THE EPIC OF STEEL

THE EPIC OF STEEL

THE EPIC OF

STEEL

DOUGLAS ALAN FISHER

Harper & Row, Publishers, New York, Evanston, and London

THE EPIC OF STEEL
Copyright © 1963 by Douglas Alan Fisher
Printed in the United States of America. All rights reserved. No part of this
book may be used or reproduced in any manner whatsoever without written
permission except in the case of brief quotations embodied in critical articles
and reviews. For information address Harper & Row, Publishers, Incorporated,
49 East 33rd Street, New York 16, N. Y.

FIRST EDITION

B-N

Library of Congress Catalog Card Number: 63-8131

Contents

Preface   **vii**

1   Before Man Knew Iron   **1**
2   Iron, Earthly and Celestial   **5**
3   Steel in Antiquity   **21**
4   From the Catalan Forge to the Blast Furnace   **25**
5   England Leads the Way   **35**
6   Prelude to the Industrial Revolution   **48**
7   Miners, Smiths, and Metallurgy   **55**
8   Iron and Steel in Colonial America   **66**
9   Rise of the Young Republic   **88**
10   The Industrial Revolution Comes to America   **97**
11   Invention of the Bessemer Process   **114**
12   The Steel Age Begins   **123**
13   Enter Automobiles, Exit Horses   **137**
14   Alloy Steels—I—Historical Development, 1819–1961   **152**
15   Alloy Steels—II—Alloying Elements   **168**
16   The Fabulous Coal Chemicals   **197**
17   Wire and Wire Products   **218**
18   Plates, Pipes and Tubes, Rails and Bars   **230**
19   Coatings for Steel   **242**
20   World Iron and Steelmaking Resources   **248**
21   The Blast Furnace, 1881–1960   **267**
22   Goliath Is Challenged   **279**
23   Electrical Processes for Making Iron and Steel   **290**
24   Steelmaking Processes—Twentieth Century   **302**
25   Steel in the Atomic-Space Age   **313**

Notes   **325**

Index   **336**

Tables

1 Number of Active Furnaces and Output of Pig Iron in Great Britain, 1788–1806   52

2 Relationship Between the Production of Bessemer Steel, Bessemer Steel Rails, the Growth of Railroads, and Percentages of Steel Rails in the United States: Selected Periods, 1867–1900   125

3 Relative Growth of Iron and Steel Production in the United States: Selected Periods, 1880–1904   128

4 Relative Production of Heavy and Light Steel Products in the United States and Percentages of Hot-Rolled Products: Selected Periods, 1905–1955   150

5 World Production of Chromite, by Countries, in Short Tons, 1950–1954, 1960   173

6 Free World Production of Cobalt, by Countries, in Short Tons of Contained Cobalt, 1950–1954, 1960   176

7 Free World Production of Columbium and Tantalum Mineral Concentrates, by Countries, 1950–1954 (Average) and 1960, in Pounds   178

8 World Reserves of Manganese Ore   181

9 World Production of Manganese Ore, by Countries, 1950–1954 (Average) and 1960, in Net Tons   182

10 World Production of Nickel, by Countries, 1950–1954 (Average) and 1960, in Net Tons of Contained Nickel   187

11 Estimated World Tungsten Reserves   192

12 World Production of Tungsten Ore and Concentrate, by Countries, 1950–1954 (Average) and 1960, in Net Tons   194

13 World Production of Vanadium in Ores and Concentrate, 1950–1954 (Average) and 1960 in Net Tons   196

14 Coal-Chemical Materials, Exclusive of Breeze, Produced at Coke-Oven Installations in the United States in 1960   204

15 Steel Industry Employment Costs Per Hour, United States and Eight Other Countries, 1952–1960   252

16 World Production (1961) and Planned Capacity of Crude Steel and Castings (1965)   254

17 Electric Furnace Steel Production in the United States, Percentages of Alloy and Carbon Steels: Selected Periods, 1911–1961   295

18 Growth of Electric Furnace Steel Production in the United States: Selected Periods, 1908–1961   297

19 Production of Steel, by Processes and Percentages, of Total Production in the United States: Selected Periods, 1875–1961   304

20 Steel Production in Selected European Countries, by Processes: 1958   305

FIGURE 1 Map: Principle Iron Ore Resources of the World   257

Preface

When I joined the public relations staff of U.S. Steel during World War II, I had not the remotest idea that I would one day write a history of the steel industry.

In the course of my work for the corporation, I wrote several books which required research in the history of steel. My curiosity aroused, I read further on my own.

Early in my research, I found a number of excellent histories of steel from antiquity to the late nineteenth century, but I was appalled to discover that for a metal as important as steel, no comprehensive history had been written in English in this century. The last such work was *History of the Manufacture of Iron in All Ages,* by James M. Swank, published in 1891.

I decided to try to fill the gap, little realizing what this work would mean. The more I read, the more I found there was to know. It soon became apparent that the story of iron and steel, beginning some five thousand years ago, spread out in many directions—woven in the social, economic, political, and other tissues composing the fabric of civilization. In addition to tracing the technology of iron and steel—my first objective—I could not follow the other ferrous strands as far as I would have liked in a single volume. Yet I hope that the book as now written will give the reader some grasp of how iron and steel, more than any other industrial metal, shaped the environment in which man lived from primitive times to the present. It will also acquaint him with some of the significant uses of the two metals, from arrowheads and implements to automobiles, skyscrapers, and missiles.

I need hardly add that the book is not confined to a history of steel in the United States. This account is international in scope, embracing the nations where the chief technological advances were made. For American readers, however, there are chapters dealing with the domestic industry from colonial days onward.

I enjoyed an invaluable advantage in having the cooperation of U.S. Steel officials and technicians. More than twenty specialists, each an authority in his line, reviewed the text for technical accuracy.

In expressing my indebtedness to U.S. Steel personnel for their part in making the book possible, I should like to mention them in the order in which they began lending me a helping hand. I gratefully salute J.

vii

Carlisle MacDonald, former Assistant to Chairman and Director of Public Relations of U.S. Steel. When I confided to him what I was writing in my evenings and holidays, he heartened me with encouragement, as he had done some years earlier in Paris when he was correspondent for the *New York Times* and with his warm heart and strong arm supported me and set my feet on the path that led to a reunion with him later at U.S. Steel. To Mr. MacDonald's successor at U.S. Steel, Phelps H. Adams, now Vice President–Public Relations, I owe a great debt. Believing in my work as a historian of the industry, he helped to give me faith in myself. Phelps Adams, a man who puts his beliefs into acts, made possible the internal review that established the technical accuracy of my book, and enabled it to reach the publisher. Roger M. Blough, Chairman of the Board, strongly believing in the need for a history such as I was writing, lent the prestige of his office on my behalf. For his kindness to me I shall always be extremely grateful. To Richard F. Miller, Assistant to Administrative Vice President–Research and Technology, I am indebted more than to any one person for assuring that the book is technically sound. He not only read my text and gave valuable advice, but shepherded the chapters among appropriate technicians. Last to be mentioned by name, but by no means least, is Harold E. McGannon. A walking technical encyclopedia, Harold knows more about the history of steel from ancient times to the present than anyone else of my acquaintance. He nursed me through the first and second drafts, and went over the last one with a fine technical and historical comb. Lastly, I would like to say to the many specialists who took time from their busy work to review portions of my history, "I can never thank you enough."

A writer may spin a novel out of his own head, based on his experiences, but he cannot write a history without a multitude of fellow workers— those authors, living and dead, who pass his desk, each leaving precious grist for the mill. Some of them never left me, but lingered close by, summoned back from time to time, as tried and proven friends, in the entire writing of the book. To all of them, the great and the obscure— from Aristotle, writers of cuneiform tablets, and biblical scribes to contemporary authors—I wave grateful thanks as they take their leave.

January 1, 1963   Douglas Alan Fisher

King Solomon and the Ironworker—The ironworker is awarded the seat of honor on King Solomon's right at a feast on completion of the temple, according to a Hebrew legend. (*Painting by Professor C. Schussele, 1864*)

Before Man Knew Iron

Man is a tool-making animal.
—Benjamin Franklin

STONE AGE TO METALS AGE

For at least 90 per cent of human existence, the life of man has been little above that of an animal, because, like an animal, he preyed on what he found ready-made in nature. Earliest man was a food gatherer. He existed just above the starvation level, keeping body and soul together by the use of his bare hands and teeth in catching game and fish, digging grubs and roots, or picking wild fruits and berries. Groping for a better way to sustain existence, man extended the use of his hands and the energy of his body by employing sticks, shells, or broken pieces of stone or bone. With these first crude tools, man began his slow emancipation from complete dependence on the forces and whims of nature.

Man made his next step forward when he learned how to chip stones into rude axe heads and primitive knives. Still later, he discovered flint, which could be flaked off into thin sharp edges, admirably suited for shaping into skin scrapers and arrow points. He progressed gradually from a food gatherer to a proficient toolmaker and skillful hunter. This longest period of man's history is known as the Paleolithic, or Old Stone Age. It began at some indeterminate time in the remote past and merged about 8000 B.C. into the Neolithic, or New Stone Age.

During what has been described as the "neolithic revolution," man learned to plant seed, domesticate animals, spin and weave, and bake pottery. The distinguishing technological feature of this period was the polishing and grinding of stones.

More a farmer than a hunter in the advanced centers of civilization, man settled down in villages and developed community life. During the New Stone Age, man first became acquainted with metals.

Neolithic man was fond of adorning himself with necklaces, bracelets, and other trinkets made from beads of pierced shells or brightly-colored stones. Seaching for suitable stones or shells, his eye was attracted by a yellow, glittering object in the sands and gravel of a stream. He picked it up and found that it was soft and could easily be hammered into beads and other articles of adornment. This yellow object was pure gold and was, generally, the first metal used by man. The discovery of gold may have taken place in other ways. It is one of the few metals existing in a pure, or free, state and is widely distributed in nature. Imperishable, ductile, and beautiful, gold became man's most prized metal; only iron, because of its greater utility, was valued above it in certain times and places.

Savage man in his search for gold, sometimes found lumps of a dark stone which he mistook for gold. This was copper which also exists in a free state in nature. On hammering the new stone, man discovered that it, too, was malleable and so he beat copper into beads and strung them together with gold and pretty stones and shells. At an unknown later date in the New Stone Age, he came across silver which likewise is found in a free state. These first three metals—gold, copper and silver—were looked upon as soft stones, for at that time man had no knowledge of metals as such.

Smelting and Casting Begin

In hammering native copper, the prehistoric smith discovered that when it was beaten sufficiently it became hard and he soon became proficient in beating, bending, grinding, and polishing the metal into knives, spearheads, and skin scrapers. The use of hammered copper marks the transition from a stone to a metal culture in almost every ancient civilization and is of paramount importance in the prehistory of man. The shaping of native copper is fixed tentatively in the sixth to the fifth millennium B.C.[1] Copper is believed to be the first luxury of the Old World to have evolved into a necessity. This period of history is known as the Copper Age and in the centers of high civilization it extended to around 3000 B.C., when the Bronze Age began. Ancient ruins have yielded copper relics that date back to 4500 B.C.[2]

From an industrial point of view, the history of man may be divided into two major parts: the Stone Age and the Metals Age. The second, which has, thus far, lasted only 1 per cent of total human existence, did not actually begin until man learned that metals do not always exist in a pure state, as he had found gold, copper, and silver, but are also intermixed with rocks and soils in what we now call ores. Primitive man made the startling discovery that with the aid of fire he could smelt certain stones from which metal flowed. It is generally accepted that copper was the first metal smelted by man. The beginning of metallurgy has been variously ascribed to Sumeria, Egypt, Southern Arabia, and Asia. The region on which most authorities agree is in the Caucasus Mountains between the Black and Caspian Seas. Reduction of copper is believed to have been practiced in that region well before 3000 B.C., for by that date copper products and not the unworked metal alone were being exported to Sumeria. At all events, reduction of the oxide and carbonate ores of copper, such as malachite, azurite and others, has been traced in the Near East to the fourth millennium B.C., and the industry was fully developed by 3500 B.C.[3] From the Caucacus Mountains, which abound with minerals, fuel, and water—and where the earliest metal remains have been found—metallurgy spread to the Ural Mountains, Persia, Central India, China, Mesopotamia, and Egypt. It reached the Mediterranean area and Central Europe somewhat before *circa* 2000 B.C.[4]

The discovery that certain stones could be smelted by fire, yielding a substance superior to the original stone, was one of the most dramatic leaps in the history of mankind. For untold centuries man had labored to shape intractable and stubborn stones which were liable to splinter or break in the process, or afterwards in use. Metal provided a far better tool-making material which could be hammered without breaking. Malleability was a prime factor in the eyes of the ancients. Moreover, a metal tool was more durable than one of stone. Once a stone or flint blade broke, it could not be repaired, whereas a metal weapon or implement could not only be resharpened but could also be melted down and rehammered or cast anew.

The casting of copper must have followed very closely the transmutation of green and blue stones into liquid red metal. The art of casting presumably developed in Mesopotamia. From there it traveled to China and India. It was in the Orient that the foundry first flourished industrially. The Eastern foundrymen achieved exceptional mastery in the technique of casting, particularly bronze, and produced colossal images. The secrets of Chinese casting filtered back westward to Egypt, Greece, and Rome. Gold, silver, lead, copper, and bronze were cast in the ancient world.[5]

Copper gave man the most satisfactory material he had yet known for clearing forests, growing crops, building sturdier houses, and constructing more seaworthy boats. Copper products which appeared at different periods, some hammered and others cast, included daggers, knives, nails, needles, seals, axes, arrowpoints, rings, arm and foot bangles, pins, bowls, pots, mirrors, tubes, cups, fishhooks, chisels, tweezers, harpoon heads, and spearheads.[6]

THE BRONZE AGE

Copper was replaced by bronze as man learned to alloy copper with tin and this next cultural stage in man's history is appropriately known as the

Bronze Age. The discovery of bronze taught man an important metallurgical lesson, namely, that the fusing of two relatively soft metals could yield a product that was harder than either. Bronze could be hammered into thinner and sharper edges than copper and was fashioned into knives and forceps, man's first surgical instruments. Since the art of casting was already known, bronze was cast shortly after it was introduced. It is claimed that well-executed bronze castings were made as early as 3000 B.C.[7] Because bronze lent itself easily to casting, the metal found its glory in objects such as statuary and works of art; it was also cast into ornaments, keys, ship prows, urns, stoves, shields, furniture, and many other products of the founder's skill.

Production of metals in the ancient world was laborious, costly and on a small scale. All metals were in short supply. Bronze drove out stone and copper tools and implements very slowly. Possession of metals was a prerogative of the nation's ruler and was, in general, restricted to his household and the priestly classes. The royal army was equipped with bronze armor and weapons and the king's own craftsmen might labor for him with bronze tools, but the ordinary worker had to be content with polished stone tools, while the peasant still reaped with a flint sickle and opened the earth with a wooden plow.

The search for new sources of copper and tin, but more especially tin, which was the scarcer of the two, gave a strong impetus to exploration and trade, the distinguishing economic features of the Bronze Age. From the centers of civilization trade routes fanned out to England, Europe, Africa, Siberia, China, and India. By caravans and ships, the products of international trade were exchanged—copper, tin, silver, gold, amber, textiles, precious stones, spices, incense, silk, lumber, food, furs, perfumes, glass, pottery, ivory, dyes, and last, but not least, slaves.

Metals were the chief sources of power and wealth in the ancient Near East and wars were fought over the possession of rich deposits or to wrest metals already mined as booty or tribute from the vanquished. The Bronze Age saw the rise of the first great empires in Sumeria, Assyria, Babylonia, Egypt, Persia, and the realm of the Hittites.

Iron, Earthly and Celestial

When the temple in Jerusalem was completed Solomon invited to a feast all the artificers who had been engaged in its construction. As the throne was unveiled, the guests were outraged to see that the seat of honor on the king's right, as yet unawarded, had been usurped by the ironworker. Whereupon the people in one voice cried out against him and the guards rushed forward to cut him down.

The king silenced their protests and turning to the stonecutter, said: "Who made the tools with which you carve?"

"The ironworker," was the reply.

To the artificer of gold and silver, Solomon said: "Who made your instruments?"

"The ironworker," they answered.

To the carpenter, Solomon said, "Who forged the tools with which you hewed the cedars of Lebanon?"

"The ironworker," was again the answer.

Then Solomon turned to the ironworker: "Thou art all men's father in art. Go, wash the sweat of the forge from thy face and sit at my right hand."

—*An Old Hebrew Legend*

The writings of explorers who visited the New World several hundred years ago, and the chronicles of later navigators, left vivid descriptions of how primitive peoples reacted after they became acquainted with iron. We are indebted for this information to the noted authority on metals, T. A. Rickard, who gleaned it from the writings just referred to. In the course of world exploration which began toward the close of the fifteenth century, Rickard reminds us, numerous ships were wrecked, and entire vessels or their dismembered parts were cast upon the shores of the seven seas. These craft contained nails, spikes, bolts, chains, anchors, and other fittings of wrought iron, and inquisitive natives examining the foundered craft or stray pieces of wreckage on their beaches or rocky coasts, discovered articles of iron and apparently learned quickly and with great joy the utility of the metal above any substance they had yet known. By means of this "drift iron," primitive peoples over a wide area were introduced to the metal. Iron was tough, strong and malleable and could be hammered with stones into spear and arrow points, knives and other implements. Once these properties of iron were known to savage people it became positively precious to them and their desire for it knew no bounds.[1]

The most valuable possessions of the Eskimos were their hunting weapons and in their passionate eagerness for iron, says a Danish explorer who visited Greenland in 1605; "they were willing to sacrifice their greatest valuables, such as their bows and arrows," and when they had nothing left to offer in exchange, "they stripped themselves to the skin and offered to make away with all their clothes they possessed." One Arctic navigator told of two instances when a child was offered in exchange for an iron knife.[2]

In the South Seas, according to tradition, the first iron known to the natives came from the sea. When Captain Cook revisited New Zealand in 1773, he reported that the people "were extravagantly fond of nails above every other thing," and like the Tahitians and Hawaiians, offered "their daughters and sisters promiscuously to every person's embrace in exchange for our iron tools."[3]

METAL FROM HEAVEN

The hunger for iron of primitive people, nearer our own time, must have been experienced by Stone Age savages when they first became acquainted with the metal. This was obtained from meteorites. The chance discovery of meteoric iron was made by peoples of a Stone Age culture in various parts of the world and at different epochs. When it first occurred is lost in the dim reaches of prehistory, possibly four to six thousand years ago. Since the discovery was probably repeated in much the same way in different regions, we may picture how it may have taken place.

Stone Age men, searching for stones suitable for shaping into tools and weapons, may have come across a whole meteorite or the fragments of one. The latter discovery was possible because meteorites sometimes shatter into thousands of pieces, ranging in weight from a few ounces to several pounds or more. Although there are some stone meteorites, most of them are largely iron. A stone meteorite would have been regarded as an ordinary stone by primitive men, but a meteorite of iron would have been very different in appearance, and much harder and heavier. It would have been looked upon as a new, strange kind of stone, the men having no knowledge of metals as such. If it was a whole meteorite the men discovered, they managed to chip loose a sample or two. When the specimens were struck with a stone hammer, they did not split or crack like other stones, but surprisingly, yielded to the hammer blows. However the discovery took place, the first iron known to man came from meteorites, and once he had learned to beat this tough, malleable substance into sharp points for arrow and spearheads and into knives and skin scrapers, he prized it above all other material for tools and weapons.

Ancient writings give unmistakable evidence that falling meteorites, or "stone showers," were well known to man.[4] Thus, at a very early time, he concluded that iron had a celestial origin and his next step was to believe that the firmament was made of the metal. In nearly all languages at the early centers of civilization, the word for iron meant "metal, or something hard from the sky." In early Egyptian writings iron was called *ba-en-pet*, variously interpreted as "hard stone from the sky" and "marvel from heaven." Iron was named *parzillu* by the Assyrians and Babylonians, *barsa* by the Sumerians and Chaldeans, and *barzel* by the Hebrews. A popular translation of these ancient terms is "metal from heaven."

Having descended from the abode of the gods, iron assumed a mystical and at times a sacred property in the eyes of the ancients. Superstitions and taboos grew up around the metal. Moses commanded the children of Israel after they had passed over into Jordan,[5] "There shalt thou build an altar unto the Lord thy God, an altar of stones: thou shalt not lift up any iron tool upon them." There were numerous later references which show that the Hebrews valued iron highly. We are told in I Kings that Solomon's temple was "built of stone made ready before it was brought thither: so that there was neither hammer nor ax nor any tool of iron heard in the house, while it was in building."[6] However, iron was used in construction of the temple, for we read in I Chronicles that David, before his death, gathered materials for his son Solomon's holy edifice: "And David prepared iron in abundance for the nails for the doors of the gates, and for the joinings."[7] He also "gave for the service of the house of God . . . one hundred thousand talents of iron."[8]

TWO PHASES OF IRON CULTURE

There were two distinct phases of man's iron culture. In the first, he secured the metal from meteorites and in the second he discovered that there is an earthly as well as a celestial iron and he learned to smelt the former. The Iron Age, proper, is generally regarded as that period in history when the metal was smelted and manufactured for use on a sufficient scale to become man's basic metal, and as such, to have affected radically the course of civilization.

There can be no doubt that iron was smelted sporadically here and there, with the secret lost and found again over a long period, many centuries before the true Iron Age began. Estimates by authorities on the beginning of ferrous metallurgy vary from roughly 4000 to 1500 B.C.—a difference of 2,500 years. This wide variation is due in part to the assumption by some antiquarians that the discovery of iron relics at an ancient smelting site indicates the existence of a true Iron Age culture, and in part to the failure by others to distinguish between heaven-sent and man-made iron in surviving relics. Between meteoric and smelted iron there is a recognizable difference. Meteoric iron contains from 5 to 26 per cent nickel, with an average of about 7 per cent. Nickel imparts toughness and some corrosion resistance to iron and steel. In meteoric iron, primitive man actually had an iron-nickel alloy, closely akin to steel, and in some respects superior to any industrial metal he manufactured up to the 1880s when nickel steel was applied with such spectacular success to armor plate that it revolutionized naval tactics. Nickel steel was, in fact, first called "meteor steel." On the other hand, smelted iron contains only traces of nickel or none at all.

The statement has been widely circulated and handed down from writer to writer, that the Iron Age may go back as far as 4000 B.C. in the earliest centers of civilization—Egypt, Chaldea, Babylonia, Assyria, and China.[9] It has been asserted by archaeological authorities that iron was known to the Egyptians at least as early as 3500 B.C. This opinion is based largely on the discovery of iron artifacts in the Great Pyramid of Gizeh, built *circa* 2900 B.C. and in a grave at Abydos, Egypt, dating from 2600 B.C. Both relics are in the British Museum. It is apparently assumed that if iron was manufactured in Egypt in 2900 B.C. it must have been known there even earlier, which would account for the authorities extending the date back to 3500 B.C. Specimens of the metal from both relics have been analyzed for nickel and showed only traces of it, which would throw doubt on their meteoric origin. The pyramid piece was taken from an inner joint, with no opening or joint connecting with it from the outside by which the iron could have been placed after the building of the pyramid. In spite of this evidence, Rickard inclines to the belief that the two specimens were of celestial origin, for he says "it is difficult to explain how the Pyramid specimen happened to be in the place described; apparently it was due to some accident, for whether celestial or terrestial, such a piece of iron must have been rare and precious at that date; even the Abydos specimen of about three centuries later, was carefully wrapped as if it were highly prized."[10]

The remains of what was probably an iron dagger found at Ur of the Chaldees, was considered proof that iron was smelted by 3100 B.C. until an analysis revealed a 10.9 per cent nickel content, unquestionably establishing its meteoric source. In a grave at Gerzeh, Egypt, of the predynastic period, that is, prior to 3400 B.C., several necklaces strung with iron and gold beads were unearthed. The presence of 7.5 per cent nickel content in the iron definitely indicates that it came from outer space.

The smelting of iron in Egypt as early as 3500 B.C. is hard to reconcile with evidence that the metal was extremely scarce in that country more than 2,000 years later. From the tomb of Tut-ankh-Amen, Pharaoh of Egypt for six years in the middle of the fourteenth century B.C., three iron objects were removed—the blade of a dagger, part of an amuletic brace-let and a miniature head rest. The three iron relics were found in the wrappings of the mummy and presumably were placed there because they were among the Pharaoh's most treasured possessions, more highly prized than the gold of which the ornate sarcophagus was made. It seems likely that iron of such rarity and value came from the heavens. Further-more, there is good reason to believe that the industrial use of iron did not begin in Egypt before the thirteenth century B.C., in the days of Rameses II, and that the metal did not become prevalent until the twenty-second and twenty-fifth dynasties, between 945 and 718 B.C.[11]

In Mesopotamia and other parts of the Near East iron appears to have been scarce in the second millennium B.C. A contract at the time of Ham-murabi, King of Babylon (2067-2024 B.C.) speaks of iron as extremely rare and costly; it was worth fifteen to twenty times as much as copper. The inference is that the only iron available was that obtained from stray meteorites.

Forbes says that the first smelting of iron was due to the accidental mistaking of iron ore for copper ore. There can be no doubt, he asserts, that the smiths first attempted to shape smelted iron as they did copper and bronze by hammering it in a cold condition. In this they were unsuc-cessful. They had to learn that iron must be red hot for shaping. The earliest wrought iron was soft, and its cutting edge dulled quickly. The new metal represented no improvement over bronze for tools and weap-ons and was manufactured in small quantities, mostly for ornaments. There was no incentive to smelt iron on a larger scale until the smiths made important metallurgical discoveries, to be described later, which enabled them to forge iron into a form superior to bronze. Forbes says that around 1400 B.C. the Hittites discovered the "steeling" of iron which gave them a monopoly of "true iron" for another two hundred years.[12] By the term "true iron," he was probably referring to a new form of iron that outclassed copper and bronze in durability and hardness.

To sum up the problem raised by the conflicting dates for the earliest smelting of iron, there is this to be said: If it took place as far back as 3500 B.C., or possibly 4000 B.C., it would have been contemporaneous with the Copper Age and have preceded the Bronze Age in the centers of the high-est civilization. It is almost universally accepted that iron metallurgy fol-lowed that of copper and bronze. The surest guide to the existence of an iron industry at any time and place is the quantity in use. If we find that iron was rare and precious as in beads and necklaces, it seems likely that it was meteoric or the product of isolated smelting, the secret of which may have been lost, only to be rediscovered again here and there. If the smelting of iron had been established as early as 3500 B.C. in Egypt, why was it so rare and precious 2,100 years later that three iron objects, probably of meteoric origin, were secreted near the body of Tut-ankh-Amen?

BIRTHPLACE OF THE IRON AGE

The birthplace of the true Iron Age has been attributed to various regions. The preponderance of authoritative opinion favors the southern slopes of the Caucasus Mountains between the Black and Caspian seas, in a region known as Chalybia. The Chalybes were famous at a very early time for their iron, and Herodotus refers to them as "a people of iron-workers" and says that the Greeks obtained both iron and steel from them.[13] Aristotle wrote that the Chalybes obtained iron from mines "on the southern shores of the Black Sea . . . the best and hardest of all kinds of iron known is that of the Chalybes."[14]

From its original center in the Caucasus Mountains the industrial use of iron is believed to have spread to the Hittites whose homeland was in Anatolia, now western Turkey. Speaking of iron, Ceram says that the Hittites knew it at a very early period, and by 1600 B.C. appear to have had a certain monopoly in its manufacture, thus confirming the statement of Forbes regarding a monopoly, but differing with him by two hundred years. If the Hittites learned the iron trade from the Chalybes, then the latter must have been active in the new industry much earlier than either 1600 B.C. or 1400 B.C., for the Hittites were certainly smelting iron for some years before they learned the technique that gave them a monopoly in it. How much earlier did the Chalybes smelt iron? There is no way of knowing. Ceram goes on to say that in early Hittite history "iron was five times more expensive than gold, forty times dearer than silver." He considers it likely that the first iron weapons were "qualitatively by no means equal to the tried and true stone and bronze weapons," which would bear out the opinion of Forbes that until "true iron" was known it was considered inferior to copper and bronze.[15]

The Hittites possessed rich and abundant iron ore and became renowned as ironworkers. Their conquests were due largely to the possession of superior iron weapons and war chariots. Destruction of the Hittite Empire, *circa* 1200 B.C. by invading Thraco-Phrygian peoples, terminated the Hittites' iron monopoly and caused a dispersion of ironmaking by driving Hittite smiths from their homeland. Preceding these emigrant smiths, however, the knowledge of ironworking had filtered from the Hittite Empire into the Syrian lowlands around 1400 B.C. It was the Philistines who brought iron into Palestine, where a fairly advanced iron industry existed as far back as 1350 B.C. The Hittites have been credited with the initial development and exploitation of the formidable light war chariot, made largely of iron. With war chariots "after the fashion of the Hittites," the Canaanites routed the Israelites, who, we read in Judges, "could not drive out the inhabitants of the valley, because they had chariots of iron."[16] In their despair, "the people of Israel cried to the Lord for help; for he (Captain of the Canaanites) had nine hundred chariots of iron, and oppressed the people of Israel cruelly for twenty years."[17]

Summing up the evidence it may be assumed that the Iron Age had its birthplace in the Caucasus Mountains sometime before 1600 B.C. or 1400 B.C. and was firmly rooted in Palestine by 1350 B.C. If a date is to be taken for the start of the Iron Age, that is, when the metal began to assume industrial importance, then a middle point of 1500 B.C. may be as good as any.

By 1000 B.C., the smelting of iron was no longer the secret or monopoly of any nation and there must have been a rush to get into the iron business, primarily for the advantage of iron weapons for offensive or defensive war. A passage in I Samuel tells how the Philistines, after subduing the Israelites, deprived their victims of iron weapons: "Now there was no smith to be found throughout all the land of Israel; for the Philistines said, 'Lest the Hebrews make themselves swords or spears.' "[18] These cases were not unusual. Iron weapons gave such an upper hand that it was not uncommon for the victor to deny them to the vanquished and to carry off their smiths.

The military advantages of iron hastened its spread in the ancient world and at the same time intensified warfare. It was through the peaceful uses of iron, however, that it made its greatest impact on early cultures. Hard and tough, capable of being forged into many forms, iron furnished a new, superior material for tools and implements, and as such raised the economic level of every society that entered into the Iron Age.

Ancient inscriptions and texts abound with the mention of iron. There are ninety-five references to iron and four to steel in the Old Testament. Tubal-cain, seventh generation from Adam, is described in Genesis as "an instructor of every artificer in brass and iron."[19] A verse in Deuteronomy indicates that the Israelites became familiar with iron during their captivity in Egypt: "But the Lord hath taken you and brought you forth out of the iron furnace, even out of Egypt."[20] Canaan, the Land of Promise, is described by Moses as "a land whose stones are iron."[21] The declaration in Job that "iron is taken out of the earth," leaves no doubt that smelting already existed in his day.[22] Another passage in Job reveals that steel, or what then passed for steel, was also in use: "He shall flee the iron weapon, and the bow of steel shall strike him through."[23] Axes, saws and harrows of iron are recorded in the reign of David, who lived about 1,000 years before the birth of Christ.[24]

SPREAD OF IRON AGE CULTURE

The Middle East, China, Japan, and India

Iron was known to the Chaldeans, Babylonians, and Assyrians. The largest accumulation of iron relics ever found consisted of 176 tons of iron bars, weighing from 9 to 44 pounds each, together with finished articles of iron, such as chains, plows, and horse bits. The find was unearthed at Khorsabad, in what was apparently a storehouse of Sargon II, King of Assyria in the seventh century B.C. At the site of ancient Nineveh, destroyed about 600 B.C., iron artifacts were collected including scales of armor and a perfect helmet inlaid with copper bands.

Iron is mentioned in the most ancient of Chinese writings extant and may have been known in China in 2600 B.C. If so, it undoubtedly was meteoric. The earliest written record of iron manufacture in China dates from *circa* 1000 B.C. Before 500 B.C. iron had found its way into agricultural and domestic use. The Chinese were noted at an early time for iron castings. The art of ironmaking was brought to Japan by invaders from the Asiatic mainland, probably from Korea, about the first century of the Christian era.

In India, according to the writings of antiquity, iron was manufactured before 1000 B.C. An early medical book describes nearly one hundred surgical instruments of iron for delicate operations. Herodotus, in his comment on the army of Xerxes, said that the Indian contingent was "clad with garments made of cotton, and had bows of cane and arrows of cane tipped with iron."[25] The famous pillars of Delhi and Dhar have excited curiosity because of their remarkable state of preservation. Both pillars were made by welding together discs of wrought iron and were erected about A.D. 310. Metallurgists who have examined specimens of the Delhi pillar agree that its preservation is due primarily to the purity of the atmosphere and not to intrinsic qualities of the iron.

Other iron relics found in India confirm the belief that the manufacture and application of the metal was highly developed at one time in that country. Wrought-iron beams, some of them 35 feet long and 8 inches square, were discovered in the ruins of a temple at Konarak, built around A.D. 1240.

India's greatest claim to metallurgical fame rests, however, on the manufacture of wootz steel, a true steel, which was fashioned into the renowned swords of Damascus, and was imported into Britain as late as the early nineteenth century.

Greece and Rome

The Egyptians or the seafaring Phoenicians, or both, contributed to the knowledge of ironmaking among the Greeks, who, according to their own records, first learned of iron from the Chalybes. Homer, who lived about 850 B.C., mentions iron a number of times in his poems. He even alludes to the tempering and hardening of iron in his description of Ulysses plunging a firebrand into the eye of Polyphemus, which he likens to the smith who "plunges the loud-hissing axe into cold water to temper it, for hence is the strength of iron." Even so, iron was apparently not abundant in his day nor at the time of the Trojan War about which he wrote. Homer relates the offer of Achilles of a "mass of iron, shapeless from the forge," at the funeral games of Patroclus. The address of Achilles to the Greeks, in offering the prize, shows how highly iron was regarded:[26]

> Stand forth, whoever will contend for this:
> And if broad fields and rich be his this mass
> Will last him many years. The man who tends
> His flocks, or guides his plough, need not be sent
> To town for iron: he will have it here.

Rome benefited from the metallurgical knowledge accumulated and handed down by older nations—the Egyptians, Phoenicians, Greeks, and others, but more particularly the Greeks, who were the principal tutors of the Romans in all arts including that of metallurgy. The Romans appreciated the utility of iron and were quick to apply it for peaceful and warlike purposes. Italy was not rich in natural resources but both native copper and rich iron ore deposits were available in the island of Elba, famous in antiquity for its iron ore. Rome also obtained "superior iron" from the province of Noricum, now Styria and Carinthia, in southeast Austria. By the beginning of the Christian era iron was in common use throughout the Roman Empire. The carpenters, masons and shipwrights of Rome were equipped with a variety of iron tools. Agricultural implements, hinges, bolts, keys, nails, and chains are but a few of the many uses to which iron was applied by the Romans.

Europe and Britain

Iron traveled westward through the Mediterranean, carried by the Phoenicians and Greeks, and overland via the Danube Valley by the Etruscans. The iron industry of Spain, originated by the Phoenicians, flourished under the successive rule of the Greeks, Carthaginians and Romans. It led the world for many hundred years, surviving, after the downfall of Rome, under the Moors who became masters of a greater part of the country in the first half of the eighth century A.D.

The Phoenicians, followed by the Greeks, were also the metallurgical instructors of the Gauls, who, from an early time, became proficient in mining and metalworking. The Gauls had a highly-developed iron industry by the time Caesar invaded their country. Large heaps of cinders, predating the Roman invasion have been found in various parts of the country. Caesar attributed the resistance of the Gauls as the most formidable enemies of Rome to the proficiency in iron smelting and the forging of weapons.

Archaeologists and students of history divide the Iron Age of Central and Western Europe into two periods, the Hallstatt and the La Tène, which took their names from cemeteries rich in bronze, iron, ceramics, and other relics found in Hallstatt, north of the Alps in Upper Austria, and in La Tène, situated on Lake Neuchatel, Switzerland. The first epoch extended from 900 to 500 B.C. and the second from 500 B.C. to the start of the Christian era.

The Hallstatt culture is traceable over a wide area, from Hungary to Spain and Portugal, but it had little influences on the British Isles, north Germany or Scandinavia. Relics found in sepulchers of more than one thousand Hallstatt cemeteries have made it possible to reconstruct the society existing in that period. With iron tools the people cleared the forests for farmlands. As the soil yielded more food, the population increased. It was in the latter part of the Hallstatt epoch that the custom of burying chieftains with their chariots first began north of the Alps. The chariots were light and luxurious, mostly four-wheeled with the hubs and spokes covered with forged iron.

During the La Tène epoch, culture in all respects showed a marked advance. Numerous cemeteries of this period have been found from the Danube and the Rhine to the Saone and Seine. The tribal chiefs and war heroes were buried more sumptuously with their chariots and gear. A high percentage of them were interred in full battle uniform, with their swords, javelins, and lances beside them. In the La Tène period, the chariot had become two-wheeled, generally drawn by two horses, with a place for the driver and warrior. The tongue was wooden, but the accessories were of metal, mostly iron. Ornamentations on the vehicle and the harness were openwork bronze. Some of the bridle mouthpieces were of bronze, others of iron.

The Celts who began coming to Britain about 800 B.C., probably from northern France, may have brought the art of ironmaking in their earliest invasions. At one of their first settlements in Wiltshire, a lump was found which "might be an early iron slag."[27] Britain was then in the Bronze Age. A hoard of bronze objects, possibly dating from the sixth century B.C., found in Glamorganshire, contained three relics made of wrought iron— the hilt of a sword, a spearhead and a socketed sickle. These and a few other isolated finds of iron, do not indicate the existence of an iron culture. The true Iron Age, when the metal was produced on a sufficient scale to be of common use, came rather late to Britain—probably not earlier than 450 B.C.—largely because until that time the bronze industry, by reason of superior techniques, held sway over the island's metal markets. During the late Bronze Age in Britain, new methods in casting bronze gave the metal a distinct advantage over iron which was wrought but not cast in that period. In addition, the bronzesmith was able, through improved hammering techniques, to shape and decorate the alloy in large sheets. Bronze products made by the British and Irish were so highly regarded that they were exported widely to Europe.

In 1942, the British Royal Air Force was constructing a landing field on a sandy waste in western Angelsey, an island off the coast of Wales. Peat was needed to prepare the ground and an obvious source was a group of bogs bordering a series of nearby lakes, among them Llyn Cerrig Bach. The peat was scooped up in power shovels, loaded into trucks and dumped in heaps on the landing site. Harrows drawn by tractors spread the peat evenly over the ground.[28]

One day the teeth of a harrow became entangled in an iron chain. Subsequently, other metal objects and animal bones were turned up in the peat. The finds eventually came to the attention of competent authorities who recognized them as relics of the early Iron Age in Wales. It is believed that the relics came from a bog adjacent to Llyn Cerrig Bach. The metal finds are of bronze and iron, remarkable for their variety—swords, part of a dagger, spears, a shield boss; fittings of vehicles, bridles, bits, rings, and other parts of harness; and miscellaneous items, such as gangchains, currency bars, tongs, sickles, cauldrons, and a trumpet. Every object has been identified as of the early Iron Age, made within the last two hundred years or so of Celtic independence preceding the Roman conquest. Roughly, the dates are from the first century B.C. to A.D. 43.

Sir Cyril Fox, who has written a report of the discovery, advances the theory that Llyn Cerrig Bach was a sacred site and that the relics were a votive offering or offerings of a Celtic tribe of the spoils of victory to a god or the indwelling spirit of the pool. Such rites, he explains, were practiced not only by the Celts of the north, but also by the Gauls. On this theory, Sir Cyril believes that there may not have been just one deposit made at Llyn Cerrig Bach; the site may have been held sacred generation after generation. Furthermore, Sir Cyril comments, the absence of Celto-Roman objects supports the votive-offering theory. The establishment of Roman Peace in 77-78 A.D., he believes, would have put an end to the existing social order which encouraged ritual based on violence. "I hold then," Sir Cyril concludes, "that the votive-offering [theory] is the more likely one, and that the Druids in all probability controlled the ritual."

Although the Romans, during their 500-year rule of Britain, established a large and thriving iron industry they did not, on the whole, says Schubert, introduce "any new technical processes."[29] They were content, as they were in other provinces of their Empire, to continue the practices they found in use by subjugated peoples. Iron and bronze were used side by side for a time, but iron slowly pushed out bronze, as it had done in earlier civilizations. Iron was found to be the superior metal, generally, for tools, weapons and implements.

Ironmaking as an industry was established in Britain by the Celts during their successive invasions, followed by incursions of the Belgae who were partially Germanic. The period from 450 B.C. to the Roman conquest in A.D. 43 is termed the Early Iron Age in Britain. During the first part of the Early Iron Age, bronze continued in use but iron gradually took over as the chief metal and was forged in to swords, daggers, knives, awls, shears, sickles, and other tools and implements, particularly for agriculture, the main source of livelihood. Each successive wave of arrivals introduced iron objects peculiar to its culture.

A distinctive feature of the Early Iron Age in Britain was the use of currency bars of definite weight, which excited the curiosity of Caesar. Generally made of iron, they were about a yard long and were used as barter money in exchange for corn, cattle, etc., or were tendered as fees to the tribal chief in ironmaking districts, where they were forged into weapons, tools and other articles by the chief's smithy.

The Belgae brought from the Continent the heavy, wheeled plow with an iron coulter and plowshare. The heavy plow, capable of turning a deep furrow, even in clay soil, initiated an agricultural revolution in Britain, which was extended by the Anglo-Saxons. Other relics of the last phase of the Early Iron Age were iron gang-chains and firedogs. The gang-chain was spaced with six hinged collars, about two feet apart, to go around the slave's neck. The ornamented iron firedogs graced the central hearth of the great hall in the manor house or castle.

EARLY IRON SMELTING

When iron smelting began in the centers of advanced civilization, primitive smiths already possessed a considerable amount of metallurgical lore. They smelted gold, silver, copper and lead, and produced bronze; they cast metals and had become adept in the use of mouth-blown tubes, and bellows made of animal skins to create greater heat by means of a forced draft. There can be no doubt that the first iron smelters treated the metal as they did copper and bronze, and in so doing encountered difficulties. Consequently, smelted iron remained inferior to bronze for weapons and tools until the smiths learned new techniques in the manufacture of iron. Thus the Iron Age represented a distinct metallurgical advance.

In principle, iron smelting is simple. Iron has a strong affinity for oxygen, which explains why most iron ores are oxides. Iron ores also contain varying quantities of other elements such as silicon, sulfur, manganese and phosphorus. The smelting, or reduction, of iron ore is based primarily on the affinity of oxygen for carbon under certain conditions of heat. When iron ore is heated in the presence of a small excess of carbonaceous material, such as charcoal, various reactions take place, depending on the temperature, the proportion of carbon present and the protection of the iron from direct contact with air. At the comparatively low temperature of 1650° F., the iron ore begins to yield some of its oxygen which combines with carbon to form carbon monoxide gas, and when the temperature reaches 2190° F., a spongy, porous mass of relatively pure iron is formed, intermixed with bits of charcoal and extraneous matter liberated from the ore, known as slag. If the temperature approaches 2400° F., a radical change takes place: the iron begins to absorb carbon rapidly, somewhat as a blotter absorbs ink, and at this point, the iron starts to melt. In the smelting process charcoal plays a dual role; it generates heat and furnishes carbon for a chemical reaction with oxygen in the ore.

The sponge stage is as far as the primitive smith got, with some exceptions, in his crude furnace. With a pair of tongs he removed this pasty lump weighing about twenty-five pounds, and hammered it on an anvil to drive out the cinders and slag and to compact the metallic particles. When the lump became too cool to be worked further he heated it in a charcoal forge, hammered it again and repeated the process until he had a compact mass of iron. This was wrought iron, and contained generally from 0.02 to 0.08 per cent carbon. The minute amount of carbon in wrought iron is just enough to make the metal tough and malleable. In the improbable event that the temperature in this type of furnace approached 2400° F., the iron sponge would absorb from 3 to 4.5 per cent carbon and melt. This is cast iron. So high a proportion of carbon makes iron hard and somewhat brittle. It is liable to crack or shatter under a heavy blow and cannot be forged at any temperature.

The original iron smelting furnace was a bowl-shaped hole in the ground lined with clay. A constant draft was supplied by two or more pairs of bellows, formed of animal skins, pressed down by the hands or feet. The air was led into the furnace over the rim by nozzles or tuyeres of clay or bamboo. Later, in eastern or southern Asia another type of bellows was evolved, in which a wooden or bamboo piston moved up and down forcing air through a tuyere into the furnace. Two cylinders were kept in operation to maintain a constant stream of air.

Different types of iron smelting furnaces were developed for local needs. Where there was a steep bank or cliff facing strong prevailing winds, the furnace was often dug into the side to obtain a natural draft. Such furnaces were much favored by the Romans. Sometimes a mound of willow branches covered with clay was built over the bowl-type furnace with an opening at the top and apertures around the base for the admission of air. The bowl-furnace persisted in use for centuries and was used by the Romans side by side with more advanced types. It is still common in parts of Africa today.

The smelting furnace was gradually built upwards with side walls of stone, surmounted by a stone shaft three to four feet high, through which materials were charged, and with a tapping hole at the base.

The Japanese developed a process peculiarly their own, called the *Tatara* method. It employed a primitive bowl-shaped furnace, with a pair of bellows at each side to provide an air blast. A mixture of iron sand and charcoal was charged into the furnace. Depending on the temperature attained, the length of time the ore was exposed to hot carbon and the location of the ore in the furnace, it was possible to produce three ferrous products: *Wako,* a high carbon (0.9 to 1.8 per cent) high quality steel, suitable for forging into swords; *Wasen*, a pig or cast iron; and *Watetsu*, a low carbon wrought iron, suitable for forging into domestic utensils. Apparently some steel was also made by heating iron sand and charcoal in a clay crucible, similar to the wootz process of India.[30]

Charcoal was the principal fuel used until its replacement by coke in the eighteenth century A.D. Charcoal was known from time immemorial in Mesopotamia where it was used in powdered form as a pigment in prehistoric pottery. Finely divided iron ore and charcoal, or other carbonaceous material, were mixed together and charged into the furnace. A fire was started and the furnace was kept in operation until a pasty lump of iron intermixed with cinders and slag was formed.

New Metallurgical Tricks

Wrought iron was excellent for many purposes, but until the ancient smith learned several new metallurgical tricks, the soft ductile metal represented no improvement over copper and bronze tools and weapons because it bent easily and did not retain a cutting edge. The reason for such behavior of wrought iron was its low carbon content. But some wrought iron made in ancient times contained a higher percentage of carbon and was therefore harder and made better weapons. Moreover, low carbon iron cannot be hardened by quenching and hammering. The ancient smith worked by a trial and error method, and, not understanding the metallurgical principles involved, his results were not always uniform. In some areas, the iron ores contained a fairly high proportion of other elements, such as manganese, which strengthens iron. The manganese, becoming alloyed with the iron in the furnace, produced a superior iron so that the ores became justly celebrated, although the reason for it was unknown.

What the ancient smith had to learn, in substance, was to add enough carbon to wrought iron so that the metal could be made hard by quenching after forging. Quenching was known in very early times. It will harden iron with a moderate amount of carbon, say, one-third of 1 per cent. It is possible that in the primitive furnace, if the temperature were high enough and the lump of iron were kept sufficiently long in contact with hot charcoal, and away from direct contact with the air, the pasty sponge might absorb considerable carbon. Then if the smith quenched the iron he would find that it became very hard and he may in time have discovered how to produce the same results by the rule-of-thumb method. Or, he may have learned the same mysterious lesson in repeatedly heating iron in the charcoal forge before hammering it on the anvil into a tool or implement. In the forge, the outer surface of the iron would absorb enough carbon from the charcoal for the metal to be hardenable by quenching. In other words, the iron had a thin hard shell, while the interior remained relatively soft. This process is called carburizing, **or** case-hardening, and is used today in some forms of steel. What very likely passed for steel in ancient times, with some exceptions such as the wootz steel of India, was carburized iron. At all events, the smith ultimately learned how to smelt iron containing enough carbon for the metal to be hardenable by quenching and forging, and also how to carburize it in his forge. He gained insight into another technique: while the quenching of iron makes it hard, it also causes it to become brittle, a highly undesirable property. The iron smelter of early times found out that if quenched iron is reheated to a relatively low temperature, the brittleness is eased without too drastically lessening the hardness. This process is called tempering.

These rules of the trade were not discerned readily by all early peoples, for wrought iron swords were known to have bent in battle. The iron swords of the Gauls, for instance, were said to have "bent and the edges turned against the Roman armor so that after every stroke the Gaulish warrior must straighten the sword with his foot against the ground before he could strike a second blow."[31] Meanwhile, the Roman soldier with a sword of Spanish steel could do his deadly work.

The Iron Age did not come fully into its own until iron smelters were skilled in five techniques which were not practiced by the copper and bronze smiths: (1) adding a correct flux, such as crushed seashells or limestone, to form a slag for taking away extraneous matter in the ore, (2) reheating and rehammering the pasty lump from the furnace to drive out the cinders and slag, (3) carburizing, (4) quenching, and (5) tempering.

Cast Iron in Ancient Times

It has been widely assumed that no cast iron was produced prior to the fourteenth century A.D. There is abundant evidence that occasionally by accident and sometimes by design, cast iron was produced before the Christian era. The more carbon iron contains—up to something over 4 per cent—the lower the melting point of the iron will be. Occasionally in the ancient furnaces the temperature was high enough and the iron was sufficiently imbedded in hot charcoal away from contact from air, so that part of the spongy iron lump absorbed enough carbon, say from 2.5 to 3 per cent, for the melting point of those parts of the metal to be lowered to a stage where iron becomes liquid. When such results were produced and iron flowed from the furnace, later solidifying into lumps, the early smelter threw them away as worthless because such iron was not malleable, even when reheated. Many fragments of discarded cast iron have been found at sites of pre-Roman and Roman smelting furnaces, attributed to the Hallstatt epoch, and indicate that the production of molten iron was frequent. However, it was probably accidental.

Other primitive smelters, on seeing the molten iron, apparently surmised that it might be cast like copper and bronze and eventually learned how to produce molten iron deliberately in special furnaces. Aristotle was familiar with the melting of iron. "Iron is softened during the operation," he says, "but soon it hardens again. This is the only way of making steel. A pasty scoria swims on top, while the separated iron falls to the bottom."[32] Pausanias, writing two centuries after Aristotle's day, speaks of "Theodorus the Samian (sixth century before Christ) who invented how to pour iron and fabricate statutes with it." Pausanias refers to an iron statue of Hercules and also an iron throne, the head of a lion and a wild boar, all of iron, commenting that "The working of iron into statues happens to be the most difficult, and a matter of the greatest labor." Later, Pliny, speaking of iron, says, "How wonderful that with the refining comes liquid iron like water, afterwards broken into pieces."[33]

China has supplied the greatest number of early iron castings. Literary references to the casting of iron in China have been traced to the sixth century B.C. and Chinese cast iron objects of great beauty have been found, made in the second century B.C. At that time a flourishing iron industry existed in China. Most of the early iron relics from China are cast iron, not wrought iron. A cast iron statue of Buddha a little over sixteen feet tall, was the product of a Chinese foundry of the sixth century B.C. The largest cast iron statue known—a lion twenty feet high and eighteen feet long—dates from *circa* A.D. 954.

IRON'S DEMOCRATIZING INFLUENCE

As the production of iron increased, ownership of the fabricated metal was no longer the prerogative of the royal household. It became possible for the farmer and craftsman to possess iron tools and implements. Iron became the poor man's friend and as such, had a strong democraticizing influence. In terms of civilization, this meant an increase in the complexity of institutions, writes Carleton S. Coon in *The Story of Man:* "Craftsmen multiply until they cease to be tame purveyors to kings and priests, and work primarily for the people. Their standards of excellence and their price ceilings are not set by royal overseers, but by their own guild chiefs whom they themselves have elected. Thus during the Iron Age did a middle class grow big enough to produce its own institutions."[34]

The Iron Age not only spread over a wider area than the Bronze Age, but it penetrated much deeper. Iron was welcomed everywhere because it was cheaper than bronze and greatly superior to it for most purposes. It tended to drive out bronze just as in a much later time iron, in turn, was largely replaced by steel.

Steel in Antiquity

Then join you with them, like a rib of steel,
To make strength stronger.
                    —William Shakespeare

We are told that in the sepulchers of Thebes and Memphis, butchers were represented as using tools of iron and steel; that the Persians, Medes, and Parthians manufactured steel long before the Christian era and that the Parthian arrow was tipped with steel.[1] The Assyrians are said to have been familiar with the making of steel, a belief arising from the discovery in ancient Nineveh of knives, saws, picks and hammers, reportedly of steel.[2] The Scriptures are quoted to prove the antiquity of steel. The prophet Jeremiah asked, "Shall iron break the northern iron and steel?"[3] Job, it will be recalled, says ". . . the bow of steel shall strike him through."[4] The Greeks are reported to have used steel armor as early as the time of Homer.

In reading these references to steel, it is well to bear in mind that many ancient languages had several words for steel, or used the same word to denote both iron and steel and even non-ferrous metals. What generally passed for steel was probably, with some exceptions, carburized or case-hardened iron with which we become familiar in the last chapter. Weapons, antedating 1000 B.C. have been found with the points or blades of a nearly glass-like hardness, the result of quenching high carbon iron.

THREE PROCESSES KNOWN IN THE PAST

True steel of a very high quality was, however, made in the ancient past. There is no doubt about the authenticity of wootz steel, manufactured in India. Aristotle, in 384 B.C., described its manufacture. It was shipped to Damascus in ancient Syria, where artisans tempered and hammered it into the famous swords which took their name from that city. Swords of Damascus were so supple that they could be bent from hilt to tip, while at the same time they were capable of taking a cutting edge that perhaps has never been surpassed. In an ancient parchment, written in Syrian characters, discovered in the remains of an armorer's shop, we have a description of how these weapons were hammered and tested for a ruler or officer of high rank:[5]

Let a high dignitary furnish an Ethiop of fair frame and let him be bound down, shoulders upward, upon the block of the God Bal-hal, his arms fastened underneath with thongs, a strap of goat skin over his back, and wound twice around the block, his feet close together lashed to a dowel of wood, and his head and neck projecting over and beyond the end of the block. . . . Then let the master-workman, having cold-hammered the blade to smooth and thin edge, thrust it into the fire of the cedarwood charcoals, in and out, the while reciting the prayer to the God Bal-hal, until the steel be of the color of the red of the rising sun when he comes up over the desert toward the East, and with a quick motion pass the same from the heel thereof to the point, six times through the most fleshy portion of the slave's back and thighs, when it shall become the color of the purple of the king. Then, if with one swing and one stroke of the right arm of the master-workman, it severs the head of the slave from his body, and display no nick or crack along the edge, the blade may be bent round about the body of the man and break not, it shall be accepted as a perfect weapon, sacred to the service of the God Bal-hal, and the owner thereof may thrust it into a scabbard of asses' skin, brazen with brass, and hung to a girdle of camel's wool dyed in the royal purple.

Aristotle's description of the manufacture of wootz was brief: "It is produced by heating on a charcoal hearth about one pound weight of malleable iron, cut into small pieces, with about 10 per cent of dried wood, in clay crucibles, the covers of which are luted with clay."[6] Since then, the manufacture of wootz steel has been described in more detail; the descriptions vary but the basic principle is the same in all. Iron for conversion into steel was smelted from a magnetite sand or other similar material, crushed into small pieces and washed. The furnace was about four feet high, somewhat conical in shape, with clay tubes inserted near the base for admission of an air blast from two skin bellows worked alternately by hand. The fuel was charcoal and after the furnace had been heated, small quantities of the granular ore were sprinkled at frequent intervals on top of the hot charcoal, which was replenished from time to time. No flux was used. The resulting spongy lump of iron was removed from the furnace and subjected to repeated hammering and heating to expel the slag.

The iron thus obtained was shaped into bars twelve inches long by one and one and one-half inches wide and one-half inch thick. The bars were cut into small pieces and several of them, making up about two pounds, were packed in a clay crucible with carbonaceous material such as dry wood, chopped small, and the contents were covered with two or three green leaves. The top of the crucible was sealed with clay. Two dozen such crucibles were piled together into a furnace and heated with charcoal under blast for several hours. In this phase the iron absorbed sufficient carbon to have a low enough melting point to become fluid. The furnace and the crucibles were allowed to cool down together, after which the crucibles were removed and broken open, yielding small cakes of high carbon steel. The cakes were heated several hours under blast in a charcoal fire to a temperature just below the melting point and turned over in the current of the bellows in order to remove excess carbon. Finally the cakes were hammered into discs about five inches in diameter weighing from two to five pounds, and offered for sale to merchants. This was the original crucible process.

The Persians also made steel—apparently by the cementation process —and their product was second in renown only to the wootz steel of India. In the cementation process, alternate layers of wrought-iron bars and carbonaceous material, generally charcoal, were heated to red heat in closed pots away from direct contact with air. The heating continued for ten days or longer, depending on the size of the bars, the temperature maintained and the degree of "steeling" desired. The iron absorbed sufficient carbon from the charcoal to be converted into steel.

In some Eastern countries there arose a variation of the cementation process. The mass was heated and then hammered into bundles, or faggots, over and over. There was an incomplete diffusion of carbon from the high carbon bars to the low carbon bars, giving a surface appearance called watering which has been inaccurately called damascened steel.

What has been described as natural, or raw steel, was produced directly from suitable ores, chiefly those containing manganese and relatively free of impurities such as sulfur, arsenic and phosphorus. The method employed was different from that used in smelting iron. The furnace was pre-heated for several days. A greater proportion of charcoal and a corresponding less proportion of ore were charged into the furnace. At the higher temperature attained, and in the presence of greater quantities of carbon from the excess charcoal, the iron absorbed enough carbon to become steel.[7]

The crucible, cementation, and natural steel processes were the three methods used to produce steel from ancient times to the middle of the nineteenth century when the Bessemer process was invented. The secret of the crucible process appears to have been lost, at least to the Western world, until Benjamin Huntsman revived it in 1740. The cementation and natural steel processes never completely died out, and the former was practiced in the United States in the present century.

STEEL PRIMARILY IN WEAPONS

Ancient Sparta's military invincibility may have been due more to steel weapons than to the superior physique and training of its soldiers, as historians have taught us to believe. In January 1961, Lyle B. Borst,

Professor of Physics at New York University, reported that examination of metal fragments, dating from as early as 650 B.C., collected at the site of ancient Sparta, showed them to be of "very high quality steel with few impurities." The specimens had long been regarded as Spartan iron money, but analysis revealed them to be steel with a carbon content ranging from 0.2 to 0.8 per cent, and containing virtually no sulfur, phosphorus, or manganese. How the steel was made is not known, but Dr. Borst has had "the opinion expressed" that the carbon may have been added in the original smelting and not by cementation, which would mean that the steel was produced by the natural process. He believes that the Spartans made steel in sufficient quantities to arm all of their troops at a time when steel was not manufactured elsewhere in Greece. In Dr. Borst's opinion, Sparta's steel weapons prevailed over those of bronze and soft wrought iron possessed by other Hellenes. The situation was to be duplicated later when the steel swords of Roman legionaries hacked down the soft iron weapons of the Gauls, as was pointed out in the previous chapter.[8]

The Romans became proficient artisans in the metalworking trades, including the manufacture of iron and steel. Rome, however, bowed to Spain as the premier producer of iron and steel in the West, and when the Romans became master of the Iberian peninsula about 140 B.C., they found that they could learn more about ferrous metallurgy from the natives than the conquerors could teach them. The Roman legions were equipped with Toledo steel swords which were said to have been "so keen that there is no helmet which cannot be cut through by them."[9]

While some wootz steel may have reached the sword makers of Toledo, the smiths of that city and other localities in Spain produced high quality steel. Some of it was an alloy steel, analysis of specimens having revealed the presence of tungsten, manganese and nickel. The tungsten and manganese were added to the molten iron in the form of wolfram which contained both of these alloying elements. Pulverized nickel was also frequently added.

Steel had other military uses than in weapons. The collection of Early Iron Age relics, found in the peat bog of Llyn Cerrig Bach, Anglesey, Wales, in 1942, contained the earliest known sample of steel discovered so far in Britain. It was probably made sometime between 150 B.C. and A.D. 50. Among the finds were twenty segments of wheel tires, presumably for war chariots. One of these fragments has been analyzed and was found to have a carbon content of 0.74 to 0.96 per cent. It was made by the cementation process. The analysis further revealed a low phosphorus and sulfur content and about 0.05 per cent manganese.[10]

From the Catalan Forge
to the Blast Furnace

The chief glory of the later Middle Ages was not its cathedrals or its epics or its scholasticism; it was the building for the first time in history of a complex civilization which rested not on the backs of sweating slaves or coolies but primarily on non-human power.

—*Lynn White, Jr.*

Before the final collapse of the Western Roman Empire, the production of metals in Europe had begun to decline in the third century A.D., and continued on the down grade for about five hundred years. Iron suffered less than all other metals. It was still needed for tools, farm implements and above all for weapons. These demands, however, were only enough to keep the iron industry feebly alive over most of Europe, except in northern Spain where it still retained some vigor. The first indication of renewed activity in ironmaking on the European mainland appeared around the eighth century in the Eastern Alps. It was followed by a revival in the mining and manufacture of other metals, spurred particularly by the discovery of rich silver and copper ores in Germany.[1]

The growth in the mining and manufacture of metals was due to the prodigious expansion in population, trade, industry, and agriculture, which took place during the Middle Ages.[2] Ironmaking prospered all over Europe. The call for greater quantities of the metal came from almost all fields of activity. The artisans who hewed the stones and built the cathedrals, churches, and other edifices during the great era of Gothic building, as well as other craftsmen such as the armorer, weaver, ship builder, horseshoer, harness and carriage maker, all made their demands felt upon the smelter and forgeman. A host of improved farm implements created a large and growing market for iron. But it was the manufacture of firearms and cannon, after they revolutionized warfare, that provided the most powerful impetus to the iron industry.[3]

After four hundred years of rapid growth there was a sharp reduction in the output of all metals from roughly the middle of the fourteenth to the middle of the fifteenth centuries. The decline began with the Black Death which swept away 35 to 65 per cent of the urban population and was accentuated by the wars which ravaged the Continent, particularly the Hundred Years War between France and England. After recovering from this long period of depression, the iron industry entered upon a prosperous era, extending from 1460 to 1530. In addition to the expanding European market, trade in iron opened up overseas. Styria, Carinthia, Hungary, Westphalia, the Basque provinces, and above all, Sweden, were the chief exporters. Swedish iron was the most prized and highest priced of all medieval irons. Before the end of the sixteenth century the rapid expansion in iron mining and smelting came to an end. It was to be another two hundred years before industry in general on the Continent was to grow as rapidly as it had expanded in the late fifteenth and early sixteenth centuries.

PRECURSORS OF THE BLAST FURNACE

While the iron industry languished over most of Europe in the early centuries of the Christian era, it kept on uninterruptedly in northern Spain where it had existed for hundreds of years. The metallurgical skill of the Catalonians was encouraged by the Visigoths who held sway over most of the peninsula from the fifth to the eighth centuries A.D., when their kingdom was destroyed by the Moors. The latter provided still greater incentive to the iron industry of Spain. During their dominion over that country the Catalan forge was developed.

The Catalan forge represented the first important metallurgical advance in iron smelting since classical times. The hearth was usually a slightly cup-shaped stone about thirty inches square, built up with stones at the front and on two sides to a height of three feet. Since the furnace was generally placed against a hillside, the hill itself formed the back wall of the structure. A short distance above the hearth near the base of the front wall, was an opening for the admission of the nozzle, or tuyere, of the leather bellows. As furnaces grew a little taller and a stronger draft was needed, a flue was extended from the top of the furnace along the surface of the ground a short distance up the hill. The hearth was filled with charcoal to the level of the tuyere. On top of this layer, charcoal and iron ore were piled in two separate columns, the charcoal at the front of the furnace and the ore toward the back. A blast of air from the bellows caused the burning charcoal to give off hot carbon monoxide gas which combined with oxygen in the ore, reducing it to a pasty mass of iron, essentially free of slag. The lump of iron was removed from the hearth and hammered to compact the metal and to drive out any remaining cinders and slag. Afterwards it was beaten into bars which were marketed to the smiths. The furnaces preceding the Catalan forge were capable of producing only fifty pounds of iron at one time. The Catalan forge could yield 350 pounds of metal in a five-hour heat and for this reason assumed importance as a commercial producer.

In the eighth and ninth centuries iron smelters in Austria, Saxony, and along the Rhine, in an effort to increase the capacity of the Catalan forge, raised the height of the furnace shaft to ten feet and later to sixteen feet. This became known as the *stückofen,* or *wolf* furnace, because the large metallic mass extracted from it was called a *stücke* or *wolf.* Later, in France the lump of iron was called a *loup* and in England a *bloom,* the latter term being derived from the Anglo-Saxon *bloma.*[4] The primitive English furnace took the name of bloomery. It never did evolve into the high bloomery or *stückofen.* Britain copied the blast furnace after Continental models, without going through the intermediate stages.[5] All these taller furnaces in Europe, whatever their names, were essentially a Catalan forge extended upwards in a quadrangular or circular shaft.

The *stückofen* was the final development of furnaces in which malleable iron was produced directly from the ore. The *stückofen* yielded an iron mass weighing from 400 to 700 pounds—compared to 350 pounds in the Catalan forge—which was cut into two equal parts called *stücke.* Each half was divided into smaller sections which were worked on the forge into bars and other forms for the trade. The annual production of a *stückofen* was from 100 to 150 tons but it did not work the year round, generally being shut down during dry summer months.[6]

In the earliest *stückofen* the air blast was supplied by a pair of leather bellows operated by the feet or hands. Charcoal and ore were charged into the top of the shaft and were replenished from time to time as the smelting proceeded. By degrees the furnaces grew taller until the stack reached a height which a blast from humanly operated bellows was unable fully to penetrate. The solution to this problem was provided by the application of water power. It had been driving simple rotary mechanisms such as grain mills for centuries, but when it was applied to operate shafts and cams is not known. As early as the first decade of the thirteenth century, water power was driving bellows and hammers in the silver mines of the South Tyrol and soon spread to the other European ironmaking regions. The Cistercians, who played a prominent role in the erection of ironworks operated by water power on the Continent, probably introduced this productive device into England when they settled there and there is evidence that such a mill was built at a Cistercian abbey in Yorkshire about 1200.[7] The water-driven bellows were heart-shaped and consisted of two wooden boards at the top and bottom, with collapsible sides and back made of ox or horsehide. The bellows at first were quite small— about five feet long and two and a half feet wide at the back end, the widest part. As the furnaces were built taller, the bellows grew in proportion in order to provide a blast powerful enough to reach the upper portions of the furnace stack. In England the largest bellows were twenty feet in length and four feet in width at the back.[8] There were usually two bellows attached to a furnace, working alternately and thus supplying a steady blast of air. Water-driven bellows caused a relocation of the iron industry. Formerly the site of an iron-smelting furnace was determined primarily by the accessibility of wood for charcoal and frequently the furnace was built deep in the forest, often on the mountain slope. Water was needed for quenching and other purposes but not in sufficient volume to turn a water wheel. Now the iron smelters came down into the valleys and built their furnaces near the banks of swiftly running streams and rivers.

True Blast Furnace Is Born

The transition from the *stückofen* to the blast furnace was gradual. In the taller furnaces the iron ore remained exposed to the reducing action of charcoal for a longer period, and this, combined with higher temperatures from the water-driven blast, generally, but not always, caused some of the iron to melt and trickle from the bottom of the furnace, where it solidified. This iron, having absorbed enough carbon to transform it into cast iron, which is brittle and unworkable in the forge, was an annoyance to the smelter whose object was to produce low carbon wrought iron. As yet he had no use for cast iron and returned it to the furnace to be remelted. In the early part of the fourteenth century, a new term began to appear among iron smelters—*flüssofen,* that is, a flow oven, clearly indicating that it was capable of producing molten iron. It was also known in German as a *hochofen* and in French as a *haut fourneau.* The increasing appearance of molten iron running from the furnace presented the smelter with a problem. We are left to conjecture what may have passed through his mind. In the proportion that iron flowed from his furnace, the quantity of wrought iron which he obtained was lessened. At the same time, the return of the solidified iron to the furnace for remelting interfered with his operations as a producer of wrought iron. Bronze was then being cast in many forms. Among the chief—if not the chief—cast bronze products were church bells. The iron smelter was certainly familiar with the bronze foundry industry. What could have been more natural than for the producer of cast iron and the bronze foundryman to have been brought together? The circumstances under which this may have occurred are obscure, but it appears most likely that church bells were the first cast iron products extensively produced, followed by a much greater demand for cast iron cannon and cannon balls.

Alert to these new outlets for cast iron, more smelters adjusted their furnaces to produce the metal in a molten state and the true blast furnace came into being. During this transition period, some furnaces, notably the *blauofen,* could be worked to produce either wrought iron or cast iron, depending on the demand. Since the evolution of the blast furnace was gradual, and was under way for some time, it is impossible to set a year for its first appearance. From the tenth century onward we hear of *stückofen* and *flüssofen* in various parts of Germany, and it is generally recognized that the blast furnace was brought to completion in the Rhine provinces, with the French, Belgians, and Germans probably sharing honors in this great technological triumph. There is a record of a *flüssofen* in operation at Marche-les-Dames, Belgium, in 1340 and of *hauts fourneaux* existing near Liége in 1400.[9] These furnaces were capable of producing molten iron. In 1409, there was a blast furnace in the valley of Massevaux, France, and it is claimed that there were many such furnaces in that country by 1450.[10]

Water power was responsible for a second important technological advance in the iron industry: the introduction of a mechanical hammer.

Ever since man worked malleable metals, the smith wielded a hammer to refine and shape the hot plastic mass on the anvil. Hand forging required that the hot piece of metal be small enough for one man to manipulate. Now the tilt hammer came to the aid of the smith. It was a long wooden arm with a head of iron weighing several hundred pounds. The axle shaft of the water wheel caused the arm to rise and fall rhythmically, beating the hot iron. The tilt hammer could perform the labor of twenty men and greatly increased productivity. It was used to do the first rough kneading of the large mass, while the smiths with their ringing hammers still did the finishing work on small sections. Tilt hammers were known to have existed in the iron-producing regions of Europe during the Middle Ages, but they did not appear in England until the late fifteenth and early sixteenth centuries.[11]

CASTING METHODS AND PRODUCTS

Church Bells and Cannon

The making of church bells and cannon was dependent on the combined skills of the iron smelter and founder. The art of casting had never been lost in the Dark Ages and medieval foundrymen attained a high degree of proficiency. The revival of metal casting in medieval times and the consequent development of new techniques in foundry practice were due to the demand for church bells during the great era of cathedral and church building throughout the Christian world. Italy was the birthplace of the revival of the art in the seventh century. By 1150, so great was the demand for church bells that bell founding had become a well-established trade. As cathedrals grew in size, bellfounders were asked to cast larger bells, and since a bell had to be cast all in one piece, this led to improved methods in molding and casting.

After the casting of iron church bells became an established trade, Italy and England gained pre-eminence for their cast iron bells. Thousands of bells ringing throughout Christendom before the end of the Middle Ages bear witness to the activity and the number of the bellfounders. Since they were the most experienced artisans for casting large objects, they were called upon after the invention of gunpowder, to turn their talents to gunmaking. The close relationship between the two trades was typified in the trademark of a fifteenth-century English foundryman whose shield bore a replica of a bell and a cannon.

For many years after the introduction of cast-iron cannon, it was not unusual for a foundryman to alternate between casting bells and cannon in his pit. In the intervals of peace he recast cannon into bells, which in turn were melted and cast into cannon at the behest of Mars. Just as bellfounders set up shop in a churchyard, so we find them, turned gunfounders, casting cannon at the site of a military operation.

The earliest guns were cast in bronze and the first are said to have been produced in the city of Ghent in 1313. Soon afterwards, cannon were made of wrought iron bars placed lengthwise and welded together with iron rings. Guns of both metals were the mortar type and were called bombards. Edward III was the first English monarch to employ cannon which he did in his invasion of Scotland in 1327.

The first cannon balls were of hewn stone or molded concrete because of their cheapness and also because the earliest cannon could not stand the greater explosive charge needed for metal balls. But stone and concrete proved to be too brittle for siege purposes. Bronze balls were too expensive. Although it was feasible to use balls of wrought iron, the labor involved in forging iron of the correct size was excessive. The problem of suitable projectiles was solved by the use of cast-iron balls which could be reproduced in quantity from the same mold. Cast-iron shot were produced in such quantity that by the middle of the sixteenth century they consumed more iron than any other product.

Although large guns fabricated of wrought iron served armies for siege purposes up to the fifteenth century, they were unable to withstand the heavier powder charges then being introduced and their manufacture was too slow and costly to meet the growing demand for ordnance. Toward the end of the fourteenth century the bellfounders began to switch their trade to that of gunfounding, at first producing bronze cannon until they were superseded by iron about 1550.

The casting of iron cannon became one of the first manufactures in which England excelled. The seat of the industry was in the Weald of Sussex. For about two hundred years, from the time of Henry VIII to the latter half of the eighteenth century, the Weald had a virtual monopoly in the production of cast iron guns, which, because of their superiority, were sold all over the Continent. The export of cannon from the Weald reached such a scale in the reign of Elizabeth that in 1573 complaints were made to the Privy Council that "merchante shippes that doe finde themselves marvailouslie molested and otherwhiles robbed by reason of the great stoare of ordenance that hath both ben convayed and solde to strangers out of this Realme, whereby their shippes are so well appointed that no poore merchante shippe maie passe, thorow the seas." In response, the ironmasters in the Weald were forbidden to sell ordnance abroad except by license.[12] Other restrictive measures were taken in later years up to 1602, when the further casting of cannon was prohibited, but all regulations proved to be ineffective. Ordnance continued to be smuggled out of the country. Gunrunning in the English Channel was a normal incident in the commercial life of Sussex at that time, and Kipling's story of demicannon being carried under wool sacks to Rye is based on history.[13] But the Spaniards profited most. It was said that when the Spanish Armada, consisting of 130 ships, sailed forth to invade England, most of the 2,400 cannon aboard were of English manufacture.[14]

In the early period of cast iron, its high cost limited its application to ordnance and to products for the wealthy, but more productive furnaces and greater economies in casting eventually brought the price of cast iron products within the reach of nearly everyone. The casting of firebacks became second in importance only to cannon and shot. In the seventeenth century, firebacks began to give way to cast-iron stoves. Their development, which brought comfort and improved health to millions, was due entirely to the art of iron casting. Before 1800, stovemaking became one of the most extensive and profitable iron manufactures in Europe and America. Other products of the founder which opened up large markets were pots, kettles, skillets, gridirons, grave slabs, clock weights, and cog wheels for machinery.

Direct Furnace Casting—the Cupola

From the inception of the blast furnace in the early 1300s up to about 1700, iron castings were made directly from the molten metal as it poured from the hearth. For large products such as bells and cannon the metal was allowed to flow directly into the molds. To make smaller castings such as cannon balls and firebacks, the molten iron was allowed to run from the furnace into a reservoir from which it was taken in a long-handled ladle and poured into molds. Since some of the iron solidified before it could reach the molds, the method was wasteful, and furthermore restricted casting to the furnace site. In France about 1700, it first occurred to foundrymen to let the molten iron solidify in small sections and then remelt them in a separate furnace, called a cupola. The molten iron was allowed to run from the furnace into a sand trough which fed a number of smaller lateral troughs. This configuration struck the early ironworkers as resembling a sow with a litter of suckling pigs. The larger casting became known as a sow, the smaller as pigs, and the iron itself as pig iron. The last two names persist to this day. The pigs were of a size that could be easily handled and reserved for a time when castings for the trade were to be made, or they could be shipped to a distant point.

The remelting cupola was an impotrant step forward. It freed the foundry from direct dependence on the site of the blast furnace, but the blast furnace and foundry often remained side by side for convenience. At the same time, the remelt furnace allowed pig iron to become an article of commerce, making it possible for a small foundry to exist in a region where no iron was smelted, and thus extended the geographical horizons of the iron industry.

The original French cupola was quite small. The first cupola similar in appearance to those of today was invented in 1794 by John Wilkinson, one of the most progressive ironmasters of that period in England. In order to melt larger quantities of iron for the manufacture of cannon and other ordnance material, he built the cupola up to blast furnace size and added a number of improvements in its construction and operation. He is credited as being the first person to apply steam power to blow the blast of a cupola.[15]

Malleable Iron Castings

Up to this period, iron was produced commercially in two forms— wrought and cast. The first, because of its very low carbon content, was strong, durable, and ductile; the second, because of its higher carbon content, was hard and brittle, with weak resistance to impact. Because iron castings were brittle, they were limited to products that were not subjected to severe strain or rough usage. Ironmasters began to search for ways to produce cast iron which possessed the tough and ductile properties of wrought iron. In the first quarter of the eighteenth century, the great French scientist, René Antoine de Réamur, applied his brilliant mind to the problem in an effort to aid the languishing French iron industry. In 1722, he published a treatise explaining his experiments. What he did was to imbed pig iron castings in iron ore and heat them at bright redness for many days. Oxygen in the ore removed almost all of the carbon from the iron, rendering it quite similar to wrought iron. His process was at first limited to small castings because large castings remained hard and brittle in the interior, but this limitation was eventually overcome by others. European malleable iron was called "whiteheart," because of the white or gray color of its fracture. The American variety, developed by Seth Boyden nearly a century after Réamur's experiments, became known as "blackheart," because of the dark color of its fracture.

CAST IRON INTO WROUGHT IRON

Although cast iron was readily acceptable for use in bells, cannon, firebacks, and stoves, it met resistance from many smiths and their customers, who were skeptical of the newfangled cast iron and still preferred time-honored wrought iron for products susceptible to casting such as locks and keys, grilles, gates, clockweights, to name a few. There were also many products for which wrought iron was preferable because it is "tough" and can withstand repeated shocks which might shatter cast iron. In this category were horseshoes, nails, tools, wagon wheel rims, farm implements, and plow points. Thus there still existed consistent demand for wrought iron and, as we have seen, some furnaces such as the *blauofen*, could be operated to produce either wrought iron or cast iron.

The problem confronting the ironmaster was to convert brittle cast iron into wrought iron. The solution involved remelting and purifying the cast pig iron into wrought iron. For this reason it is known as the indirect process. Where, when, and how the process was developed is unknown. Very likely it originated among the Walloons in Belgium, where the first written reference to it appeared in 1620, but at that date the process had reached a fair degree of development.[16] Different methods were later introduced but they all involved the same basic principle, in which excess carbon and other elements in pig iron were oxidized out in a charcoal forge, called a finery, not unlike the early American blacksmith's forge.

The finery was filled with charcoal which was heated with bellows to a high temperature. Three or four pigs were thrust endwise into the fire and stirred with a long iron bar to expose different parts of their surface to the blast of the bellows. The ends of the pigs melted off in drops, and the molten iron was purified by the oxidizing effect of the blast. As the metal became purer, its melting point was raised and it solidified in pasty particles which adhered together to form a spongy bloom. This was removed from the forge and given a few strokes of the hammer. It was then carried to the tilt hammer which was applied dexterously to beat the iron into a thick, short, square shape. It was returned to the refinery and brought to red-heat and again worked under the tilt hammer until it was in the shape of a bar about three feet long with square knobs at the ends. This was called an ancony. In the final step the ancony was carried to a second forge called a chafery, where it was reheated and then beaten into bars of different shapes and sizes for the trade.

The iron bar was the standard wrought iron product sold by the iron industry. It constituted the stock of iron from which the smith drew to forge whatever products were in local demand. He was the local manufacturer of products needed in the home, on the farm, in industry, and war, from remote times down to the Village Blacksmith of Longfellow and considerably later. In England bars of wrought iron were generally sold at the market town or fair, and it was customary for the bailiff to buy what iron was needed for the farm and to employ the village smith to fashion it into nails, horseshoes, mattocks, hay-forks, sickles, bolts, hinges, hoops, and countless other products. "The iron-bound bucket that hung in the well," existed at least as early as 1331. In medieval England iron was most commonly sold by the "piece," twenty-three of which made a hundred-weight.[17] Forged steel was marketed by the "garb," meaning a hundred, which was an ancient weight equivalent to twenty-seven pounds.[18] Swank says that the garb was also known as a "sheaf," which contained thirty small pieces.[19] Raw steel was sold by the "cake." Allowing for a loss in forging, the cake would weigh approximately thirty-six pounds.[20] The price of steel was about four times that of iron.[21]

STEEL

As we learned in the previous chapter, the manufacture of steel did not die out after the collapse of the Roman Empire. It continued to be made by the cementation and direct, or natural, processes in Britain during the Roman occupation and later through the medieval period. Steel was produced elsewhere, because Schubert tells us that in the middle of the sixteenth century steelworkers were brought into England from Germany and also that steel was imported into England from Sweden.[22]

England Leads the Way

Gold is for the mistress—silver for the maid—
Copper for the craftsman, cunning at his trade,
"Good!" said the Baron, sitting in his hall,
"But Iron—Cold Iron—is Master of them all."
— *Rudyard Kipling*
Cold Iron

When the Roman legions withdrew from Britain around 410 A.D. most of their civilizing influences "fell into oblivion."[1] One craft, however, continued in unbroken tradition, even through England's Dark Ages which followed the departure of the Romans—the craft of the smith. The Anglo-Saxons, who took over the land, still needed iron for swords and other articles of war, for tools and agricultural implements. The smith was held in such high esteem that he was treated as an officer of the highest rank and his person was protected by a double penalty.

After Christianity was established in Britain in the seventh century, the monks were noted for their skill as ironworkers. St. Dunstan, who lived in the tenth century, is said to have had a forge in his bedroom and to have been a skilled blacksmith and metallurgist.

The conquest of England by William the Conqueror in 1066 was followed by a peaceful invasion of industrial and trading classes from Normandy who contributed much to the development of the English iron industry and other resources. The second infusion of skills into the British iron industry was due to Edward III through his dual policy of encouraging native manufacturing by inviting artisans to come over from the Continent, while at the same time restricting imports of foreign goods. No iron manufactured in England or imported into it could be sold or carried out of the kingdom under penalty of forfeiting double the quantity to the king. By virtue of these measures the iron industry extended its activities during the reign of Edward III, but the metal was still so scarce that the iron pots, spits, and pans in the royal kitchen were classed among the king's jewels.

The low output of iron in medieval England is explainable by the continued use of the low bloomery long after the blast furnace had appeared on the Continent. Even after the introduction of the blast furnace in England, the bloomery was extensively employed in the sixteenth and seventeenth centuries.

The English ironmasters did not have to go through the evolutionary steps from the low bloomery to the blast furnace because it had already been accomplished in Europe. Schubert says there is no evidence that the high bloomery, or *stückofen,* representing the intermediate stage in the development of the blast furnace, was ever built in Britain. The English simply jumped over the *stückofen* and went directly from the low bloomery to the blast furnace. It was for reasons of national defense that the English finally erected their first blast furnace around 1496. It belonged to the Crown and was built in the Weald of Sussex by Henry VII to make cast iron for the royal artillery as the monarch strengthened his northern borders against a Scottish invasion. Other blast furnaces soon followed in the Weald which became the busiest iron center in England. It reached its peak in the reign of Queen Elizabeth, when, instead of importing iron, England began to export it in large quantities, mostly in the form of ordnance. Shipbuilding and the founding of cannon were said to be the sole manufactures in which the English excelled in the reign of James I, from 1603 to 1625. England continued to import the finer grades of iron and considerable quantities of steel from Europe, chiefly from Sweden, Germany, and Spain.

THE HISTORY OF WIRE

The use of wire goes far back into antiquity. It was first used entirely for ornamentation. A crown made of wire leaves was said to have been worn by Queen Shubab of Sumeria as long ago as 3745 B.C.[2] We are not told of what material the wire was made but it is known that the earliest wire was of hammered gold and silver. Gold rings were the most common form. A necklace partly of gold wire was unearthed at Denderah, Egypt, presumably worn by the Pharaoh who ruled over that country about 2750 B.C. The thirty-ninth chapter of Exodus describes how wire was prepared for the ceremonial robes of Aaron: "And they did beat the gold into thin plates, and cut it into wire."[3] There is also a record of wire having been made about 800 B.C. by the artisans of Nineveh, the capital of ancient Assyria, now Iraq.

The first evidence that wire was employed for purposes other than ornamentation was found in the ruins of Pompeii which was buried under an eruption of Vesuvius in 79 A.D. This relic was bronze wire rope and its perfect construction leads to the conclusion that the making of wire rope was well developed at that time. It is also the earliest known example of wire made of other material than a precious metal. Bronze wire was eventually replaced by iron. For many centuries, wire, first of bronze and then of iron, was made by heating a lump of metal and then beating it on an anvil into flat, thin sheets. These were slit into narrow strips by a chisel and elongated into wire by further hammering.

The wire industry may be said to date from the time that man discovered how to form it by drawing it through a die. The earliest reference to a die is in a Latin manuscript written by a monk, Theophilus, sometime between the ninth and eleventh centuries. He describes how wire was drawn through three or four rows of holes in an iron draw plate. The metals used were lead and tin.

Progress in wire drawing is closely related to the use of chain armor by knights in the Middle Ages when it was discovered that a suit of mail was more effective than a breastplate of solid metal, thereby opening up a new era in the history of European armor. The new armor consisted of hundreds of small chains, the round links of which were made of iron wire. Coats of mail, attributed to the fourth and fifth centuries, have been found in Danish peat bogs, fashioned of rings welded and riveted in alternate rows, made by hammering. The Vikings who ravaged England and northern Europe in the eighth and ninth centuries wore suits of mail which became the chief knightly armor until the close of the thirteenth century. Wire for the earliest suits of mail was undoubtedly made by the hammering method but it is considered possible that at a later period the wire was drawn.

Wire Drawing Introduced

The nation that developed wire drawing on a commercial scale was France. There were reported to be eight wire drawing establishments in Paris in 1292, all working with brass. By the middle of the fourteenth century the Germans stole the march on the French and made Nuremberg the European home of wire drawing. At first the wire was pulled through a die by sheer human force, a few inches at a time, in a painfully slow process. The Germans invented a machine operated by a hand crank, which pulled the wire through a die plate. Lengths of six to twelve feet could be produced, the ends of which were heated and forged together. The next step was taken about the middle of the fourteenth century by Rudolph of Nuremberg who applied water power to draw the wire and the modern wire industry was born.

Wire was consumed in large quantities in England for carding wool. The nation depended on foreign supplies, not only for ready-made wool cards but for almost all other wire it sold. The story has been handed down by successive writers that wire drawing was introduced into England by a group of Germans who were granted permission by Queen Elizabeth in 1565 to enter the country for the purpose of digging metallic ores. Shortly afterwards, the story says, the first water-driven wire mill was erected in England and before long the native industry was freed of dependence on imports.

Schubert has amplified this story and slightly amended it. He concedes that it was a desire to make England independent of imported wire for the wool trade that brought about erection of the first water-driven wire mill in that country about 1566-1567. He places the mill in the immediate vicinity of the Cistercian Abbey at Tintern, Monmouthshire.

Eventually, other wire mills were set on their feet in Britain, more than two centuries after the method had been introduced by Rudolph of Nuremberg. The British wire industry became very lucrative. Wire was manufactured into wool cards, pack needles, bird cages, mouse traps, knitting needles, rings, and rods for curtains, and chains for keys. The number of persons engaged in the manufacture of wire products in England in 1597 was estimated at more than five thousand.

SLITTING MILLS AND NAILS

An important feat of technology in this period was invention of the slitting mill which found its greatest application in preparation of nail rods for manufacture of the humble but indispensable nail. The ring of the carpenter's hammer driving in nails has gone down through the ages. Copper nails were used on tire rims of primitive vehicles in the Bronze Age. The Bible relates that when David, about 1000 B.C., made plans to build a temple he "prepared iron in abundance for the nails for the doors of the gates and for the joinings."[4] Christ was nailed to a cross.

From remote times until the close of the eighteenth century when nail-making machines were invented in America, nails were made by hand. A wrought-iron nail rod was cut into the approximate length of a nail, placed in a vise or simply on an anvil, and with deft strokes of a hammer, the point and head were shaped. A skilled worker could forge as many as two thousand small nails a day. These were called wrought, or cut, nails.

A water-driven machine for slitting flat bars of iron into nail rods was known a little before or after 1500 in the Liége district of Belgium and also in Germany. A flat bar was heated and then cut into strips by passing between a series of revolving discs. The first license to set up such a mill in England was granted to Bulvis Bulmer in 1588. Whether he utilized the privilege is not known, but a slitting mill is supposed to have been erected in Kent, England, in 1590 by Godfrey Box (also spelled Godefroi de Bochs), a native of Liége, Belgium. Richard Foley, an English iron-master, set up a slitting mill in Worcestershire about 1625. There is a well-known story that he went to Sweden disguised as a beggar and there learned the secrets of the slitting mill while fiddling for the workmen. On his return to England, he is supposed to have built his slitting mill. Schubert discounts this "romantic story" because the new invention was not introduced into Sweden prior to 1626, or perhaps a few years later. Although Foley's slitting mill was not the first in England, it represented an improvement over contemporary mills and remained the prevailing type in Britain until near the end of the eighteenth century.[5]

The slitting mill stepped up productivity in the nail trade prodigiously, and for a period nail-making consumed more iron, in England at least, than any other product. A thriving nail trade had its center in Birmingham where women and girls were employed as "nailers" in numerous blacksmith shops, "wielding the hammer with all the grace of their sex."[6]

RISE OF THE TIN-PLATE INDUSTRY

The resistance of tin to oxidation must have become apparent at a very early time, and some authorities say that the application of a thin coat of tin to various metals by dipping them in molten tin is very old. The Romans coated copper vessels with tin to make containers for food and drink. Although there are some references to coating iron with tin in the first century of the Christian era, the modern industry dates from about 1240 when the tin mines of the Erzgebirge mountains in Bohemia, which were an important source of tin in antiquity, were rediscovered and the plating of iron sheets was revived. The methods used in the process were concealed there for several hundred years. Through the efforts of the Duke of Saxony, it is said, the secrets were finally penetrated, and in 1620 tin-plating began in the Hartz Mountains, where tin ores had been known in the Bronze Age. The Saxons were also vigilant in guarding their techniques, but the news of their success reached Wales and inspired Captain Andrew Yarrington in 1665 to try to filch the secrets of tin plate manufacture from the Germans. In an account of his adventures, he wrote that eleven knights, noblemen and gentlemen advanced a "sum of monies" for defraying "my charge of travelling." He was accompanied by an "Able Fireman" who understood the nature of iron and an "Ingenious Interpreter." With their aid, he succeeded in learning the "whole art of making and tinning the plates," but he does not explain the process. Several years after his return to England, Yarrington and his backers attempted to duplicate the German methods but with little or no success. Yarrington claimed that persons high in the king's favor were granted patents for tin-plate manufacture.[7]

The tin-plate trade languished in England for about half a century after Yarrington's secret mission to Saxony. The man who vitalized the business and made it a commercial success was Major John Hanbury. He owned an ironworks at Pontypool, Wales, and as early as 1697 operated what a contemporary described as "an excellent invention . . . for driving hot-iron . . . by the help of a rolling engine moved by water . . . into as thin plates as tin." With his rolled iron sheets, Hanbury at first manufactured pots, kettles, saucepans, and other products which he was able to do at one-third the prevailing cost. In 1720, he branched into the manufacture of tin plate. Whether he began at once to substitute rolled for hammered sheets is not recorded, but by 1728 he was doing so, and by 1730 his sheets for tin plating were definitely on the market. Other tin-plate manufac-turers experimented with the rolled sheets and were described as de-lighted with their superior quality. The manufacture of rolled iron sheets, the accessibility of tin mines in Cornwall and abundant water power laid the basis for the rapid ascendancy of Wales as the tin-plate center of the world. Plating iron with tin is basically a simple process. The iron sheet is immersed in molten tin, but the trick is to give an even, adhesive coating. This requires a meticulously clean surface and since the smoother the sheet the more thoroughly it can be rid of rust and minute dirt specks, it is understandable why Hanbury's rolled sheets gave such a boost to the Welsh tin-plate industry.

Origin of "Tin Cans"

Tin plate was used almost exclusively in open vessels and in ornamental work until it was found to be an ideal material for hermetically sealed food containers. In 1765 an Italian scientist, Spallanzani, without any knowledge of germs, developed the theory that *something* in the air caused food to spoil, that heating food in sealed bottles would kill that *something* and that the sealing would keep out contaminating air. He ap-plied his theory with some degree of success but made no practical appli-cation of it. Modern canning is due indirectly to the French Revolution and Napoleon. In 1795 the French government offered a prize of 12,000 francs to anyone who would find a way to preserve food for French sailors at sea. Nicolas Appert, a Parisian confectioner, who may or may not have heard of Spallanzani's pioneering work, entertained a similiar theory and persisted in the face of repeated failures for nearly fifteen years until he canned food to his satisfaction in glass bottles. So skeptical was the world at the time of the possibility of preserving food indefinitely by canning that Appert was required to have sample bottles of preserved food travel around in French ships for a two-to-three-year testing period. His food stood the tests, and in 1809 Napoleon's government awarded him the prize.

Appert's success interested the tin-plate trade across the Channel; in 1810 an Englishman, Peter Durand, patented a process for preserving food in cans made of tin-plated iron sheets, and the "tin can" was born. He named his container a "tin cannister." The British chose the first word and called the containers "tins" while in America the second word was contracted to "can." The new container was first used extensively to preserve meats for British soldiers and sailors who made the term "tinned bully beef" known throughout the Empire.

Tin-plated cans were at first made laboriously by hand. An expert tin-smith could turn out ten a day, but the output was later stepped up to sixty. The cans were, consequently, expensive and were worth more than their contents.

Wales, already the tin-plate center of the world, entered upon an ascending wave of prosperity in furnishing its product to the new and expanding market of the food industry. Improved methods in tin-plate production and the substitution of Bessemer steel for wrought iron around 1880, gave a better and cheaper can. World leadership of the Welsh tin-plate trade, which depended on the United States as its chief customer for 70 per cent of its output, went unchallenged until passage of the McKinley Tariff Act in 1890 enabled the American industry to become firmly established and finally to take over the crown.

FROM CHARCOAL TO COKE IN THE IRON INDUSTRY

The more the iron industry expanded, the more it threatened its own extinction by devouring the fuel on which it depended. For 150 years the chief ironmaking nations of Western Europe were torn between the need of timber for charcoal on the one hand, and for building material and domestic fuel on the other. Nowhere did this problem become as acute as in England, with dramatic consequences which we shall see presently.

Charcoal replaced wood as a fuel in smelting metals during the Bronze Age. Heat from a log is fitful, whereas charcoal burns steadily with a fairly even heat that can be lowered or intensified by the amount of air blown upon it.

The ease of making charcoal and the great abundance of forests in earlier times favored the use of this fuel. Logs were stacked into a conical pile that was covered with mud or turf, except for a small area at the top. Holes were left open at the base of this dome-shaped mound that functioned like an oven. Once the logs were ignited, the mud or turf prevented air from directly reaching the wood for complete combustion. The internal heat passing upward, caused the logs to give off their fluids and sap juices in the form of steam or heavy oils, leaving behind a gray porous substance of almost pure carbon and weighing one-third of its original weight—charcoal. Charcoal burning was a slow process and generally took place in the forest where the timber was cut.

Charcoal was consumed not only in the iron-smelting furnace but also in the refinery forge, both requiring large quantities of fuel for every ton of iron produced and refined. Extensive as were the forests of Europe, trees were not quickly replaced and the appetite of the "voracious" iron mills was causing more and more concern in England from the early fourteenth century onward. Charcoal burners preferred oak and chestnut trees and the former were also the choice of the shipbuilders. The denuding of forests also threatened to deprive communities of firewood. Loud complaints arose in various parts of the realm. The charcoal burners were considered a public menace and the ironworkers became even more unpopular, being described by a religious writer as "heathenish in their manners, puffed up with pride, and inflated with worldly prosperity."[8]

Although some steps were taken to preserve the island's timber resources, notably through a system of coppicing which required the replacement of felled trees, the situation went from bad to worse and was aggravated by Henry VIII's dissolution of the monasteries in the late 1530s and through the sale of their possessions, including vast tracts of well-preserved woodlands. Most of the new owners, as well as tenants of property retained by the Crown, hastened to sell off the timber, particularly to ironmasters.

Complaints against the destruction of forests grew more frequent and louder and were loudest of all against the loss of timber for shipbuilding because "shipping is the walles" which prevented enemies from invading England. Tough oak was desired for English ships of war and merchant vessels at a time when the mother country was expanding overseas and clashing with Spain.

By the time of Queen Elizabeth, the country was on the horns of a dilemma. How should the need for timber be balanced between the iron and shipbuilding industries? The good queen apparently started with a compromise. In the first year of her reign, 1558, an Act was passed forbidding the cutting of timber in certain parts of the realm "for the making of iron," exception being made of the Weald of Kent, the county of Sussex and certain parishes in Surrey. Five years later, further restrictions were imposed, but these were not severe enough; in 1581, Queen Elizabeth signed a law which provided that "no new iron works should be erected within twenty-two miles of London, nor within fourteen miles of the river Thames," nor in certain parts of Sussex near the sea. The Act further forbade the use of wood in the prescribed areas, with certain exceptions, for conversion into "coal or other fewel, for the making of iron-metal in any iron-mill, furnace or hammer." These restrictions were not rigidly enforced and the British iron industry continued to devour its own tail. Finally in 1584, an Act was passed forbidding the erection of any new iron works in Surrey, Kent, and Sussex, and ordered that no timber one foot square at the stub should be used as fuel "at any iron-work."

Another reason for the contraction of the iron industry was the constant rise in operating costs. The price of wood in England tripled between 1588 and 1630 and continued to soar. In 1550 a typical ironmaster found that charcoal represented 50 per cent of his total operating costs and by 1750 had climbed to 80 per cent. Squeezed by ruinous operating costs, many ironmasters gave up in despair. Abandonment of furnaces all but wiped out the English charcoal iron industry. Swank, quoting Simon Sturdevant, reports that in 1612 there were "800 furnaces, forges, or iron mills" in England, Scotland, Ireland and Wales, adding that a few years later the number of furnaces in that total were estimated to be 300.[9] In 1717—a few years after Abraham Darby first smelted iron with coke—there were only fifteen furnaces and fourteen forges in the British isles.[10] If these figures are correct, the English iron industry in a little more than a century had shrunk approximately 96 per cent in the number of furnaces and forges. Seventeenth- and eighteenth-century England still depended heavily on Sweden for iron, with Russia and the American colonies augmenting her supplies.

Search for Another Fuel

What should be done to save the forests and the iron industry of England occupied the attention of many minds. The best that Parliament could do was to restrict the production of charcoal and iron and increase imports, with the tragic results which have been recorded here. If England was to continue to smelt iron and not confine herself to refining imported metal, it was imperative that another fuel be found.

It was inevitable that England should eventually turn to coal, of which she had immense reserves. The conversion of coal into coke dates back to antiquity. In China and India, a crude coking process was carried out simply by setting fire to piles of coal. After combustion was well under way, turf or wet straw was spread over the pile to seal off most of the air. The coke obtained was used to forge iron and steel implements and weapons. One of the earliest known references to the coking process was made by Theophrastus, a pupil of Aristotle. In his *History of Stones*, written about 371 B.C., Theophrastus observes:

But the Lipara stone empties itself, as it were, in burning and becomes like the pumice, changing at once both its color and density; for before burning it is black, smooth and compact. . . . Certain stones there are about Tetras, in Sicily, which is over against Lipara, which empty themselves in the same manner in the fire.[11]

In the latter part of the sixteenth century, the coking of coal was practiced in England, where the coke was substituted for charcoal in the brickmaking, brewing, dyeing, and brass industries. In view of the depressed state of the iron industry, it was but natural that a number of enterprising people thought of replacing charcoal with coke in the blast furnace. The first attempt to smelt iron with coal was made in Yorkshire by Thomas Proctor who obtained a patent in 1589 for a process utilizing coal mixed with peat and charcoal. It was unsuccessful. A few years later the Countess of Cumberland sought a license to smelt iron with mineral coal and peat. Further attempts to smelt iron with coal were more frequent in the following century, including one by John Rovenson (also spelled Robinson) who obtained a patent in 1613, granting him the sole right in England and Wales to refine iron with coal.

The name of Rovenson brings up the controversial figure of Dud Dudley, natural son of Edward, fifth Lord of Dudley. Dud Dudley, in his book *Metallum Martis,* claims to have smelted iron of good quality with "pit-coles" at the rate of "3 tuns" per week in 1619 and to have been granted a patent in that year by James I. He claims further to have "made annually great store of iron, good and merchantable," which he sold for four pounds per ton against the going price of six pounds per ton for charcoal iron.[12]

Dud Dudley Debunked

Dud Dudley wrote *Metallum Martis* forty years after his first experiments. The book won him undisputed recognition as one of the great inventors of the iron and steel industry, as the man who finally united coal and iron in Britain, and as such he has gone down in the history books. Beginning in 1921, skepticism regarding the assertions of Dud Dudley began to rear its head. Finally, H. R. Schubert entered the jousting lists, and in an article, "The Truth about Dud Dudley," published in the November 1950 issue of the *Journal of the British Iron and Steel Institute,* unseats Dudley from his place of honor.[13]

Schubert bases his rejection of Dudley's claims on two recently discovered documents. The first, dated May 25, 1618, is an agreement between John Robinson of Westminster and Edward, Lord Dudley. Robinson's patent of 1613 granted him the sole privilege in England and Wales to make and refine iron with coal for a period of thirty-one years. In developing his process he had been aided by Lord Dudley financially, and also by sharing knowledge which Dudley had gained in his own experiments. Now the two men entered into a partnership in which, for anticipated profits, Robinson assigned his patent to Lord Dudley. There were other conditions which need not be elaborated here. The result was that Lord Dudley secured for himself an exclusive patent in 1622 for fourteen years. The agreement strongly indicates, says Schubert, that serious attempts were made to smelt iron with coal in the vicinity of Dudley at that time, but there is no record that any met with success.

At the time the experiments took place, Schubert continues, Dud Dudley was a youth of eighteen or nineteen before he went to Oxford. Although Dud Dudley never acknowledged so in his book, he very likely knew of the experiments and, says Schubert, "it is not impossible that Dud Dudley made use of experience gained by the trials of 1618 for his own first attempts, which he claimed to be completely successful." Dudley asserts that they were made in 1619, whereas, Schubert points out, he was a student at Oxford from September 1619 to March 1622.[14]

"There is not the slightest evidence on record," writes Schubert, "that

Dud Dudley had any success with his trials," but on the contrary, "his assertions of successfully smelting iron with coal are contradicted by a second document." This is a deposition made by William Cope in the Court of Chancery, London, in December 1635, acknowledging that Dud Dudley had devoted great labor and expense to the invention of a means for making iron with coal, but distinctly denying that he "made the said iron with seacoles or pitt coles," as the latter had alleged.[15]

Schubert concludes that "Dud Dudley, despite all his claims, did neither invent the method for producing iron with mineral coal, nor was he successful in any of his attempts made in various ironworks in the Dudley area."[16]

R.A. Mott, in an article published in the *Transactions of the Newcomen Society* for 1934-1935, says that after a thorough study of the records, he concluded that Dudley was "an opportunist, vain, boastful, and untruthful and that there are no grounds for including him among the pioneers of the iron industry."[17]

Abraham Darby, Father of the Coke Furnace

Whether Dud Dudley produced "Merchantable Iron" with "pitt coles" or not, his secrets died with him. At best, his work was experimental. The man who brought the process to completion and introduced a bright new era into the iron industry was the English Quaker, Abraham Darby.

In his youth, Darby was apprenticed to the iron trade, and after finishing his apprenticeship in 1699 he went to Bristol and there set up a business to make malt mills. He journeyed to Holland, presumably in 1704, and it is generally believed that while there he studied the methods used in casting brass pots, which at that time constituted an important English import. In 1706, with several partners, he established a foundry for casting brass pots. His interest soon turned to cast iron and as a result of his experiments he patented a process for casting "bellied" iron pots in sand, which was a marked improvement over loam or clay then in use. Darby's partners did not share his growing enthusiasm for the cast iron business and so he left Bristol and leased an ironworks in Coalbrookdale near the Severn River in Shropshire. The region was rich in charcoal timber and iron ore and the Severn was both a source of power and a transportation artery for his products.

Darby intended to smelt iron with charcoal, but the steadily rising cost of the fuel soon became an insuperable barrier to profitable operations. Instead of abandoning his enterprise or restricting his output, as many of his competitors were doing, this resourceful man looked about for a substitute. He must have known that raw coal had been tried without success, and there is reason to believe that he may have experimented with it, for there are entries in his journal of 1709 for the purchase of "Coles." There are also entries for the purchase of "charking coles" in his accounts of 1708 and 1709, but whether these refer to charcoal or coal is not known. It appears certain that in those years he was in the throes of experimentation. From his experience as a malt mill maker, Darby was familiar with the use of coke, which was used in appreciable quantities for drying malt. It is highly possible that he smelted iron with coke on a commercial scale as early as 1709, for in that year he sold large quantities of pig iron, as well as cast iron pots, kettles and firebacks. Finally, Darby's records show that by 1711 the new fuel had proved satisfactory. It may be concluded, then, that this epochal event took place not later than 1711 and more likely a few years earlier.

Coke consists almost entirely of carbon and was then made in a process similar to that used in baking wood into charcoal. Smelting with coke was more efficient and economical than charcoal and Darby was able to offer cast iron pots, kettles and other small ware for sale at a price that was within the reach of the majority of the population. By bringing the price of these iron products to a level which the average citizen could afford, Darby has been hailed as a great benefactor to the English people.

Acceptance of the new process by the English ironmasters and their customers was slow. This is not surprising. Coke-produced pig iron, being high in carbon, was brittle and although suitable for cast wares, the forgemen found difficulty in converting it into wrought iron for shaping into plowshares, edge tools, locks and bolts, wagon tires, hoes, and many other products. Smelters who wished to sell their products to forgemen did not want it known that it was made with coke. Charcoal remained the fuel used not only for converting pig iron into wrought-iron bars, but also for smelting iron intended to be made into bars.

Coke Smelting Established in England

It was Darby's son, Abraham Darby II, who is credited with overcoming the opposition of forgemen to coke-produced iron. (Incidentally, the ironworks at Coalbrookdale have remained in operation ever since their founding, managed by five generations of Darbys whose active interest continued in the works until recent years.) Abraham Darby II, a worthy son of his father, sought to enlarge the market for his coke-iron, particularly in the nail trade of the Midlands which was then the largest consumer of iron. He encountered obstacles because the nail trade insisted on charcoal iron. Between 1749 and 1750, he succeeded in producing a quality of iron in his coke-fired blast furnace which the nailers and other forgemen could convert satisfactorily into malleable iron, but the technique he employed is not known. The story is told that for six days and nights he stayed on the bridge of his furnace, waiting until the flow of iron was of the quality he was searching for and when he was assured that success had been attained he collapsed and had to be carried by the workmen to his home.[18] This accomplishment has been erroneously attributed to his father upon his successful smelting of iron with coke.

Others in addition to Abraham Darby II doubtless had a hand in improving the efficiency of the coke blast furnace and its products so that they became acceptable to the forgemen. After 1760, the coke smelting process spread rapidly in Britain and the great forgemasters began to buy coke iron. The iron industry took a new lease on life in England and Wales, and it has been said that the iron industry of Scotland was created by the new fuel. By 1796, charcoal furnaces had all but disappeared in Great Britain. Output increased from 17,000 tons in 1740 to 68,000 tons in 1788.

Iron castings of improved quality and lower price led to their increasing substitution for wood, copper, lead, brass and other materials, thereby expanding the markets for iron. But cast iron made its greatest gains by replacing wrought iron. Increased productivity in iron smelting and casting made it possible for cast iron products to undersell wrought iron wares of the forges, which were costly to operate due to the large consumption of expensive charcoal and the wages of highly-skilled forgemen and smiths. The eighteenth century witnessed a struggle between the foundrymen and the forgemen, with the thinning ranks of the latter giving way before the implacable advance of the former. In less than one hundred years after Darby's death, the quantity of coke-iron produced in the world increased from a negligible amount to more than one hundred million tons a year.

Prelude to the Industrial Revolution

Man without tools is nothing;
With tools he is all.
            —Thomas Carlyle

THE FIRST ROLLING MILLS

There is some evidence that the remote ancestor of the massive rolling mill of the steel industry was a pair of hand-driven rolls about one-half inch in diameter used in the fourteenth century to flatten strips of gold and silver, and perhaps lead.[1] It is certain that the first rolls of which there are actual records were small hand-operated cylinders used to roll flat metals which were ductile enough to be worked in a cold condition and were employed by goldsmiths and others who manufactured jewelry or works of art.

The commercial development of rolling was taken out of the hands of workers in precious metals who produced on a small scale and were satisfied with small machines. The greater availability and increased use of lead and tin which are ductile enough to be shaped cold, induced some men to substitute rolling for hand-hammering methods. In 1615, Solomon de Caus of France rolled lead and tin into sheets for making organ pipes. His mill was hand-operated. He also rolled lead into sheets for the flashings and gutters of buildings.[2] From then on, rolling mills were gradually improved and as they grew larger in order to produce for a widening market, horse power and then water power were substituted for manual operation.

All of the mills mentioned so far were for rolling metal in a cold condition. The rolling of heated metal appears to have arisen in connection with the slitting mill. This mill, it will be recalled from the previous chapter, was used to slit flat iron sheets (also called plates) into nail rods and was known in Belgium and Germany around 1500. Accounts of the earli-

48

est slitting mills do not say whether the bars were flattened into sheets by hammering or rolling to prepare them for the slitting mill. Schubert says that since plain-surfaced rolls were known in the English iron industry in the days of Bevis Bulmer, who took out the first English license for a slitting mill in 1588, it is possible that the rolling of bars preliminary to cutting may also have been done in the earlier slitting mills. He adds that mills for rolling bars into flat plates are mentioned in an inventory made in 1609 of a disused steel works in Sussex, which had been erected in 1565. The rolls were apparently driven by hand and not by water power. "All this," Schubert says, "justifies the conclusion that Bulmer's slitting mill and a few others built in Britain before Foley's day [Richard Foley, who established a slitting mill in 1625] had iron rollers for rolling the bars into plates and large iron shears for mechanical cutting."[3] In such rolling mills, the iron had to be in a red-hot condition. Thus, it seems safe to assume that the hot-rolling of iron took place at least as early as 1588 and probably some years earlier. In 1697, Major John Hanbury, at his ironworks in Pontypool, Wales, was operating a rolling mill to flatten bars into sheets as an independent machine and not as an adjunct to the slitting mill. By 1720, rolling mills were in common use both in England and on the Continent.[4]

Grooved Rolls

Until the early part of the eighteenth century, the rolls were smooth-surfaced iron cylinders which pressed hot metal into thin flat sheets. The next step in the evolution of the rolling mill was momentous. By constructing the rolls with grooves in their surfaces it was possible to roll iron into various shapes. In a sense, the rolls functioned as cylindrical dies. Grooved rolls were first employed to form lead pipes. Such a mill was brought from England to France in 1728. The rolls contained seven semicircular grooves ranging from two to four inches in diameter. A rough lead pipe, formed from sheets, was passed back and forth through the appropriate grooves until it assumed a uniform external diameter.

In the same year, John Payne, an Englishman, received a patent for a rolling mill in which hammered bars were made "to pass between two large metal Rowlers (which have proper notches or furrows upon their surfaces) into such shapes and forms as shall be required." Payne seems never to have built the mill but the idea of rolling iron bars into various shapes became of lively interest at that time.[5]

Cort Combines Rolling and Puddling

Modern rolling practice is universally recognized as dating from 1783 when Henry Cort was issued a patent for a mill with grooved rolls. Cort owned an ironworks at Fontley, England. In 1780, the British Navy sent him a quantity of scrap iron, consisting mainly of old hoops, and asked him to use this material in producing iron products for His Majesty's ships. Between 1780 and 1783, he experimented with grooved rolls for producing flat, round and square bars and on January 17 of the latter year took out his first patent for grooved rolls.[6]

Having successfully demonstrated his ability to roll scrap iron for the British Navy, Cort was next urged to make use of old iron ship ballast. To convert this iron into wrought iron, he experimented with a reverberatory furnace and from it developed the puddling furnace. Until the invention of the reverberatory furnace, pig iron was converted into wrought iron by heating the pigs in direct contact with charcoal in a refinery forge. In the reverberatory furnace, there is no contact between the metal and the fuel. The hearth, containing the metal, is placed at the base of the flue. Behind the hearth, separated by a bridge, is the combustion chamber filled with charcoal or coal. Flames and gases from the burning fuel, in their passage to the flue, sweep over the iron in the hearth, oxidizing the metal.

The reverberatory furnace was invented in 1613 by John Rovenson, but it was not employed for refining pig iron into wrought iron until 1766 when Thomas and George Cranege were granted a patent in England for a similar process. It appears that the Cranege brothers used something like puddling in their process.

After numerous experiments, Cort overcame the obstacles which the "suphurous and drossy" nature of pit-coal[7] had presented to previous experimenters, and developed a puddling furnace which he patented in 1784. In his furnace, he converted scrap into wrought iron which the Navy, after exhaustive tests, declared to be far superior to any produced in Great Britain and fully equal to the best Swedish iron.

Cort's puddling furnace had an opening in a side wall through which a puddler stirred the molten metal with a long rake called a rabble. This exposed all parts of the metal to the heat and gases so that the excess carbon and other undesirable elements were oxidized out. When the metal reached a pasty granular condition, the puddler rolled it into a ball which was divided into three parts, each weighing about 150 pounds, a convenient size for removing from the furnace by tongs. Each ball was "shingled" by the blows of a forge hammer to expel the slag and to form it into two "half-blooms." Each half-bloom was passed through the rolls, the grooves of which shaped it into bars.

Cort exhausted his entire personal fortune in expensive experimentation and arranged to borrow money from a Navy paymaster named Jellicoe, who was reputedly a wealthy man. Cort put up his Fontley ironworks and his patents as security. In addition, he was to pay Jellicoe a good share of the profits and to take in Jellicoe's son as a partner. When the elder Jellicoe died in 1789, it was discovered that he had embezzled from the Navy the money which he loaned to Cort. Cort's properties and patents were seized and he was completely ruined. The firms which adopted his grooved rolls and puddling furnace were allowed to use them for ten years until the patents expired without paying Cort a farthing of royalty. Great estates were gained by ironmasters who profited by his processes, and it has been estimated that his inventions added 600 million pounds sterling to the wealth of the Kingdom.[8] In return for long years of labor and the loss of his personal estate, Cort died a poor and broken man.

Although Cort invented neither grooved rolls nor the puddling furnace, he was the first person to combine them successfully in one operation and for this reason has justly gone down in history as the father of modern rolling. The effect of his inventions on the iron trade was immediate and impressive. Whereas it had been possible formerly to produce one ton of bars in twelve hours, Cort himself was able to roll fifteen tons in the same time and the iron was of a quality which permitted it to be substituted for charcoal iron in all uses except the making of steel.[9] Large plants, which had with difficulty forged ten to twenty tons of iron a week, manufactured ten times that amount with Cort's processes and fewer men.[10] In 1788, the output of bar iron in Great Britain was 33,000 tons, and three years later puddled and rolled iron alone amounted to 50,000 tons—a growth largely concentrated in Wales.[11]

Grooved rolls and the puddling furnace brought the long era of the smith's supremacy to a close, and opened that of manufacture by machinery which now awaited the arrival of steam power.

STEAM POWER ENTERS THE IRON INDUSTRY

John Wilkinson, inventor of the modern-type cupola, brought steam power into the iron industry on a permanent basis by adapting a Watt engine to blow two blast furnaces, which, incidentally, was also the first application of the invention for a purpose other than pumping water. In 1780, he had four Watt engines producing blast at his ironworks, and his successful use of the engines soon led to orders from other ironmasters. Wilkinson extended the use of steam power in 1782 by harnessing it to drive a forge hammer and finally, in 1786, operated a slitting and rolling mill with a Watt engine.[12]

The next person to step upon the scene is another Scotsman, James Beaumont Neilsen, a native of Glasgow. Until his time the air had been blown into the blast furnace at atmospheric temperature and there was an intrenched belief among ironmasters that the colder the air, the more iron was produced. Meanwhile, John Smeaton of England, in 1760, had intensified the cold air blast by the construction of cast iron blowing cylinders to replace bellows. The cylinders were initially driven by water power and later for a time were propelled by the "fire engine" of Newcomen. But it was Watt's more powerful engine that supplied the necessary force to drive a strong blast of air into a higher column of iron ore and coke within the blast furnace stack, which actually resulted in augmenting the furnace capacity.

Neilsen added the finishing touch. As the superintendent of the Glasgow Gas Works, he experimented with the illuminating power of gas by bringing heated air through a closed tube close to the burner. A stronger light resulted. He tried a similar experiment by blowing heated air into a smith's forge fire, which became more brilliant and hotter. Neilsen thought of applying the same principle to the blast furnace and after many years of perseverance his experiments were crowned with success and he was granted a patent for his invention in 1828, but he encountered strong prejudice against his machine on the grounds that "cold air was best." But after he won over the Clyde Iron Works, the rest of the Scottish iron industry fell into line. By 1835, the use of hot blast had become established in the iron industry.[13]

The successive technological advances achieved in Britain—coke blast furnaces, puddling furnaces, grooved rolls, hot blast, and steam power—produced remarkable results as may be seen in Table 1.

TABLE 1

NUMBER OF ACTIVE FURNACES AND OUTPUT OF PIG IRON
IN GREAT BRITAIN, 1788-1806

Year	Number of Furnaces	Output in Net Tons
1788	85	76,496
1796	121	140,088
1806	173	273,113

SOURCE: James M. Swank, *History of the Manufacture of Iron in All Ages*, Philadelphia, 2d ed., 1892, p. 519.

Steam power brought about important changes in the coal and iron industries. It hastened the demise of the charcoal furnace. More effective steam-driven pumps made possible the mining of coal and iron ore at greater depths. A blast furnace could be operated the year round and the ironmaster was freed of dependence on rain and interruptions by summer droughts. Also, it was no longer necessary for furnace, forge, and finishing mill to be separate as was typical of the early years of the century.

REVIVAL OF THE CRUCIBLE PROCESS

The crucible process, as we learned in Chapter 3, was practiced in India several centuries before the Christian era in the manufacture of the celebrated wootz steel. The secrets of the process are supposed to have been lost in the intervening centuries and to have been rediscovered in England by the Quaker clockmaker, Benjamin Huntsman, in 1740. Whether India continued to manufacture wootz steel uninterruptedly from pre-Christian times to the eighteenth and nineteenth centuries is difficult to determine. We have the word of the eminent English metal-lurgist, J. S. Jeans, that "previous" to Huntsman's experiments with the crucible process, wootz steel was being imported from India into England where, because of its homogeneity, it was held to be so superior to all others that the makers of dies for coining presses were willing to pay the "fabulous price" of 5 guineas a pound.[14]

Huntsman imported "blister" steel (made by the cementation process) from Germany for his clock and watch springs, but he became dissatisfied with its uneven quality and sought to produce a more homogeneous steel. He decided to accomplish his purpose by remelting blister steel in clay crucibles, and he has been acclaimed for having "rediscovered" the "lost" crucible process and even for having invented it. It was not lost, but was still very much alive, as has been clearly shown above. It may be said that Huntsman did "rediscover" the crucible process in the sense that he worked out the secrets himself, and for this single-handed accomplishment his name deserves to go down in history laden with honor.

From the start, Huntsman surrounded his experiments with the utmost secrecy. Time and again, the steel which he made was of inferior quality, and he is reported to have buried many "hundredweight" of rejected metal. In the end, his patience and toil were rewarded, and he produced crucible steel of excellent quality. But when he endeavored to sell it to the Sheffield cutlers, they "perversely declined" to buy it because it was so much harder and denser than that to which they were accustomed.[15] Scorned by his countrymen, Huntsman found a ready market for his product in France, and when the Sheffield cutlers heard of it they sought to have sales to their foreign rivals prohibited; but they were unsuc-cessful, and Huntsman's export business quickly spread all over the Continent.

Meanwhile, the Sheffield cutlers, alarmed by Huntsman's glowing success abroad, attempted to penetrate his secrets which were unpro-tected by a patent. Huntsman, on his guard, took elaborate precautions to conceal his process from spying eyes, excluding all strangers from his premises and swearing his workmen to secrecy. As a double precaution against spying, all work was done at night. One Samuel Walker, pre-sumably a representative of the Sheffield cutlers, disguised himself as a beggar, so the story goes, and came to Huntsman's works on a cold winter evening and asked in mercy's name to be taken in and allowed to warm himself by the fire.[16] Lying on the floor, he feigned sleep, while covertly watching the operations. Bars of blister steel were broken into small pieces, two to three inches long, and placed in fire-clay crucibles. When nearly filled, a little broken glass was spread over the top which was sealed with a close-fitting cover. The crucibles were placed in a furnace where they remained three or four hours. The crucibles were then re-moved with tongs and the molten steel was poured into molds.

At all events, Huntsman's process was soon known to the cutlers of

Sheffield who eagerly exploited it. From a very early time, Sheffield had been the steel center of England and was known to Chaucer who wrote of the Sheffield knife called a "thuytel" as in common use in his day.[17] Huntsman's process really put the city "on the map," and more progress was made in the Sheffield steel trade from his death in 1776 to the close of the century than anywhere else in the world.

Improvements in Crucible Steelmaking

Crucible furnaces underwent marked improvement in order to keep pace with the growing demand for cast steel. Huntsman's furnaces were fired with charcoal. The furnace consisted of a series of "pot holes" spaced about 3 feet apart, center to center, in a wall. The pot holes were on the floor level, with handles on their doors for opening and closing the hole. Each pot hole was about 3½ feet high, 2 feet deep, from front to back, and 1½ feet wide. This was large enough to accommodate two crucibles of 75 pounds capacity, each surrounded with a layer of charcoal several inches thick. Each pot hole was connected at the bottom with a flue leading to the cellar for the admission of air and at the top with a flue leading to the main chimney for the escaping gases.[18]

To begin the operation, two crucibles were placed on iron bar stands in a pot hole and packed in charcoal up to their necks. The fire was ignited and when the crucibles were at white heat, the "puller out" charged them by means of a "charger," a funnel-shaped device which fitted over the mouth of the crucible. The covers were closed on the crucibles and the pot hole was filled with charcoal which was renewed several times before the "steeling" was completed. The first heat took from four to five hours and the second and third heats, because of the high temperature remaining in the pot hole, required shorter periods. Control of the furnace was under the charge of the head melter, who, with the puller out, regulated the rate of melting. When the steel was properly melted and any necessary ferroalloys had been added and melted, the puller out, with his arms and legs protected by wet sacking, introduced the long pulling-out tongs into the pot hole, lifted out the crucibles and placed them on the floor. After the clay lid was removed and the slag was skimmed off, the crucible was carried in single tongs, or double-handled tongs for two men, to the molds into which the molten steel was poured.[19]

The crucible furnaces, from Huntsman's day on—at least up into the twentieth century—appear to have been worked continuously from Monday morning until Saturday noon. To produce 25 tons of steel a week in a charcoal-fired furnace of the Huntsman type, required at least 12 pot holes. Charcoal consumption was high. From 2½ to 3½ tons were consumed to produce one ton of tool steel and 1¾ tons for one ton of ordinary grades of steel.[20]

Miners, Smiths, and Metallurgy

I have seen the metal worker at his task at the mouth of his furnace, his fingers burned and scarred like a crocodile's skin. . . . At night when he should be free he must still work on until his task is done, sometimes longer than his strength can stand.

—An Egyptian Metal Worker
Source Unknown

A man who could transmute earth by fire into a metal could not help but be looked upon as a magician, a sorcerer, or a demigod. By the same token, the metal itself was considered to have mystical properties which could be used for malignant or benign purposes. All sorts of superstitions and taboos grew up around the use of iron and the person of the smith.

In primitive society, there was apparently no middle ground for the smith. He was honored or despised, but always held in awe. We are afforded a glimpse of how the ancients looked upon the smith by examining the culture of people living today in primitive society. In some African tribes, the smiths are virtual slaves of an inferior social status. The Somali never enter a smithy or shake hands with a smith or marry his daughter. In other tribes, the word "smith" is a term of abuse though it is considered unwise to insult him because his curse is very expensive to buy off. Some tribes, however, hold the smith in great honor as the maker of deadly weapons. Corn and other foods are cultivated for him and the community builds his smithy. He ranks with the chief medicine man and only medicine men and their kin are allowed to be smiths. In certain tribes of northeast Africa, the smiths and their families constitute a separate clan in which the craft is handed down from father to son. They marry only among themselves, for marriage with an outsider is considered dangerous. They and their products are held to be unclean because the weapons which the smiths make lead to the spilling of blood.

Weapons must be purified by rubbing with cow fat or butter when taken over in exchange for food.

In parts of the East Indies, the smiths are believed to be magicians possessing magical power to work dangerous metal. Their tools are worshiped, for they perform mysterious work and the spirits of the tools protect the smith and his family.

Such, in brief, is the picture of the smith in primitive society. As civilizations developed, he gained in prestige and his services were sought far and wide, if only for practical reasons, because rulers were dependent on him for their weapons and tools. The victor in battle was careful to carry off the enemy's smiths, not only to have them for himself but also to deprive the vanquished of their services. Sennacherib mentions that when he conquered Babylon he took the smiths among his booty and Nebuchadnezzar did the same when he destroyed Jerusalem. The domination of Palestine by a handful of Philistines seems to have been due to their excellent smiths and the Philistines took pains to see that the Jews were deprived of their own, for "There is no smith found in all the land of Israel, for the Philistines said, lest the Hebrews make them swords and spears."[1]

As time passed, the smith continued to grow in esteem. In pre-Christian Wales the smiths were allowed to sit near the Druid priest of the household in the king's presence. The Welsh smiths were believed to wield mysterious powers and their censure was dreaded by the Celts. Later, in Christian Wales, the king's smith, who fashioned his weapons of war, belonged to the upper class of society and ranked as a high official at the royal court. In Anglo-Saxon times the smith had gained such recognition that his person was protected by a double penalty and he was treated as an officer of the highest rank. It was not uncommon for Anglo-Saxon monks to manufacture iron, and we read that St. Dunstan, who lived in the tenth century, had a forge in his bedroom and was reputed to have been a skilled blacksmith.

MINING AND METALWORKING

Mines were exploited on a fairly large scale in Egypt, Greece, and elsewhere, particularly for gold and silver. In the dawn of civilization, all mines belonged to the ruler of the land and the labor in them was performed by slaves, who were generally captives of war or convicts. The rattle of chains and the groans of the enslaved accompanied the sound of the miner's pick in the ancient mines. The Greek historian, Agatharcides, has left a vivid picture of how gold was mined by slaves in Egypt. They labored in narrow shafts, stooped over, unable to straighten up. Children were assigned to the smallest passageways. "These workers," wrote Diodorus Siculus, another Greek historian, "can take no care of their bodies and have not even a garment to hide their nakedness . . .

there is no forgiveness or relaxation at all for the sick, or the maimed, or for the old . . . but all with blows are compelled to stick to their labor until worn out they die in servitude."[2] Much the same conditions prevailed in the silver mines of Greece and later in the mines operated by the Romans in subjugated countries.

The Middle Ages

Most of our knowledge of mining, metalworking, and metallurgy, as practiced in the Middle Ages, has come down from two men: Vanoccio Biringuccio and Georgius Agricola. Birringuccio's *Pirotechnia*, written in Italian and published in 1540, a year after his death, was the first printed book describing the metal arts and the processes of ore reduction. Agricola was the Latin name of George Bauer, a German. His *De Re Metallica*, written in Latin, was also published a year after his death, which occurred in 1555. Although Agricola borrowed from *Pirotechnia*, particularly in his description of steelmaking, he drew on his own extensive knowledge of mining and metalworking which he elaborated with German thoroughness. *De Re Metallica* remained the standard textbook on mining and metallurgy for more than 180 years. For translating this work from Latin into English we are indebted to Herbert and Lou Henry Hoover who completed their monumental task of scholarship in 1912.

Although the smiths were greatly in demand during the Middle Ages and were often granted privileges beyond other skilled workers in order to attract their services, their hours were long and their work in smoky forges was arduous. It is not surprising that they became known as "blacksmiths." Speaking of the "iron smiths," Biringuccio tells us "the unhappy workmen are never able to enjoy any quiet except in the evening when they are exhausted by the laborious and long day that began for them with the first crowing of the cock. Sometimes they even fall asleep without bothering about supper."[3]

The life of the miners was even more wretched; they toiled underground in dangerous conditions and often did not see the light of day for long periods. The twenty-four hours of day and night, Agricola informs us, were divided into three seven-hour shifts, the three remaining hours being spent between the shifts in entering and leaving the shafts. The day shifts extended from 4:00 A.M. to 11:00 A.M. and from noon to 7:00 P.M. The night shift began at 8:00 P.M. and ended at 3:00 A.M. Generally, a miner worked two shifts during the twenty-four hours, although in some mines he was not permitted to work two shifts in succession, says Agricola, "because it often happens that he either falls asleep in the mine overcome by exhaustion from too much labor, or arrives too late for his shift, or leaves sooner than he ought." The *Bergmeister*, or manager of the mine, did not allow the third shift "to be imposed upon the workmen unless necessity demands," Agricola continues. "In that case . . . they keep vigil by the night lamps, and to prevent themselves falling asleep from the late hours or from fatigue, they lighten their long and arduous labors by singing, which is neither wholly untrained nor unpleasing."[4]

Agricola shared the belief current in his day that demons and gnomes inhabited the mines. The demons were of "ferocious aspect" and could only be "expelled and put to flight by prayer and fasting." But many of the gnomes were friendly and even helpful. "They appear to laugh with glee and pretend to do much, but really do nothing. They are called little miners, because of their dwarfish stature, which is about two feet. . . . Sometimes they throw pebbles at the workmen, but they rarely injure them unless the workmen first ridicule or curse them."[5]

Seventeenth and Eighteenth Centuries

Conditions of labor among miners and metalworkers improved in the seventeenth and eighteenth centuries with a definite movement toward unionism taking form toward the close of the period. However, in accordance with the custom prevailing among workers of all kinds, the workday was long. In Sweden during the seventeenth century, the "hammersmiths" were confined to their place of work from 6:00 P.M. Sunday until the same hour the following Saturday. During the week they lived in a cottage near the shop separated from their families. Each day their bodies became more blackened with soot, which they did not bother to wash off until they reached home on Saturday. The nailsmiths were less fortunate in their hours, their day beginning at 4:00 A.M. and ending at 9:00 P.M., but they enjoyed the advantage of being allowed to sleep home at night.[6]

Plenty of cheap strong liquor played an important role in the life of the Swedish ironworker. Each Saturday night the smith was allowed to "fetch a few quarts" at the office, sometimes as many as ten per man, and then "the cups were bravely drained." Inadequate wages were frequently made up by generous gifts of liquor, and bonuses were generally paid in strong spirits. The construction of a new hammer was celebrated with three and a half quarts per man and on festive occasions the "alcohol flowed freely." To be kept at their tasks, the charcoal burners deep in the forests "had to be generously plied with drink."[7]

In England during the eighteenth century, it was still a time-honored tradition that a brewhouse was essential to every well-equipped furnace or forge. An extra allowance of ale was dispensed when special exertions were called for. In the early years of the century, the hours were from 5:00 A.M. to 8:00 P.M., with a half-hour break at eight in the morning and one hour at noon. Toward the end of the century the hours were from 6:00 A.M. to 8:00 P.M. with the same breaks during the day. The nailworkers toiled longer hours than the smiths—from 6:00 A.M. to 11:00 P.M. or midnight.[8]

As the Industrial Revolution gained headway in England, workers in the mining, metalworking, and textile industries began uniting for common action. From 1777 onward, unionism developed rapidly among the craftsmen in the great steel center of Sheffield, and in 1787 the cutlers there engaged in a strike. In and around Sheffield, other groups such as scissors-smiths, spring-knife makers, and saw-smiths formed unions. These unions, however, were on the fringe of the iron industry and there is no evidence of similar activity on the part of smelters, founders, and forgemen before the nineteenth century.

Mining Methods

The exploitation of ore deposits at different levels was practiced in classical times. Shafts in the silver mines at Larium, Greece, were usually not more than 150 feet deep but some went as far as 350 feet. Ventilation was a serious problem in ancient mining, but a far more formidable one was the drainage of water which was to plague miners for centuries and limit the depth of mines until Newcomen and Watt invented the steam engine and applied it to mine pumps.

Agricola describes in detail the methods, machinery, and implements used in mining during his day. One subterranean system for pumping water required ninety-six horses, to be drawn upon in relays, as motive power. Such machinery vividly shows that mechanical invention had been pushed as far as it could go with wood as the chief material and with water, men and horses supplying the motive force, and why, to remedy this critical situation, men substituted iron for wood and steam for water power.

Haulage of ores in ancient mines was performed in buckets or leather sacks. Resinous torches or pieces of skin soaked in fat served for illumination. Later, earthenware or metal lamps were placed in niches cut into the rocks. Lamps were also hung from the roof of the gallery. The earliest miners used stone tools but those of the Greeks and Romans were made of iron.

In Agricola's time, ore was occasionally hauled from the mine in baskets, or sacks made of oxhide, but it was generally done in buckets made of staves encircled with iron hoops. The smaller buckets were pulled up by machines operated by men and the larger ones by machines turned by horses. The mine cart was a small open truck bound together with iron bands. "A large blunt pin fixed to the bottom of the truck runs in a groove on a plank in such a way that the truck does not leave the beaten track," says Agricola, giving us an early example of a vehicle moving on a track. These trucks were employed only in the longest tunnels.

In the sixteenth century, according to Agricola, some mine shafts were sunk to a depth of 660 feet. Narrow tunnels were also dug into the sides of mountains or hills. In these, the miners worked in a prone position and "to avoid wearing away their clothes and injuring their left shoulders they usually bind to themselves small wooden cradles. For this reason, this particular class of miners, in order to use their iron tools, are obliged to bend their necks to the left, not infrequently having them twisted."[9]

The simplest machine for bringing up ore or water from the mine was a windlass with cranks turned by two men. While one bucket rose, the other descended. Another windlass for raising heavier loads from a greater depth was more complicated and was operated by three men. There were more intricate machines with cogs and wheels for hauling larger quantities of ore from shafts as deep as 240 feet, turned by two men or four horses, depending on the size of the machine. In all these machines, buckets were used to hold the ore.

Once the ore was removed from the shaft, it was taken down the mountain in various ways, says Agricola. In winter, boxes filled with ore were placed on a sledge and drawn down the mountain by horses or dogs. Sometimes two or three sacks of ore were placed on a small sledge "higher in the fore part and lower at the back. Sitting on these sacks, not without risk of his life, the bold driver guides the sledge as it rushes down the mountain into the valleys with a stick, which he carries in his hand."[10] Ore was also carried down the mountains in pack saddles by horse and mules, or in two-wheeled carts and four-wheeled wagons, depending on the season and the steepness of the grade.

RAISING WATER FROM THE MINES

Since the greatest obstacle faced by the miners was the removal of water, the most ambitious and intricate machinery was designed to overcome it. Where a relatively small amount of water was encountered, drains made of hollowed logs were placed along the sides of passageways. When the water was in such volume that it impeded mining, it was raised in leather bags or buckets or was pumped out of the shafts. When done with bags or buckets, the machinery employed depended on the depth of the mine. One machine was activated by a man turning a crank, another by a treadmill and a third, which far excelled the other two, says Agricola, was built where a surface stream could be diverted to pass by the mine and turn a large water wheel which caused the axle, bearing the chain and dippers, to revolve.

Agricola describes various kinds of suction pumps and what he calls rag and chain pumps. In the latter, an endless chain with little balls every six feet, raised water through a pipe. Where no river could be diverted to turn a water wheel, a huge and complex machine was installed to drive a rag and chain pump in a subterranean chamber 50 feet in diameter, strongly supported with beams and posts 40 feet long and 1½ feet thick. Through the top of this chamber there extended an upright square axle 45 feet in length and 1½ feet wide and thick. As this axle revolved, it turned a 24-foot toothed wheel, which, in turn, moved cogs and a drum, the latter causing the chain and balls to circulate within the pipe, drawing up water. This subterranean machine which could draw water from a depth of 240 feet, required a team of thirty-two horses. "Eight of them work for four hours, and then these rest for twelve hours, and the same number take their place," writes Agricola. The horses descended to the machine by an inclined shaft "which slopes and twists like a screw." At Schemnitz, in the Carpathian Mountains, there was such a subterranean machine consisting of three suction pumps at different levels and the entire system entailed the use of ninety-six horses. The lowest of these pumps was 660 feet underground.[11]

VENTILATING MACHINES

The mechanical inventiveness of miners in the Middle Ages did not stop at machines for removing ores and water, but was also applied to the vexatious problem of ventilation. This was known to the ancients, for Pliny tells of shaking linen cloths in the shafts to freshen the air.

The simplest ventilating devices made use of prevailing winds like modern ventilators on the tops of buildings. A barrel with a wooden wing attached to it was spun around by the wind exposing a "blow-hole" through which the air entered and passed down a wooden conduit into the shaft. Another device employed fans made of thin boards tipped with goose feathers attached to an axle inside of a stationary drum. There were two blow-holes on the drum, one toward the top and the other at the bottom. A workman turning a crank caused the fans to revolve, drawing in air through the upper blow-hole and expelling it through the other into a conduit leading into the shaft. Where there was an abundant water supply this type of ventilator could be driven by water power.

Bellows were the most effective ventilators; they could be used either to force fresh air into the mines or suck out the "heavy and pestilential vapours" from a depth of 120 feet. For the first purpose, the nozzle of the bellows was placed within a conduit leading into the mine; for the second, the position of the bellows was reversed, drawing air from the shaft and discharging it into the atmosphere. Three double bellows or a set of triple bellows could be operated by one man working treadles with his feet. Both systems of bellows could also be operated by a horse either mounted on a treadmill or driven round and round in a circle to turn an axle, as blind oxen and donkeys were trained to turn grist mills in ancient times.

FROM ARISTOTLE TO THE ALCHEMISTS

Controversies raged in the ancient world over the question: Are metals good or evil? Should or should they not be mined? Those who condemned metals contended that since nature had buried them deep in the earth they were not intended to be used by man. Many were the philosophers and poets who inveighed against metals, particularly gold and silver, as the cause of wickedness in men.

Agricola cites the words of a host of "detractors" of gold and silver, who, he says, "next raise an outcry against other metals, as iron, than which they say nothing more pernicious could have been brought into the life of man," and he quotes the famous lines of Pliny:[12]

Iron is used not only in hand to hand fighting, but also to form the winged missiles of war, sometimes for hurling engines, sometimes for lances, sometimes even for arrows. I look upon it as the most deadly fruit of human ingenuity. For to bring Death to men more quickly we have given wings to iron and taught it to fly.

Agricola comes vigorously to the defense of metals, contending that those who speak ill of them condemn as wicked "the Creator Himself, when they assert that He fashioned some things vainly and without good cause, and thus they regard Him as the Author of evils, which opinion is certainly not worthy of pious and sensible men." He concludes that evil is not in the metals themselves but in the men who use them for evil purposes.

The attitude of the ancient moral crusaders who felt that in digging metals, man, in his folly had opened a Pandora's box, may have been influenced by the mysteries surrounding metals. The Peripatetic school, which greatly dominated thinking down to the seventeenth century, was based on Aristotle's theory that the physical universe is composed of four elements: earth, water, air, and fire; that they are transmutable and never found pure and are endowed with certain fundamental properties which acted as an "efficient" force upon the material cause—the elements. Transmutation of the elements in the earth produced two "exhalations," the fiery one (probably meaning gases), and the other damp (probably meaning steam). The former produced stones, the latter metals. Hence, all metals, since they become liquid when heated must be in large part water, and like water solidify when cold. Therefore metals are "cold and damp."[13]

If this sounds bewildering and confusing to modern ears, it is nothing compared to the effusions of the alchemists who, in the main, based their views on the Peripatetic theory, with many fanciful additions of their own. Alchemy, which originated with the Muslims, reached its zenith in the Middle Ages when libraries teemed with more material on this occult science, apart from religious and classical works, than any other subject. The alchemists mingled superstition, demonology, astrology, incantations—even sex was not omitted—in their attempts to make gold and silver from baser metals. Most of the great intellectual leaders of the later medieval centuries believed in alchemy, but Agricola was not taken in by it, because, as he said, in spite of the alchemists' assertions, there was no record of their having become rich, though everywhere they "are straining every nerve night and day . . . to heap up a great quantity of gold and silver."[14]

To the views of the alchemists, the astrologers added their bit with the result that by the early sixteenth century alchemy reached "the absolute apogee of muddled thought derived from the Peripatetics, the Alchemists and the Astrologers."[15] According to the astrologers, metallic ores and all things born are influenced by the heavens. Every metallic ore received a special influence from its own particular planet. Thus the influence on gold is the sun, on silver the moon, on tin Jupiter, on copper Venus, on iron Mars, on lead Saturn, on quicksilver Mercury.

The belief was also widely held that metals grow in the earth like plants. "Good investigators," says Biringuccio, made a drawing of a large tree with many branches planted in the middle of the base of a mountain. "From its principal trunk extend various branches . . . exactly like real trees in mature forests. They think that these grow and enlarge continually and draw themselves toward the sky, ever converting into their own nature the most disposed adjacent materials so that finally the tips arrive at the summit of the mountain and emerge with clear sign," sending forth various mineral veins.[16]

Meanwhile, on the practical level of the furnace and the forge, men were carrying on processes handed down from the past and improvising others on their own part. From the earliest times, one of the surest guides to the smith was the color of the metal at different stages of heat. It was necessary, says Biringuccio "to know all the colors that are shown and thrown off in cooling," and how these colors are acquired in cooling. "You quench them at the proper state of these colors if you wish them more or less hard in temper."[17] Varied indeed were the recipes for quenching baths, jealously guarded by the smiths. Recipes from one of the earliest books published in 1531, says, "Take snayles, and first drawne water of a red die of which water being taken in the firste moneths of haruest when it raynes," boil it with snails, "then heate your iron red hote and quench it therein and it shall be as hard as steel." Or, "Ye may do the like with the blood of a man of age, and of sanguine complexion, being of a merry nature and pleasant . . . distilled in the middst of May." Belief in the efficacy of some of these solutions died hard and still survived into the early eighteenth century.[18]

SCIENCE IS APPLIED TO METALLURGY

Science, at its beginning in the early seventeenth century, concerned itself but little with practical metallurgy. Even the great French mathematician and philosopher, Descartes, whose principal works appeared between 1620 and 1640, borrowed from the alchemists in his belief that metals were formed under pressure deep in the earth by combinations of sulphur and mercury, and that the resulting metallic parts rise through crevices in rocks until they become lodged there to form veins of ore. Another French scientist, Jacques Rohault, who derived most of his ideas from Descartes, did not deny as late as 1671 that the alchemists might succeed in their search for the philosopher's stone, but he regarded it as "almost inconceivably improbable."[19]

Another school of thought which dominated chemistry during the greater part of the eighteenth century was the phlogiston theory. This theory originally expounded by Becker and elaborated by Stahl, held that all matter capable of burning contained a substance called phlogiston (from the Greek, meaning "burnt"), which was given off during combustion. A substance that had been burned could regain phlogiston by being heated with a material rich in phlogiston. All matter which burned readily was considered to contain a large amount of phlogiston. Charcoal was given as an example, since after its combustion little visible residue remains. The phlogiston theory was universally accepted until Lavoisier proved, after careful weighing, that a metal when calcined gained in weight exactly as much as was taken from the air. Later, after the discovery of oxygen in the air by Scheele and Priestley, Lavoisier demonstrated that combustion is due to oxygen rather than a loss of phlogiston, and the phlogiston theory was exploded.[20]

René Antoine de Réamur may be looked upon as the first person to attempt to combine science and metallurgy and as the first applied scientist in the modern sense of the term. His *Memoirs on Steel and Iron,* published in 1722, was the first significant book on iron and steel since *Pirotechnia* and *De Re Metallica.* Réamur began his work on ferrous metallurgy with a practical aim in view: to produce iron castings with the quality of wrought iron. His initial experiments had but little success and he then turned his attention to steel, also for a practical purpose—to help the domestic industry, since all high quality steel was then imported into France.

Réamur considered iron ore to be composed of "ferruginous parts" and parts containing sulfur and salts. He assumed that when steel is heated the sulfur and salts are driven out of the molecules into interstices between them; on quenching, the rapid cooling prevents the sulfur and salts from entering the molecules, thus cementing them firmly together and giving a hard, quenched steel; on tempering, the sulfur and salts return only partially to the molecules and the metal becomes proportionately soft. "If we interpret sulfur and salts as carbon, and molecules as cementite, and interstices as the lattices in the gamma phase," Mehl observes, "Réamur is describing our modern knowledge with extraordinary accuracy."[21]

Réamur clearly recognized that, invisible to the lens, changes in steel brought about by heat affected the properties of the metal. He realized that wrought iron was the purest form of commercial iron and that it was the addition of some other substance which converted it into cast iron and steel. This material which he called sulfur and salts was, of course, carbon.

The fact that varying percentages of carbon caused the differences in hardness of wrought iron, cast iron and steel, gained recognition slowly. Bergmann made some headway in 1781 but he confused carbon, which he isolated, with phlogiston, and he held stubbornly to the phlogiston theory. His views were combated by Vandermonde, Berthollet, and Monge who claimed in a report to the Académies des Sciences in 1786 that carbon was the element which all were seeking as the cause of the differences between iron and steel. This theory was proven by Clouet in 1798 and by Pepys in 1815, both of whom succeeded in making steel by heating iron and a diamond together. Then, in 1827, Karsten in Germany isolated the carbide from soft steel and showed it to be a compound of iron and carbon. It was not until 1888 that F. Abel dissolved steel in chromic acid and showed that the residue, carbide, had the chemical formula $Fe_3 C$.[22]

Iron and Steel in Colonial America

Under a spreading chestnut-tree
The village smithy stands;
The smith, a mighty man is he,
With large and sinewy hands;
And the muscles of his brawny arms
Are strong as iron bands.
. . . .
Week in, week out, from morn till night
You can hear his bellows blow;
You can hear him swing his heavy sledge
With measured beat and slow,
Like a sexton ringing the village bell
When the evening sun is low.

—Henry Wadsworth Longfellow
The Village Blacksmith

FIRST IRON ENTERPRISES IN NORTH AMERICA

It has been claimed that the North American Indians knew how to smelt iron and copper and that iron was smelted by the Vikings who came to these shores about A.D. 1000 and continued their visits for three and a half centuries. An iron sword, an axe, and the "grip" of a shield found in 1930 lying close together near Beardmore, Northern Ontario, have been identified by Norse archaeologists as dating from A.D. 900 to 1000, but these are considered to have been of European manufacture.[1] It is the consensus of American archaeologists that no metal was smelted in North America in pre-Columbian times. The Indians did, however, beat meteoric iron into beads, knives, chisels, and drills, but in very small quantities.

Falling Creek, Virginia

The early American colonists, struggling to adapt themselves to a strange land and climate, clearing virgin forests to make into tillable lands and pastures, were compelled to be self-sufficient, weaving their own cloth and making their own soap, candles, and many other essential items. Apart from food and raiment, their greatest need was iron and one of their first concerns was its manufacture. From the beginning and for a great many years, iron was scarce and expensive.

The first discovery of iron ore by English settlers in North America was made in 1584, as a result of an expedition sent by Sir Walter Raleigh to Roanoke Island off North Carolina. His explorers brought back such encouraging reports that in the following year Raleigh sent another expedition to prepare a permanent settlement on the island. An iron mine was found there and was reported "to hold iron richly," but apparently none was taken out or shipped to England.[2]

Among the first group of colonists to reach Jamestown was a blacksmith named James Read. It may have been he who forged the first native iron about which Captain John Smith wrote four months after the colony was established: "As yet we have no houses to cover us, our Tents were rotten, our cabbins worse than nought; our best commoditie was Iron which we made into little chisels." In 1609, enough iron ore was shipped from Jamestown to England to be smelted into sixteen to seventeen tons of iron described "so good as the East Indian Marchants (officials of the East India Company) brought y^t of the Virginian Company, preferring y^t before any other Iron of what Country soever. . . ."[3]

It was to be another decade before the matter of ironmaking in Virginia came alive again, and it was the outgrowth of a philanthropic gift of £550 made anonymously by a person in London signing himself "Dust and Ashes." It was offered to the Virginia Company for the purpose of "bringing vp of the Infidells Children in true religion and christianity." The Virginia Company, which had been chartered by the Crown to colonize Virginia, was in a dilemma how to follow the injunctions of this unusual bequest while still furthering its major aim of starting an iron industry. Eventually it was found possible to accomplish both ends by entrusting the money to a group of men who styled themselves the Southampton Hundred or the Southampton Adventurers, and who added from their own purse "a farr greater Some toward the furnishinge out of Captaine Bluett and his Companie being 80 verie able and sufficient workmen wth all manner of prouisions for the setting vp of an iron worke in Virginia, whereof the proffitte accruinge were intended and ordered in a ratable proporcon to be faithfully imployed for the educatinge of 30 of the Infidelle Children in Christian Religion and otherwise as the Donor had required." Thus the first organized industrial venture in North America was the product of a philanthropic impulse.[4]

Bluett died shortly after his arrival. Judging from the number of his workmen, his "project was conceived in the grand manner," but what he accomplished before his death or what became of his surviving workmen is quite obscure. It is concluded that this first venture of the Southampton Hundred ended in failure.[5] Bluett's project was only one of three ironmaking ventures in the 1619-1620 period, for the Virginia Company speaks of some 150 men sent to Virginia "to set up three Iron workes." Three "master workmen" who came with Bluett promptly died. They were replaced in 1620 by three others.[6]

All three ironworking ventures, according to one estimate, terminated in failure.[7] By May 1621, the company had spent about £4,000 on ironmaking in Virginia. But the company had still not accepted total defeat; and, in 1621, Sir Edwin Sandys, treasurer and chief executive officer of the company, sent a "fourth gent," John Berkeley, reputed to know the iron business, with "20 principall workemen." Included among them were two founders, two finers and two chaffery men, indicating an intention to set up an integrated iron works, consisting of a blast furnace and a finery and chaffery for refining the pig iron into wrought iron.[8] This, apparently, was a strictly company venture, independent of "Dust and Ashes."[9]

It is not known when Berkeley reached Virginia. He selected a location below the falls of Falling Creek, a tributary of the James River, sixty-six miles above "James City" and eight miles below the present city of Richmond. Abundance of water, wood, mines, and stone, said Sandys in a letter, made the location so fitted for the purpose, as if "nature itself had applied her selfe to the wish and direction of the workmen."[10]

There were numerous and discouraging delays in completion of the works and the Virginia Company in its letters showed increasing impatience with Berkeley's progress. One letter urged him to "let us have by at least the next returns some good quantities of iron and wyne."[11] A London court entry in early 1622, noted that Berkeley had "brought that longe desired worke to so good forwardnes as to undertake so confidently to make Iron there by Whitsontyde next."[12] Robert Beverly, in a report, expected Berkeley "to finish the Work, and have plentiful Provision of Iron for them by the next Easter."[13] But tragedy struck Falling Creek before that date.

Chief Openchancanough and his warriors of the tribe inhabiting Indian Creek regarded with suspicion and hostility the strange buildings which the white men were erecting on their domain. Some preliminary firings of the furnace may have filled them with alarm. On March 22, 1622, Openchancanough and his braves swooped down on the settlement. Caught off-guard, the colonists had no chance against the superior numbers of their attackers. Reports vary on the extent of the massacre. According to one count, twenty-seven persons perished and two survived, a boy and a girl, who hid in the bushes.[14] Another version says that the Indians massacred all 348 members of the settlement except Berkeley's son, Maurice, who was absent from Falling Creek at the time.[15]

The disaster at Falling Creek ended four years' efforts to establish ironmaking in Virginia at a total cost of £5,000. The return on the investment, according to records of the Virginia Company, was "a fire shovell and tongs and a little barre of Iron made by a Bloomery."[16] The disheartened company proposed continuing on a modest scale construction of a bloomery, contrasted with the "greater waies wch we have formerly attempted." The project was to be undertaken by a few private adventurers, but appears not to have been carried through.[17] The Virginia Company was dissolved in 1624, and it was to be nearly a century before ironmaking on a sustained basis was revived in Virginia.

According to a popular version of the Falling Creek massacre, it was on that day that Berkeley intended to blow in the furnace, and although there may have been some trials, the ironworks was never in regular production. In support of this contention, Berkeley's expectation to "make Iron" and to "finish the Work" before Easter, is pointed out, as well as records of 1623 which refer to "many wilde & vaste pjects set on foot all at one time," including "3 iron works," all of which came to naught.[18]

This interpretation of events at Falling Creek has been vigorously disputed by Charles E. Hatch, Jr., and Thurlow Gates Gregory in an article published in the July 1962 issue of the *Virginia Magazine of History and Biography*.[19] Mr. Hatch is Chief Park Historian at the Colonial National Historical Park, embracing Yorktown and Jamestown. Mr. Gregory is an industrialist who figured prominently in having artifacts unearthed at the Falling Creek site brought to public notice.[20]

The authors acknowledge that "production was not sustained for any considerable period"; but they assert that "The records indicate, however, and a study of the site and remains have confirmed, that despite trials and tribulations, an integrated ironworks was erected on Falling Creek, perhaps in 1619, and that it was producing in 1620 and probably at other times. It very likely was in production and fully operational at the time the Indians struck on March 22, 1622."[21]

The re-awakened interest in the Falling Creek ironworks was due to explorations at the site in 1925 and 1955. "The observed and noted findings," say Messrs. Hatch and Gregory, included: "(1) the walls and foundations of an ironworks some ten feet below the present ground surface, (2) a sizeable charcoal pit containing a large amount of charcoal, (3) a considerable quantity of iron relics (an ax, nails, spikes, and lumps of iron), (4) a circular stone construction believed to be part of a blast furnace, (5) abundant samples of both cast iron and wrought iron, (6) large quantities of slag, and (7) the remains of an ancient wharf or pier.

In 1955 well over a ton of material was removed including numerous long rounded 'pigs' or billets."[22]

Analysis of one of the iron specimens revealed a carbon content of 3.73 per cent. The laboratory report said, "We regard this as being cast iron of the kind produced at that time." Another specimen was found to contain 3.54 carbon, and was regarded by the laboratory as "castable iron of the kind produced at that time." Two other specimens had 3.73 and 3.54 per cent carbon, respectively. Several other specimens were of low carbon content which classified them as wrought iron.[23]

Messrs. Hatch and Gregory claim that the analyses prove "the existence at the Falling Creek site of both wrought iron and cast iron."[24] They add that there is "no evidence that cast iron was made in Chesterfield County or elsewhere in Virginia for a century after the Massacre of March 22, 1622, and in this period changes in the iron process did evolve and the product reflected these changes. Falling Creek cast iron could be expected to be, and is, different in identifiable respects from cast iron of the later Colonial period."[25]

It appears to be beyond dispute that an integrated ironworks was constructed on Falling Creek. But it is generally acknowledged that, whatever degree of production the works attained, it was never in full, continuous production as a going concern. It deserves a high place of honor in the history of the American iron and steel industry, but precedence for the first truly successful iron enterprise in North America must be accorded the ironworks on the Saugus River in Massachusetts, whose checkered history will not be narrated.

Ironworks on the Saugus

Shortly after the Pilgrims landed at Plymouth in 1620, they discovered bog iron ore in the nearby ponds and marshes. Word of the discovery was sent back to England where it aroused considerable interest, as samples of ore shipped earlier from Virginia had done. The General Court of the colony in 1641 passed a measure giving encouragement to "such as will adventure for the discovery of mines," and as a reward offered the discoverer the use of the land for twenty-one years. It is doubtful if the first effort to take advantage of this inducement would have been projected on such a grand scale and pushed as vigorously as it was, but for the intervention of John Winthrop the Younger, son of the first governor of the Massachusetts Bay Colony. He was instrumental in having samples of iron ore shipped to England where he, in person, persuaded a group of hard-headed capitalists to subscribe £1,000 for the development of the iron resources of the colony. The group called itself the Company of Undertakers of the Iron Works in New England. It was a private joint-stock company which was expected to yield a profit to its investors.

In the winter of 1643-1644, the General Court offered the undertakers a twenty-one-year monopoly in the manufacture of iron within the juris-diction of Massachusetts, grants of common land and other privileges, and in return for the monopoly the undertakers were to be obligated to produce enough iron for the colony's needs within two years. These terms were unacceptable to the undertakers who, in negotiations over the next few years, drove a hard bargain with the Massachusetts magistrates. The Court yielded on some points but held to its stipulation for a price ceiling of £20 per ton on bar iron. The company was thus assured of a monop-oly in iron manufacture if it could meet the colony's needs.

Meanwhile, in the fall of 1643, Winthrop, as agent for the undertakers, set sail from England for the colony. He spent the winter reconnoitering for a site at which to build a blast furnace and chose a location south of Boston at Braintree. Work was probably begun in the spring of 1644, and a year later construction of the furnace was completed. It was a large furnace, similar in size to the one which was later erected on the Saugus River. As it turned out, the furnace was too large for the volume of water which could be obtained from the dammed pond, especially in times of drought. Furthermore, there apparently was not enough bog ore to last twenty years, as Winthrop had originally estimated.

By the end of 1644, Winthrop had decided to resign as agent for the undertakers, while at the same time they had come to the sad conclusion that he was not the man for the job and replaced him with a new agent, Richard Leader. The Braintree blast furnace remained in intermittent production for two years until a furnace was constructed at Lynn, and then it was abandoned for want of ore. Leader took over his duties as the new agent in March 1645. His first task was to build, or to finish construc-tion of, a forge for refining pig iron from the Braintree blast furnace into wrought iron. The forge presumably was in operation by 1646. Unlike the Braintree blast furnace, it was not abandoned but remained in opera-tion as a subsidiary forge for the works at Lynn.

The forge having been completed, Leader now needed a more satisfac-tory blast furnace than the one at Braintree. At Lynn, on the Saugus River, midway between Boston and Salem, he found a happy combina-tion of requirements—a plentiful supply of bog ore, extensive woodlands, a natural elevation on the river bank for a furnace-charging bridge, and a navigable stream that could be dammed above the works to provide ample water power. Construction of the new works probably began early in 1646 and the furnace and forge were completed by January 1648. The new community became known as Hammersmith.

This "birthplace of the American iron and steel industry," as the works are called, was an ambitious project and was equal to the most advanced contemporary plants in England. It consisted of a large blast furnace, with a twenty-foot stack, a forge of two fineries and a chafery, a five-hundred-pound tilt hammer, and a rolling and slitting mill, the first such mills in the New World, at a time when there were only about a dozen in Britain and on the Continent. There was an extensive water-power system by which water from a central reservoir ran at least seven water wheels. There were good storage facilities, a separate blacksmith's forge, workmen's accommodations, and a pier for small river boats which carried away the company's products. In addition to these facilities, the property included a six-hundred-acre farm where the bulk of labor was performed by indentured Scots.

Production at Hammersmith got under way in 1648, and in September of that year it was reported that "the Furnace runnes 8 tun per weeke, and their barre Iron is as good as Spanish. . . ."[26] Most of the output from the blast furnace was cast into pig iron which was hauled to the plant's forge or shipped to the one at Braintree for conversion into wrought-iron bars, the plant's chief article of sale. Some of the bar iron was flattened into strips in the rolling mill and afterwards cut in the slitting mill into nail rods, the material from which nails were made by hand.

Technologically, Hammersmith was a first-class ironworks, capable of producing quality products, which it did for nearly twenty years, but almost from the start it was plagued with troubles, mostly financial and finally ended in dismal failure and complete loss to all investors. Why was this so? Basically it appears to have been due to bad judgment and management on the part of the absentee owners in England. Neither Winthrop the Younger nor Richard Leader, his successor, were experienced in iron manufacture. The former's blast furnace had to be written off as a total loss. Leader found his operating costs outrunning his income and in two years resigned. John Gifford, the third agent for the company, was an experienced ironmaster from England, and under his regime the Hammersmith works and the forge at Braintree reached their apogee of efficiency. In 1650, the undertakers had high hopes of recovering their investment within a few years and realizing a profit. But these hopes were to be dashed. Gifford may have been a skilled technician, but he was an improvident business manager, and his accounts were said to have been in a "mess."[27] All of his transactions are not clear, but it is patent that he borrowed money to cover his operating expenses. When he was asked to render an accounting, he took the offensive himself by suing for the recovery of money which he claimed to have advanced for the company and, thus, fired the first gun in an interminable legal battle which eventually bogged down the company. The entire assets of the undertakers were taken over by creditors and the ownership of the property became incredibly snarled. Litigation was carried on in the Massachusetts courts and in England where the deplorable situation finally came to the attention of the Lord Protector Cromwell himself. Meanwhile, the works continued in operation, although haltingly, and changed ownership several times. The properties gradually fell into disrepair, and according to the best available evidence the works ground to a halt around 1670. By 1678, the plant was completely abandoned.[28]

The Hammersmith ironworks arose from its ashes in 1954, faithfully restored, in so far as it was possible to do so, as it existed in the days of the Pilgrims. Its resurrection was due chiefly to M. Louise Hawkes, whose ancestors lived at Saugus before the ironworks was built. When she heard of a plan to remove the ironmaster's house from New England, her patriotic fervor was aroused. This spirited lady initiated a movement which grew as it went along and in 1943 culminated in the formation of the First Ironworks Association, Inc., whose main purpose was to restore the Hammersmith works. The project came to the attention of the American Iron and Steel Institute which promised financial support for restoration of this historic landmark. Specialists of many kinds—archaeologists, historians, architects, metallurgists and others—combined their knowledge and skills in recreating the plant. On September 17, 1954, The First Iron Works Restoration was officially dedicated.

HEIRS OF HAMMERSMITH AND BRAINTREE

Although the ironworks at Braintree and Hammersmith were financial failures, they left a rich legacy in a corps of skilled craftsmen at a time when such men were scarce and invaluable and the growing population needed iron more than ever before. The skills of these former employees and of others whom they trained, were responsible for the actual founding of ironmaking on a solid basis along the northeastern seaboard and, in particular, for Massachusetts remaining the center of the iron industry on this continent for another century.

The first successor to Hammersmith deserves a place in history as "the oldest successful iron manufactory in New England," having remained in operation 224 years following its erection in 1656.[29] This was known as Raynham Forge, located near Taunton in the Plymouth Colony, and was built by former employees of Hammersmith. Other ironworks were built in the Taunton vicinity which became a major ironmaking center in the colonial period.

Following dissolution of the undertakers' monopoly in the Massachusetts Bay Colony, the court allowed petitioners from Concord to build a furnace which was erected there in 1660. Many other ironworks speedily followed, first in the region around Plymouth where a furnace was built in 1702.

As the higher quality bog ore gave out, the furnaces in eastern Massachusetts depended heavily on iron ores shipped from other colonies, particularly from the rich mines at Egg Harbor, New Jersey, and still later on pig iron imported from Pennsylvania, Maryland, and as far away as Virginia for remelting in forges for conversion into castings and bar iron.

IRON WORKS IN OTHER COLONIES

Rhode Island was the scene of an active iron trade in the colonial period, beginning about 1720, when Samuel Bissel, a blacksmith of Newport, began the manufacture of nails. Bog ore, as well as hematite and magnetite ores, furnished material for a number of furnaces and forges which turned out "cannon, bombs and bullets" for the French-Indian wars. Later, one of these works, Hope Furnace, cast cannon and balls for Washington's troops in the Revolutionary War. Before 1800, rolling and slitting mills and other iron manufacturing enterprises constituted the "largest branch of productive industry in the State."

There was but scant iron manufacture in Maine and New Hampshire, although in the latter state a thriving blast furnace once existed at Franconia. In Vermont, the barter system prevailed widely; when a farmer needed cauldrons, fire-dogs, a heating or cooking stove, axes, or farm implements, it was the custom to pay for them at the furnace with grain, pigs, or other country produce. The first blast furnace and forge in Vermont were erected at Fairhaven in 1788.

Iron Industry of Connecticut

John Winthrop, Jr., after being relieved of his duties as agent of the Company of Undertakers, repaired to Connecticut, where he was granted permission to establish a settlement at Pequot. Whether he actually built an ironworks there appears uncertain, but it is known that with several partners he built a blast furnace, the first in Connecticut, and also a forge, near New Haven, largely staffed with some of the unemployed from Hammersmith. Winthrop's iron venture in Connecticut, like the one in Massachusetts, did not prosper and was abandoned in 1680, presumably because the bog ore gave out.

In the next half-century numerous small ironworks, mostly bloomeries, existed along the streams and rivers in various parts of the state, supplying local needs for iron. It was nearly three-quarters of a century after Winthrop's first iron venture that development began of the rich hematite ores in Salisbury, Litchfield County, which became world celebrated and were mined for more than 150 years. Based on the local ores, Salisbury was at one period the most active ironmaking region in the United States.

As early as 1734, a bloomery forge was erected at Lime Rock, Litchfield County. The first blast furnace in the county was built by Ethan Allen, hero of Ticonderoga, and two partners in 1762, at Lakeville, then called Furnace Village. It is reported to have cast the first cannon produced in this country for service in the Revolutionary War and to have continued manufacturing large quantities of ordnance for the Continental Army. There is also some evidence that part of the iron chain strung across the Hudson River between West Point and Fort Montgomery during the Revolutionary War to prevent the ascent of British gunboats was forged from Salisbury iron. In its halcyon days, Litchfield county possessed twenty-seven blast furnaces and three slitting mills.

Connecticut's laurels do not rest solely on ironmaking. It has the distinction of being the first colony to manufacture steel. In 1728, Samuel Higley of Simsbury, and Joseph Dewey of Hebron, in Hartford County, reported to the state legislature that the former had "with great pains and cost, found out and obtained a curious art, by which to convert, change, or transmute common iron into good steel, sufficient for any use, and was the very first that ever performed such an operation in America." It was undoubtedly made by the cementation process. Their claim was supported by certificates from several smiths who had made a trial of the steel and pronounced it to be good. Higley and Dewey were granted the exclusive right for ten years "of practicing the business or trade of steel-making."[30]

New Jersey One of Early Leaders in Iron and Steel

Henry Leonard, at one time a skilled forge hand at the Saugus Works, moved to New Jersey in 1674. With his three sons, he built for one James Glover and several partners, the first ironworks in that colony. It was located at Tinton Falls near the present town of Red Bank. The ironworks were sold to Colonel Lewis Morris who was given a land grant of several thousand acres with sweeping privileges to mine and smelt ore. The Tinton Falls ironworks developed into "a heavily capitalized iron plantation."

The eastern seacoast was an ideal location for the works. The swamps were full of bog ore. The nearby salt bays furnished ample supplies of clam and oyster shells to use as a flux in the furnaces, while large tracts of woodland were at hand for charcoal.

Farther to the south, bog iron was the basis of an industrial region which flourished for more than one hundred years in a region known as the Pine Barrens, lying roughly midway between Philadelphia and Atlantic City.

Beginning in the first quarter of the eighteenth century, the first ironworks were built in the region. In subsequent years, many more were added and at one time the entire area was dotted with sizeable communities built around the ironworks, including paper mills, sawmills, glass factories, brickmaking establishments, cotton and grist mills. The largest furnaces were the Batsto and the Martha. During the Revolutionary War, the Pine Barrens were an important munitions center for Washington's armies.

Toward the middle of the last century, the Pennsylvania iron industry, using better grade ores in anthracite-fired blast furnaces, began to produce a grade of pig iron with which the Pine Barrens could not compete. In the mid-1880s, the iron industry there collapsed and whole towns were deserted. Most of them have long since disappeared without a trace and the land has reverted to its primitive state. This 100,000 acre tract has recently been purchased by the State of New Jersey for a watershed, game preserve, and park.

The earliest settlers who located in northern New Jersey came there for the purpose of smelting the rich magnetic iron ores in the neighborhood, and in 1710 erected a forge on the Whippany River in Hanover township four miles from Morristown.[31] The ore was mined at the celebrated Succassunna mine, fifteen miles distant and was carried to the works in leather bags on pack horses, and the bar iron was transported on horseback over the Orange Mountains to Newark.

At the close of the seventeenth century and in the opening years of the eighteenth, New Jersey was the only colony outside of New England producing iron. Some of the furnaces became famous in their day and the owners of almost all of them loyally turned out war material for the Continental Army.

Oxford Furnace in Warren County has been considered as "one of the most important factors in the Revolutionary period." So important did it become in the eyes of the British that they made several expeditions to capture it, all of which ended in failure. Erected in 1742, the furnace remained in blast until 1882 and in that year shared with the Cornwall Furnace in Pennsylvania the honor of being the oldest American furnaces still in operation.

In 1784, there were eight furnaces and seventy-nine bloomeries in New Jersey, and by 1802 the number had risen to thirteen furnaces, of which six were out of blast, 150 forges, and four rolling and slitting mills.

The largest operator and the most colorful figure in the New Jersey iron industry before the Revolution was a German, Peter Hasenclever, sometimes called "Baron," although his claim to the title was doubtful. In London, in 1763, he interested a number of capitalists in organizing a company to exploit the resources of the colonies. Appointed general manager, and authorized to spend £40,000 on various enterprises, he came to America the following year, bringing with him a large number of German miners and ironworkers. He bought the Ringwood Iron Company in the northern part of the state and later acquired other properties in the vicinity totalling 10,000 acres. He embarked on one of the most ambitious industrial enterprises which the colony had seen, expending large sums of money but without producing tangible results, and was finally discharged by his London superiors. At one time the company had twenty-four furnaces and forges at Ringwood, Long Pond (now Greenwood Lake), and Charlottenburg. The Ringwood Furnace and Forge was the largest of the three ironworks. All three obtained their iron ore from the Ringwood iron mines, which have been worked intermittently since colonial days. As many as six hundred persons were employed in the pits at periods of peak production.

In 1750, there was in Trenton "one Furnis for making Steel" whose product was advertised as "esteemed quite equal if not better in quality than what is imported from England."[32] It is known that steel was made in Trenton during the Revolution.

Early Iron History of the Empire State

New York was one of the last of the original thirteen colonies to set up an iron enterprise. The first in the province was built by Philip Livingston on Ancram Creek in Columbia County, fourteen miles east of the Hudson River "some time after 1734." Iron ore was obtained from the Salisbury mines in nearby Connecticut. The most important iron enterprise in New York at this period was the Sterling Iron Works, built in 1751 near Monroe, Orange County, after the discovery of rich magnetic iron ore in Sterling Mountain. Before the American Revolution, the furnace and forge came into the possession of Peter Townsend, two of whose direct descendants by the same name were identified with the iron industry of New York. It is said that the first steel made in the province was produced at the Sterling Works which is also reported to have cast anchors for the first ships of war to fly the stars and stripes. Other iron ore mines were discovered in Orange County before the Revolution and many furnaces and forges were built to make use of them.

Peter Townsend's ironworks deserve a unique place in Revolutionary history because of an iron chain manufactured there for stringing across the Hudson River from West Point. The British had early recognized the strategic importance of the river. By controlling it they could have access to Canada and to their Indian allies in the interior, and at the same time split the colonies in two. Peter Townsend was commissioned to fabricate a massive iron chain. The links were carried in ox carts to the river. Each link was two feet long and weighed one hundred pounds. The chain was five hundred yards in length. The British did not even test the strength of the chain, and it was removed at the end of the war.

Beginning of Iron Industry in Pennsylvania

Iron smelting in Pennsylvania is first mentioned in a verse written in 1692:

> A certain place here is, where some begun
> To try some Mettle, and have made it run,
> Wherein was Iron absolutely found
> At once was known about some Forty Pound.

The first successful venture in ironmaking was due to an enterprising Quaker smith, Thomas Rutter, who erected a bloomery called Pool Forge on Manatawny Creek in Berks County a few miles above Pottstown in

1716. Soon afterward, Coventry Forge, in Chester County, was built by Samuel Nutt, another Quaker. Thomas Rutter, in company with Thomas Potts, erected the third iron enterprise, the Colebrookdale Furnace in Berks County, about 1720. It contained the first blast furnace built in Pennsylvania and enjoyed a long prosperous career. Thomas Potts in his day was the most successful ironmaster in Pennsylvania. His son, John, was the founder of Pottsgrove, later known as Pottstown.

From the early eighteenth century to the Revolutionary War, the iron industry in the eastern part of the state, particularly in the Delaware and Schuylkill River valleys, expanded rapidly and made more progress than in any other colony and comprised sixty furnaces and forges, several slitting mills, and steelworks.

The Delaware River valley region saw more military action in the Revolution than any other part of the country, and its busy furnaces and forges supplied the major part of the iron for General Washington's armies. Prominent in this respect were the Warwick, Cornwall, and Durham Furnaces, probably the largest blast furnaces at the time in the colonies.

The Durham Furnace played a colorful part in the colonial history of the Delaware River Valley. It was built at Durham, near the Delaware River, about forty miles above Trenton in 1727. In order to navigate the rapids and shallows of the river, Robert Durham, manager of the works, borrowing from the Indian canoe, devised a shallow flat-bottomed bark about sixty feet long and eight feet wide and with a depth of forty-two inches. The craft became famous as the Durham boat, and, until the advent of canals and railroads, transported the greater part of freight between Philadelphia and the upper Delaware River. At one time, a fleet of several hundred Durham boats plied the river employing 2,000 to 3,000 men. General Washington knew of the Durham boats and when he was retreating through New Jersey with the British breathing at his heels, he sent word ahead to have all possible boats assembled for crossing the Delaware into Pennsylvania. Durham boats of the iron industry ferried the general and his men to safety across the stream and he kept all available craft on his side to prevent the British from following him. A little later when Washington made his historic recrossing of the Delaware at McKonkey's Ferry nine miles above Trenton on Christmas night, 1776, through blocks of ice, again it was the Durham boats which took him and his ragged soldiers to the Jersey side. From there he swooped down on the Hessians in Trenton and won a resounding victory.

Valley Forge was the popular name for the Mount Joy Forge, a relatively small iron plantation, operated by Colonel William Dewees at the time the Revolutionary War began. After the Battle of Brandywine in September 1777, the British General Howe sent a detachment to destroy the forge. On Howe's departure for Philadelphia, Washington retired to

Valley Forge where he and his ill-clad, half-starved men passed the severe winter of 1777-1778.

One of the most productive iron enterprises in Pennsylvania was the Warwick Furnace in Chester County. It was among the foremost furnaces in casting cannon and shell for the Continental Army. Warwick Furnace had the distinction of casting the first Franklin stoves which after 1742 began to replace the open smoky fireplaces of earlier days.

Described as one of the "natural glories of Pennsylvania" was the Cornwall iron ore mine, first opened in 1742, and the source of ore for the celebrated Cornwall Furnace. The Cornwall mine was the most productive in the nation prior to the development of Lake Superior ores and held that distinction for several years after Lake Superior ores came into general use. It has been mined continuously since it was opened and is now operated by the Bethlehem Steel Company.

Near Morrisville, named after Robert Morris, financier of the Revolution, there was at one time a thriving iron industry. After the Revolutionary War, the Delaware Works, consisting of forges, slitting mills, grist and saw mills, was established in the vicinity of Morrisville. Near the same spot the giant Fairless Works of United States Steel Corporation was constructed in 1952.

In 1739, the Vincent Steel Works, first in Pennsylvania, were built on French Creek. Two steel works were erected in Philadelphia before the Revolution. Produced in small quantities, steel was used mostly in swords, bayonets and edge tools.

The first blast furnace west of the Allegheny Mountains was built on Jacob's Creek in Fayette County in 1790. Two years later, George Anshutz, a German, erected a small furnace on Two Mile Run, now Shady Side, in what was to become the great steel area of Pittsburgh. It was abandoned after two years for lack of ore. Next, in 1805, a foundry was built at what is now the northeast corner of Smithfield Street and Fifth Avenue, in Pittsburgh. It cast howitzers, shells, and balls for Commodore Perry's fleet on Lake Erie and for General Jackson's forces in New Orleans in the War of 1812.

Colonial Ironworks in Delaware and Maryland

Records of colonial Delaware refer in 1661 to a place called "iron hill" and report that iron ore was discovered there by the Dutch soon after their occupation of the region, if not even earlier by the Swedes. Sir William Keith, Governor of Pennsylvania, is said to have erected an ironworks in New Castle on the Delaware River some time before 1730. A number of furnaces, forges, and rolling mills were erected in the remaining part of the century, but Delaware did not achieve the prominence in iron manufacture of adjoining Maryland.

The pioneer ironworks in Maryland was a bloomery erected at North East in Cecil County at the head of the Chesapeake Bay prior to 1716. Shortly afterwards, Joseph Farmer, an ironmaster in England, organized a company to manufacture iron in the colony. He chose a site near the mouth of Principio Creek where it flows into the Chesapeake Bay and there erected a furnace, the first ironworks of the Principio Company, as the enterprise became known. Farmer's capitalist friends in England became dissatisfied with his management of the company and replaced him by an English Quaker, John England. England was one of the most intelligent and enterprising colonial ironmasters, and when the Principio Works ran out of iron ore, he explored the region around about and found valuable deposits in Virginia, on the lands of Captain Augustine Washington, father of George. England proposed to Captain Washington that the company be allowed to build a furnace on his property in exchange for which Washington was to have two-twelfths interest in the company, reduced in a later contract to one-twelfth. The furnace on Washington's land was called the Accokeek Furnace.

Augustine Washington bequeathed the estate of Mount Vernon and his interest in the Principio Company to his son Lawrence, half-brother of George. Lawrence willed his estate to his daughter Sarah, and at her death, if without issue, to his brother Augustine. Augustine succeeded to ownership of the iron interests and George to the estate at Mount Vernon.

The Principio Company continued to acquire properties and to build additional works. In 1751, it owned four furnaces and two forges, 30,000 acres and "slaves and livestock in abundance." It stood at the front rank of colonial iron enterprises for fifty years and was the foremost producer of pig iron and possibly of bar iron. It was said that half of the pig iron exported to Great Britain prior to the Revolution came from the company.[33]

In 1777, the British destroyed the Principio furnaces, forge, gristmill, and other buildings and spiked the cannon. After peace was declared, Colonel Samuel Hughes purchased the company, rebuilt the furnace and forge at Principio and did a thriving business in the War of 1812. Again the British destroyed the works. Hughes partially repaired his ruined works and carried on for a few years but finally gave up for want of enough capital.

The Principio Works was restored a third time when two brothers, George and Joseph Whitaker, with several partners, acquired the property in 1836. A year later, they built new furnaces, forges, and other necessary facilities. Through their activities, the holdings of the original Principio Company, passing from owner to owner, eventually became absorbed in the Wheeling Steel Corporation of Wheeling, West Virginia, organized in 1920.

Next in importance after the Principio Company was the Mount Etna Furnace built in 1770 on Antietam Creek in Allegheny County.

Virginia and West Virginia

After the Indians destroyed the ironworks at Falling Creek in 1622, it was almost a hundred years before there was a revival of the industry in Virginia, and it was due to Colonel Alexander Spotswood, Governor of the colony from 1710 to 1723. He was the first person to put the iron industry of Virginia on a firm and permanent basis and was responsible for the construction of numerous iron enterprises, the first of which was in operation in 1716.

Following Colonel Spotswood's lead, many furnaces and forges were built before the Revolution. After the war, the iron industry of Virginia took a fresh start to furnish iron to the many other industries arising in the state, especially household manufactures. Nails were one of the products of the home and it was said that Thomas Jefferson required a dozen of his younger slaves to make nails, which they did at the rate of one ton a month "at a considerable profit." The iron industry of Virginia continued to prosper well into the eighteenth century and at its height consisted of eighty-eight charcoal furnaces, fifty-nine forges and bloomeries, and twelve rolling mills, although several of these facilities were in the present State of West Virginia. Before 1850, the iron industry of Virginia underwent a sharp decline, and by 1856 there were only thirty-nine charcoal furnaces and forty-three forges in the state.[34]

Early Iron Industry in Other Southern Colonies

The frontier communities of other southern colonies, particularly North Carolina, Tennessee, and Kentucky, were settled largely by Scotch-Irish immigrants who were said to possess a "genius for ironmaking." The furnaces and forges which they set up were worked fitfully, as the wants of the owners or the neighboring blacksmiths required and the supply of water permitted, furnishing the customary iron commodities for the home, the farm, and self-defense. Until the third quarter of the eighteenth century, iron was still taken in exchange for shoes, coffee, sugar, calico, salt, and other necessities, and bar iron was considered legal tender for the payment of debts. All of the early furnaces were of a primitive type and remained so in remote mountain parts. In 1883, there were two dozen bloomeries still operating in the mountains of Tennessee and a dozen in the mountains of North Carolina, the counterparts of those constructed by pioneers.

CHARACTERISTICS OF COLONIAL IRON INDUSTRY

In the American colonies iron was manufactured at first from sheer necessity for survival. Most of the earliest furnaces and forges were small and were analogous to the local sawmill or gristmill, furnishing iron in the kinds and quantities needed in the community. The bloomery was a primitive furnace of the Catalan type and produced wrought iron directly from the ore. The wrought iron was reheated in the forges and beaten into bars which were sold to the local blacksmith who was the all-round manufacturer for the settlers. The bloomeries were generally in the more remote and isolated communities, and many such furnaces remained in use until the third quarter of the nineteenth century. The blast furnace soon became the basis of regularly established ironworks. Most of the pig iron produced in the blast furnaces was converted into wrought iron in refinery forges and was afterwards beaten by trip hammers into bars for the trade, and, here again, the principal customers were blacksmiths. A considerable quantity of pig iron was cast directly at the blast furnace into pots, pans, kettles, stove plates, fire backs, and other foundry products.

A good portion of the wrought iron bars was rolled into flat strips which were cut in the slitting mill into narrow sections called nail rods, the stock from which wrought iron nails were forged by hand. There appears never to have been enough nails to go around, and the intense demand for them led to the invention of nailmaking machines in the colonial period. The colonies could boast a few plate mills where heated bars were beaten by water-driven hammers into thin sheets, some of which were afterward tinned and used in a variety of utensils, such as fish kettles, stewing pans, and coffee pots.

Wire appears to have been first drawn in this country for use in carding wool, as was the case earlier in England. It was to make wire for the wool trade which undoubtedly prompted the first known "wyer drawer" in the colonies, Nathaniel Robbinson, to petition a Massachusetts court in 1666 for aid in carrying on his craft, a petition that was denied. A year later, Joseph Jenks of Lynn, also desired "the favor of the Court to advance a sume for ye encouragement of wyer drawing, etc."; but the court judged it "not meet to advance any money on that design" and authorized the County Treasurer to "purchase a wire drawing outfit known to be in town for the sum not to exceed fifteen pounds, and to dispose of the same to those skilled in the art of making wire as shall best promote the development of the industry."[35]

From this time on, wire was made in Massachusetts and other eastern states in small quantities by individual artisans who owned a small forge, an anvil, and a wire drawing machine. Progress was slow for many years, and in 1834 there were only three wire mills—establishments separate from home artisans—in the entire United States.

These secondary works—rolling, slitting, plate, and wire mills—were not numerous in the eighteenth century, and the majority were in towns and boroughs to which the pig iron was transported.

Virtually all of the colonial ironworks were built by streams and rivers primarily for water to work the devices which supplied the blast in many bloomeries and to turn the waterwheels which operated the bellows of blast furnaces and forges, and actuated forge hammers and slitting mills, and, secondarily, for the convenience of transportation. Water was also essential for metal-cooling purposes. The site generally chosen for a blast furnace was where a bank rose from a stream or river so that a wooden bridge could be erected from the summit of the bank to a charging platform below the top of the furnace stack. Across this span, "bridgemen" or "fillers" transported the raw materials in wheelbarrows and dumped them into the furnace shaft. The blast furnace stacks were about twenty-five feet square at the base and between twenty-five to thirty feet high. About two and a half tons of ore and 180 bushels of charcoal were needed to produce a ton of iron.[36] The fluxes generally used were fresh water or marine shells. Furnaces were shut down during the freezing months of winter and during hot dry periods of summer. Bog ores found in many fresh water ponds and swamps and salt water marshes served the first ironworkers. As these became depleted and ore deposits were found farther inland, the ores were scooped from the ground surface or dug a short distance under the top soil. Mines were rarely more than forty feet deep. The earliest colonial blast furnaces and forges received forced air from large leather bellows driven by water power. There was only one tuyere in a blast furnace for the admission of air until about the first quarter of the nineteenth century when records occur of furnaces with three tuyeres. Shortly before, or after the Revolution—authorities differ— leather bellows were supplanted by wooden cylinders or "tubs," as they were called. Within the tubs were pistons which were driven back and forth by water power, forcing air into the furnace. During the colonial period, a good output for a blast furnace was twenty-five to thirty tons of iron a week.

Skilled ironworkers were scarce during the entire colonial period and especially during the Revolution. Many of them were Negro slaves or indentured servants, and even Indians were employed at some works. We read in histories of the period that drinking by the workmen of hard liquor, the "traditional lubricant for ironworkers," was one of the greatest difficulties faced by the ironmasters in maintaining production. In 1723, an act was passed in Pennsylvania prohibiting the sale of rum and liquors within three miles of any furnace under penalty of forty shillings for each offense. It was said that "whiskey drinking and fox hunting were the banes of many early forges," and that one gallon of whiskey and another of beer were consumed for every ton of iron produced. Apparently some legislatures, recognizing the institution of drinking, attempted to limit it by authorizing ironmasters to sell to their employees such quantities of rum or other strong liquor as they "judged from experience to be necessary." In spite of these measures, the men got hold of strong liquor to such an extent that frequently a furnace had to shut down temporarily, because too few of the crew were on their feet to operate it.

Iron Plantations

In the eighteenth century, there arose a social-economic community unique in the American colonies—the iron plantation. There were two chief reasons for its origin and growth. Accessibility to iron ore was a prerequisite, but the furnaces and forges could not work without charcoal, and the primary consideration for the site of an iron plantation was the presence of immense stands of timber. A typical blast furnace yielding two tons of iron daily consumed the charcoal from one acre of woodland. A wooded area of 240 acres yielding 5,000 to 6,000 cords was cut down yearly to feed a typical blast furnace.[37] In addition, large quantities of charcoal were consumed in the forges and blacksmith shops of a plantation. The Hopewell Village iron plantation in Pennsylvania devoured the charcoal made from 15,000 cords of wood a year. The woodcutters and charcoal burners far outnumbered the miners and furnace and forge crews. The woodsmen and charcoal burners working at a continually greater distance from the center of the plantation, spent most of their time in the wilderness living in crude cabins. Iron plantations varied in size from a few hundred acres to 10,000. The 20,000-acre Martha Furnace in the Pine Barrens of Southern New Jersey was exceptionally large.

The second reason for the emergence of the iron plantation was the development of many settlements into the first towns and cities on the continent. Formerly, iron was produced for local consumption. Towns and cities with their greater populations and infant industries, provided a relatively concentrated market for iron products. It was primarily to serve these new markets that the iron plantation came into being.

The iron plantation was largely a self-sufficient, feudal-like community. The ironmaster's mansion, often of beautiful Georgian or Colonial architecture, was generally on an elevation where he could observe the works. Near the furnace and forges were clustered cottages for the furnacemen, woodcutters, miners, farm hands, blacksmiths, and their families. A farm and vegetable garden was cultivated to raise food for the community. The plantation also had its own gristmill, sawmill, and blacksmith shop, as well as a store stocked with foods, medicine, cloth, hardware, and other necessities. There was generally a church and a school.

Before the Revolution iron plantations stretched from New England down to the Carolinas. Most of the ironworks in the Pine Barrens of southern New Jersey were plantations. The Martha Furnace in its heyday had a population of four hundred people, forty to fifty houses, saw and grist mills, a school, a store, numerous other buildings, and even a "hospital of sorts." But the colony *par excellence* of the iron plantation was Pennsylvania where these institutions produced the greater part of the iron smelted in the province during the eighteenth century. Dozens of iron plantations carried on their feudal way of life in the Schuylkill,

Susquehanna, and Juniata river valleys. The iron plantations reached their height of development when the Revolution broke out. Almost overnight they changed from small iron enterprises to large-scale industries straining themselves to the limit of their capacities to produce articles of war. Many of them continued in operation for a century afterward.

The Hopewell Village iron plantation remained active well into the last century. It was originated by William Bird in 1770 and at one time covered more than 10,000 acres. In 1938, Hopewell Village was established as a National Historic Site, and since then has been largely reconstructed. It is in Berks County, six miles from Birdsboro, the latter named after its founder.

THE REVOLUTIONARY WAR PERIOD

During the eighteenth century, contrary currents were at work in the British and colonial iron industries. While the former was shrinking to conform itself to England's dwindling forests, the latter was striding confidently ahead with a continent of raw materials to draw upon and a ready market for its products. In 1700 the seaboard colonies produced but 1,500 tons of iron, representing about one-seventeenth of the world's output. Fifty years later the native industry, pushing farther inland and southward, smelted 10,000 tons of iron, or about one-seventh of world production. From then on until the eve of the Revolution, the growth was spectacular; ironworks were built in every colony but Georgia, and by 1775, colonial output reached 30,000 tons, an increase of 200 per cent in twenty-five years. Between 1750 and 1775, estimated world production rose from 140,000 to 180,000 tons, or 30 per cent.[38] Thus, by 1775, the colonial iron industry had risen to a position where it accounted for 16 per cent of world production, outstripping the mother country and exceeded only by Sweden and Russia. In 1775, according to the best available records, the colonies possessed eighty blast furnaces and 175 forges compared to sixty blast furnaces and thirty-five forges in all England and Wales,[39] and the colonies were outproducing the mother country in both pig iron and bar iron. The colonies were not only supplying their own iron needs but were also exporting the metal to England. It has been estimated that between 1717 and 1776 these exports amounted to a total of 150,000 tons of pig and bar iron, averaging around 2,000 to 3,000 tons a year.[40]

Meanwhile, the British iron industry, because of a depletion of native charcoal timber, was rapidly shrinking in size, and the island was forced to import more and more iron. In 1738, England imported more than three times as much bar iron as she produced. An increased supply of pig iron for refinement into cheap bars was of the first necessity if the British iron industry was to survive, and it was but natural that those immediately concerned began to cast their eyes in the direction of the American colonies.

From the beginning, England had sought to stifle in the colonies the development of manufactures which might compete with home industries. Joseph Gee, in 1750, remarked that the British people "ought always to keep a watchful eye over our colonies to restrain them from setting up any of the manufactures which are carried on in Great Britain, and any such attempts should be crushed in the beginning."[41] But the pressure of circumstances led some wiser heads to favor a relaxation of this policy in respect to pig iron. What to do about the colonial iron industry agitated British politics off and on for forty years.

The Iron Act of 1750

In 1750, the famous Iron Act was passed. It provided for the free entry of colonial pig iron into Great Britain and of colonial bar iron into London, the later provision being amended in 1757 to include all English ports. The law specified that "no mill or other engine for slitting or rolling of iron, or any plateing forge to work with a tilt hammer, or any furnace for making steel, shall be erected," but those already in existence were allowed to remain.[42]

The Iron Act's restrictive measures were openly flouted. Furnaces and forges, slitting and plating mills were erected in many communities. The Act failed to relieve the situation in England. In the decade preceding passage of the Act, annual colonial exports to England averaged about 2,300 tons of pig iron and and thirty-five tons of bars. During the first five years of the Act, average annual exports to Britain increased to 3,100 tons of pig iron and 200 tons of bars. The colonists themselves circumvented the main purpose of the Act by working up most of their iron into articles to meet their own pressing needs, leaving little surplus for export to England. Following a depression which struck the colonial iron industry in the late 1760s, ironmasters looked for relief in the English market and exports reached as high as 4,800 tons of pig iron and 2,000 tons of bar iron in several years before the Revolution.

Iron Industry Helped War of Independence

The production of 30,000 tons of iron by the American colonies in 1775 was a remarkable achievement. "If the iron industry had not reached a relatively high stage prior to 1775," says Bining, "it is doubtful whether the colonists could have defended themselves against the British army or could have provided themselves with necessary war manufactures." He adds that French aid in munitions and military supplies, as well as in finance, was extremely important.[43]

The rebelling colonies were fortunate in having on their side the vast majority of the owners and managers of ironworks. Not only in the products of their furnaces and forges did the ironmasters contribute to the cause of liberty, but also in political and military activity. At least five signers of the Declaration of Independence were directly associated with the iron industry: George Taylor of Durham Furnace, George Ross and James Smith, delegates from Pennsylvania, Stephen Hopkins from Delaware, Charles Carroll from Maryland, and Philip Livingston from New York.

George Washington himself was the son of a Virginia ironmaster, Augustine Washington. Scores of ironmasters and ironworkers left their furnaces and forges to serve as officers and soldiers in the Continental Army. Members of the iron industry prominent among Washington's officers were Generals Daniel Morgan and Nathanael Greene and Colonel Ethan Allen. William Alexander (Lord Sterling or Stirling) owned the land on which the Sterling Ironworks were built in Orange County, New York, and may have been part owner of the works himself.

During the war, the demand for iron far exceeded the supply. Full potential production suffered for two reasons. First was the acute shortage of skilled labor. So critical did this become that all ironworkers were exempted from military service. The second factor which lowered the productive output of the iron industry was the destruction of numerous ironworks by the British. Realizing the military importance of iron to the rebelling colonies, British commanders planned some of their campaigns in order to cripple the fighting arm of General Washington, and many skirmishes and several of the major battles of the war took place at or near ironworks. The British succeeded in razing a number of the more important ironworks, particularly in the South.

The principal military items produced at the ironworks were cannon and shot, and secondarily, cast iron kettles, salt pans, ovens, and boilers for camp supplies. The bar iron from bloomeries and forges was shaped by blacksmiths into various military accessories as well as into tools needed in other industries manufacturing war equipment. It was fortunate that a few steel furnaces existed and that some had been built in defiance of the Iron Act. Rare and precious, steel was forged into bayonets and swords. The all-important musket was manufactured by gunsmiths. The colonial iron industry, handicapped by a shortage of skilled labor and the destruction of many furnaces and forges by the enemy, performed a herculean task in supplying the sinews of war to the Continental Army.

Rise of the Young Republic

> *Iron accommodates itself to all our wants, our desires, and even our caprices; it is equally serviceable to the arts, sciences, to agriculture, and war; the same ore furnishes the sword, the ploughshare . . . the spring of a watch or a carriage, the chisel, the chain, the compass, the cannon, and the bomb. It is a medicine of much virtue, and the only metal friendly to the human frame.*
>
> —*Ure's Dictionary of Arts, Manufactures and Mines*

After the Revolutionary War, the iron industry of the young republic went into a decline. It was exhausted from the war effort, technologically behind the times, and suffering from a general postwar depression, intensified by cheap English iron flooding the market. Not only were many ironworks demolished by the British during the Revolution, but large numbers of the surviving furnaces and forges were obsolete. As the older works fell into disrepair, there was no point in trying to restore them. What was needed were more up-to-date facilities. But construction materials and labor were scarce, prices for both were high, and as a consequence many of the old furnaces and forges were abandoned. Another factor which retarded the postwar growth of the iron industry was inadequate transportation.

The greatest hindrance to a revival of the iron industry, as well as to other manufactures, was the dumping of English goods directly after the Treaty of Paris in 1783. English fleets brought to American ports shiploads of manufactured goods, including iron, which were sold at a low price or disposed of at auctions. The price of European iron was below the cost of domestic production.

The owners of ironworks could hardly have maintained themselves in the opening years of the nineteenth century except for the relief which came from the embargo of 1808, the Non-Intercourse Act, and the closing of ports during the War of 1812. Iron manufacture flourished during that period, but the deflation which followed the war brought depressed conditions to the industry and ruined many ironmasters. From 1816 to 1833, a movement to protect "infant industries" grew steadily and the iron industry benefited from higher import duties enacted in that period; but in spite of this tariff umbrella, imports from Great Britain rose from 21,500 tons in 1815 to 36,000 in 1828-1829. From the early thirties to the Civil War, the general tendency of tariffs was downward and imports of iron and steel rose abruptly from 74,000 tons in 1832 to 102,000 tons in 1843-1844.[1] In spite of adverse tariffs and higher imports, the iron industry did very well for itself in the first half of the century, judging by the following figures:[2]

1810—153 blast furnaces produced 59,000 tons of pig iron and 135 bloomeries and 330 forges manufactured 27,000 tons of bar iron. There were 316 trip hammers, 34 rolling and slitting mills, and 410 naileries. The last-named turned out nearly 16 million pounds of nails.

1840—804 blast furnaces produced 316,000 tons of pig iron, and 795 bloomeries, forges, and rolling mills manufactured 217,000 tons of bar iron.

1850—377 "establishments" produced 620,000 tons of pig iron and 552 "establishments" manufactured wrought iron valued at $22 million. The tonnage was not given.

1860—286 "establishments" produced 1 million tons of pig iron and 256 "establishments" manufactured 564,000 tons of rolled iron and thirteen "establishments" produced 13,000 tons of steel.

From the foregoing it will be seen that between 1810 and 1860 pig iron production increased from 59,000 to 1 million tons, or more than sixteen times. The greater output from a smaller number of furnaces in 1860 over 1840 was due to larger furnaces, the gradual replacement of charcoal by mineral fuel, and a number of other technological improvements, principally the use of the hot blast. The general expansion of the iron industry may also be measured by the rise of iron production per capita: In 1810, it was approximately seventeen pounds; in 1840 it had risen to thirty-eight pounds and by 1860 it had climbed to fifty-nine pounds.

THE IRON INDUSTRY MOVES WESTWARD

When the Revolutionary War ended, the frontier was still fairly close to the Atlantic seaboard. Beyond the frontier stretched unbroken forests, wide plains, and formidable mountains inhabited by wandering Indian tribes, a handful of explorers, and a few scattered French outposts. Shortly afterwards one of the greatest migrations in history got under way. In a single lifetime, from 1790 to 1850, the population increased

from about 4 million, 94 per cent of which were in the original thirteen
colonies, to 23 million in thirty-one states. The pressure of population was
being felt in the East, where available farmland had been largely occupied. Seemingly unlimited acres of rich, virgin soil to be had for its occupation and development, or at low cost, drew the people westward like a
magnet. Migration on a large scale began with the opening of the Northwest Territory about 1787, and in the next thirty years multitudes poured
into that region.

When the settlers moved into the Old Northwest, they lived in primitive frontier conditions similar in many respects to those of the early
colonists along the Atlantic seaboard. Iron was scarce, especially in remote districts. Consequently, one of the first concerns of the settlers was
to establish an iron industry. It had its origins in the Western Reserve
where the first furnace, Hopewell Furnace, was built in Mahoning
County, Ohio, in 1804, two years after the territory was admitted to the
Union. The most prominent iron center of the early West was the Hanging Rock district, comprising several counties in Ohio and Kentucky on
both sides of the Ohio River. The first ironworks on the Kentucky side
was the Argillite Furnace built in 1818 near the town of Greenup. The
first furnace on the Ohio side was the Franklin Furnace erected by the
Ohio Iron Company near Portsmouth in 1827. From then on, the iron
industry in the Hanging Rock district expanded rapidly and for more
than thirty-five years was one of the leading iron-producing areas in the
United States.

Turnpikes to "Iron Horses"

A society with poor transportation exists largely on a local basis. Such
was the condition in colonial days. The chief means of transporting goods
and people were by water, but the major rivers in the eastern part of
the United States run north and south. With the rapid growth in the
size and number of cities in the East and the swelling torrent of westward migration, better interconnecting travel arteries became imperative.
The settlers in the West depended for their very existence on adequate
transportation facilities connecting them with the East.

The nation's first answer was in the form of turnpikes, which pro-
liferated in the North and South. The most famous road was authorized
by the government—the Cumberland Road, or, as it was popularly
known, the National Pike. Over this route from Cumberland, Maryland,
to Jefferson City, Missouri, vehicles of all descriptions traveled westward
in such volume that, as one observer put it, "It looked more like the
leading avenue of a great city than a road through rural districts."[3]

After Robert Fulton harnessed steam power to his *Clermont* in 1807
and sailed it up the Hudson River from New York to Albany, water
transportation began to take some of the traffic load from turnpikes.

In the next few decades there was an impressive expansion in steamboat navigation. It became one of the favorite means for families to travel westward into a region where rich, abundant acreage awaited every newcomer.

But there was still need for additional east-west transportation facilities to link up with the rivers. The problem was given its initial solution by the building of canals. The opening of the Erie Canal in 1825 began a new and romantic chapter in American history, celebrated in song and story. Cutting across New York State, it joined the Hudson River with the Great Lakes, providing an all-water route for the exchange of goods between the northwestern farmer and the northeastern manufacturer. It also became a popular avenue for the westward surge of homesteaders. The success of the Erie Canal inaugurated an era of feverish canal-digging. Pennsylvania developed the most extensive system in the nation, followed by Virginia and Maryland in the South.

Next came the puffing, wood-burning, "iron horses." The first American-made locomotive, "Tom Thumb," an experimental model with a boiler the size of a flour barrel, made its historic run of thirteen miles on August 25, 1830. On Christmas day of the same year, "The Best Friend of Charleston" began the first scheduled passenger service on this continent, although of short duration, for it was discontinued the following summer after a defective safety valve caused the locomotive to blow up. The early cars were little more than uncovered wooden stagecoaches. Occasionally, the iron straps which served as rails would come loose and curl up into "snakeheads," protruding through the floor of the carriage, injuring passengers, or derailing trains. The railroads at first were confined to the Atlantic seaboard, but soon they began to extend their iron fingers westward in a mad race with the canals to capture the trade flowing from the West.

The use of rails to guide a wheeled vehicle had long been applied in England for hauling coal wagons from the pit to the place of shipment. These first rails were wooden. Later, thin strips of forged wrought iron were nailed to the wooden tracks and this device remained in use without any noticeable improvement for 125 years. The first step toward the development of the modern rail took place in England in 1767, when cast iron plates were attached to wooden stringers in order to provide support for heavier loads of coal. Cast iron tended to crack and was gradually replaced by more dependable wrought iron. This type of flat wrought-iron rail was known as a strap rail. England continued to pioneer in the development of rails, and after many futile efforts finally succeeded in 1820 in rolling a heavy wrought-iron edge rail eighteen feet in length.

The early railroads in America generally used the strap rail fastened to wood or strung between stone blocks. Because of numerous mishaps caused by the light rails and the appearance of heavier trains, the heavy wrought-iron edge rail, imported from England, began to replace the strap rail. America had no facilities for producing the heavy rail until 1844 when the Mt. Savage Rolling Mill in Allegany County, Maryland, began manufacture of the inverted "U" rail. The T-rail, now the standard design, was invented in 1831 by an American, R. L. Stevens, and was produced in America in 1845 by the Mt. Savage mill and also by the Montour Rolling Mill of Danville, Pennsylvania. Other rail mills were soon built in the United States and by 1854 their annual output amounted to 108,000 tons, but the railroads still depended heavily on imports from Britain.

REVOLUTION IN AGRICULTURE

When the nineteenth century opened, the United States was largely an agricultural nation, with nine out of ten gainfully employed persons working on farms. Implements were crude and productivity was low. The plow was made of wood with a piece of iron or an old saw blade nailed to the share. With such equipment the farmer could raise only enough for himself and family with a small surplus left to exchange for other commodities in nearby towns. The iron, textile, and other manufactures, expanding under the impetus of the Industrial Revolution, lured workers from the farms with higher wages. Swelling city populations offered tempting markets for farm produce. To survive, and to meet the challenge of larger markets, the farmer was impelled to find labor-saving devices. From 1830 onward, inventions followed one another pell mell, and the farmer began to hitch horses instead of oxen to implements and machines for harrowing, seeding, cultivating, raking, reaping, harvesting, and threshing, most of them made more durable and productive by iron and steel. The beginning of the farmer's liberation from hand power, which dated from Biblical days, by horsepower, was made possible in the last analysis by the replacement of wood by iron and steel.

The introduction of the steel plow and the invention of the reaper were the outstanding improvements of this period. The homesteader on the plains found that the cast iron plow which he brought with him from the East, dulled quickly in the tough prairie sod and furthermore the heavy soil stuck to the blade and would not "scour off." The steel plow, first developed commercially by John Deere in 1837, answered the challenge of the prairie sod and enabled the farmer to open up larger tracts for growing grains, principally wheat. About the same time, invention of the reaper by Cyrus McCormick made it possible to harvest the bigger crops.

By means of these and other mechanical inventions during the agricultural revolution between 1830 and 1860, "the American farmer acquired the power not only to bring forth an abundance of food for every man, woman, and child in the United States but also to contribute to world surplus."[4] The agricultural revolution in its early years provided the first important market for iron, and hundreds of factories, turning out plows and other agricultural machinery, laid the foundation for rapidly developing industry.

Barbed Wire in the Opening of the West

The steel plow made it possible for the homesteader to turn the heavily matted sod, and the reaper encouraged him to open up large tracts and sow them with wheat. Before farming could be conducted satisfactorily on a large scale, the homesteaders had to solve the vexing problem of how to fence in their cultivated fields. Fences were needed to protect crops against wild animals and large herds of wandering range cattle. But the prairies provided neither stones nor timber. Sod fences and thorny hedges were tried, but both were unsatisfactory and hedges took too long to grow.

Newspapers, farm journals, and agricultural societies energetically discussed the problem of fences. Farmers were exhorted to "look the question in the face" and come up with a solution. Two men looked the question in the face at about the same time and came up with a practical answer—barbed wire. They were Joseph H. Glidden, a farmer, and Jacob Haish, a carpenter, both of DeKalb, Illinois, with the former slightly in the lead. Glidden applied for his patent on October 27, 1873, and Haish on December 22 of the same year. Haish claimed priority for his invention and fought Glidden in the courts for twenty years. A final decision recognized Glidden as the first inventor. His type of barbed wire was the kind most widely used for half a century.

Barbed wire at first met with opposition from farmers and cattlemen who refused to believe that the wire was strong enough to hold in livestock and they also feared that the barbs would injure the animals. But once the farmers and ranchers were won over to the new fencing material, the demand for it increased like wildfire.

American ingenuity set to work inventing machines that manufactured barbed wire and rolled it on spools ready for use. The first barbed wire was made out of wrought iron; but after steel replaced iron in wire in the 1870s, the greater usefulness of steel further increased the demand for barbed wire. Production soared from 10,000 pounds in 1874 to 80 million pounds in 1880. Greater productivity was accompanied by a fall in price—from twenty cents to slightly less than two cents a pound within twenty-three years.

HOMESTEADERS AND CATTLEMEN CLASH

Once the homesteaders overcame their objection to barbed wire, they began rapidly to string it on their properties which the government had given to them, or sold at a low price. Much of this land was on the vast unfenced government domain comprising 1 million square miles, known as the "cow country,"[5] which the cattlemen claimed as their own by right of squatter sovereignty, as old as the frontier itself. The ranchmen vigorously opposed the fencing of any part of this land by the pioneer homesteaders. Then, as soon as the cattlemen were "sold" on barbed wire, they hastened to fence not only their own properties but large areas of the public domain as well, in an effort to keep out the sturdy pioneers looking for new land. Accusing the cattlemen of setting up "barbed wire kingdoms," the farmers appealed to the government for help, and laws were eventually passed that forbade fencing of the public domain.[6]

"BET-A-MILLION" GATES

The man who broke the initial opposition of the cattlemen to barbed wire was the fabulous John W. ("Bet-A-Million") Gates, who rose from a poor boy to become the dominant figure in the wire industry at the close of the century and the principal founder of the American Steel and Wire Company. At the age of twenty-one, Gates became a wire salesman for his uncle, Isaac L. Ellwood, a hardware dealer in DeKalb, who had bought one-half interest in Glidden's patent for $265. Ellwood had been unable to crack the Texas market for barbed wire. His warehouses were filled with carloads of rusting, unsold barbed wire.[7]

When Gates reached San Antonio, he found the ranchmen unwilling to accept a free demonstration of barbed wire's effectiveness. He hit upon the idea of publicly proving the value of his product by staging a rodeo in the Military Plaza of the city. A herd of cattle was driven into the barbed wire arena by wild-yelling cowboys. The cattle broke in all directions, charging the fence, but the eight strands of wire held firm and the steers after one experience stayed away from the steel barbs. Ranchmen needed no more persuasion. Gates was unable to supply all the orders that poured in. The rodeo started a revolution in the cattle industry.

"It was barbed wire," says Webb, "and not the railroads or the homestead laws that made it possible for the farmers to resume, or at least accelerate, their march across the prairies on to the plains. Even the fertile Prairie Plains were but sparsely settled until after the advent of barbed wire."[8]

NAILS AND NAILMAKING

From very early times, there appears to have been an insatiable demand for nails. For a period in England, nails consumed more iron than any other product. The demand was all the greater in the American colonies where the settlers had to build homes and barns, churches, town halls, and other structures. The humble, wrought-iron nail was almost worth its weight in gold. When some colonists picked up stakes to pioneer farther west, they would burn down the old house and hunt among the ashes for the nails to use in erecting their new home. The nail certainly helped to build America, and this is an appropriate place to give it due recognition.

In colonial times, nailmaking was one of the most thriving household activities, especially in New England. During winter months, particularly, when little or no work could be done outside, entire families, including the children, would gather around the fireplace and make nails by hand. A nail rod—a long narrow strip of iron obtained from the nearest iron-monger—was cut with a pair of shears to the approximate size of the nail to be made, and placed in a vise. With a few skilled blows of the hammer, the shank and head were formed. A good worker could make as many as 2,000 small nails a day. The nails were bartered for commodities which the family needed.

It is not surprising that a few nailmakers, impatient with the slow hand process, devised nailmaking machines. The first in the world was built by Jeremiah Wilkinson of Rhode Island as early as 1777. It was a crude machine, operated by the hands and feet, but it "cut" nails and its appearance set off an intense activity to invent others. Between 1790 and 1825, the Patent Office recognized 120 different nailmaking machines. One of the most successful machines is attributed to Jacob Perkins of Newburyport, Massachusetts, who patented his invention in 1795. It was said to have been capable of turning out 200,000 nails a day. According to Swank, a nail-cutting machine patented by Josiah G. Pierson of New York, who plied his trade at Ramapo, Rockland County, was the first that "produced satisfactory results and was generally used."[9]

The new machines soon put a quietus to the household industry. Nail factories sprang up rapidly in New England, New York, New Jersey, and eastern Pennsylvania, and by 1810 there were 410 "naileries" producing 16 million nails. Cut nails, so-called to distinguish them, first from the hand-wrought variety and later from wire nails, were produced from an iron plate rolled on a small rolling mill. The iron plate was hammered to a thickness of about one-half inch, after which it was rolled to the thickness and width required for the size of the nail to be made.

Wire Nails Introduced

Cut nails, after replacing handmade nails, were the only kind produced until the greatest advance in the history of nails took place in the latter half of the nineteenth century—the manufacture of nails from wire. Two Americans are credited, by different authorities, with having introduced the wire nail to America. According to one version, Major Thomas Norton visited England in 1850 and saw wire nails being made by machines in Birmingham. On his return to America, he ordered construction of similar machines in 1851 and put them into operation—the first of the kind, it is claimed, in this country. Swank says that the first wire nails manufactured in the United States were made in 1851 or 1852 in New York City by William Hassall, who emigrated from Birmingham, England, and presumably brought with him knowledge of the English machines.[10]

Wire nails were smooth, with a tapered point, contrasted to the rough edges and blunt end of cut nails, and people at first hesitated to buy them, suspecting that they would not hold and would split the wood. For a while they were purchased only by furniture manufacturers, cigar-box makers, wagon builders, and roofers. By degrees, hardware stores began to carry wire nails, and other manufacturers ordered them in quantity lots from the mills. Many customers still clung to cut nails; and, to satisfy their demands, over 8 million kegs of cut nails were manufactured as late as 1886, compared to 600,000 kegs of wire nails. From then on, cut nails lost ground rapidly and by 1892 half of the nails made in the United States were of wire. Three years later, the cut nail was definitely on the way out. Improved machinery led to sharp drop in the price of wire nails—from twenty cents a pound in 1875 to a fraction more than one cent a pound in 1894.

Most nails were made of iron until low-cost Bessemer steel was put on the market. Two German immigrants, Michael Baakes and Father Joseph Goebbels, a priest, apparently first thought of substituting steel for iron at their factory, the Kentucky Wire Nail Works, in Covington, Kentucky. This was in 1875. Baakes was one of the most prominent nail manufacturers of the last century.

The Industrial Revolution Comes to America

A tool is but the extension of a man's hand, and a machine is but a complex tool. And he that invents a machine augments the power of a man and the well-being of mankind.

—*Henry Ward Beecher*

When the Industrial Revolution reached American shores in the early part of the nineteenth century, the sequence of technology in the iron industry was the reverse of what it had been earlier in England. There the substitution of coke for charcoal as a blast furnace fuel preceded the introduction of Cort's puddling furnace and grooved rolls. In America, the puddling furnace, grooved rolls, and other techniques were introduced before the change from charcoal to coke. The Industrial Revolution was in full swing and the iron industry was becoming a "heavy" industry while the United States was still in the charcoal era. Leaders of the iron industry did not feel the urgency of copying England's coke furnaces while large tracts of charcoal timber still remained.

The iron industry from the start in America produced for a predominantly agricultural population. It made and sold hollow ware and other castings at the furnace site. Its chief product, bars, was fashioned by the blacksmith to meet the needs of the farmer, the wagoner, the mill owner, the carpenter, and other local artisans. Generally speaking, no other intermediary was needed between the ironmaster and the consumer. It was not until the 1820s, when the first small factories came into being, that a specialization began in the manufacture of iron products. The rural population continued to be the chief market of the iron industry. Manufacture of farm machinery and implements created the first important specialty market for the iron industry, absorbing for many years a large part of its output. Hundreds of factories turned out plows, hay rakes, cultivators, reapers, and other agricultural equipment.

The two earliest iron products to create sizable industries of their own were the "pot-bellied" heating stove and the iron range. The first became widely popular early in the century, but the second was in still greater demand; its production increased by leaps and bounds and in 1850 reached a volume of more than 300,000 units.

Pennsylvania, in the middle of the century, produced more than half of the pig iron and rolled iron in the United States, but New England was the chief manufacturing center of smaller finished products of iron and steel, such as iron axes, springs, bolts, wire, firearms, and clocks. Half of the edge tools and three-fourths of the cutlery were produced in New England, and most of the textile machinery was also made there.

The iron industry was not at first technologically equipped to produce rolled products, castings, and forgings in the varieties and quantities needed in the new era which the agricultural and industrial revolutions were bringing into being. Development of the rolling mill will be considered first.

DEVELOPMENT OF ROLLING MILLS

From a metallurgical and engineering standpoint, rolling is the most practical and economical method for shaping iron and steel. At forging temperature, iron and steel are relatively soft and can be given various shapes under the pressure of rolls. Although the primary purpose of rolling is to shape hot metal, it has an important secondary purpose. Iron and steel at forging temperature consist of a relatively weak mass of large, coarse grains or crystals. In passing between the rolls, the metal is compacted in the same manner as the smith's hammer kneaded the hot iron bloom on his anvil. The large crystals or grains are transformed by the rolling into much smaller crystals, and the quality of the metal is improved. In a sense, rolling is a form of mechanical forging.

The American rolling mill, in the early nineteenth century resembled that of colonial days and was capable of rolling only flat wrought iron bars. Sheets were hammered partly by hand and partly by water-driven hammers. These methods were not only slow but were also expensive in labor and charcoal. Ironmasters, striving to adopt cheaper, mass-production methods, borrowed Henry Cort's puddling furnace and grooved rolls to produce bars. The first such installation in America was made at the Plumstock Works, near Uniontown, Pennsylvania, in 1817. Others soon followed in Pittsburgh, where there were eight in the 1820s, most of them driven by steam power. The puddling furnace was indispensable for the mass production of wrought iron to keep pace with the productivity of the rolling mill. As furnaces grew larger, the mass of puddled iron increased in size and was divided into three balls, each weighing about 150 pounds.

Sheets and Plates

Meanwhile, the growing demand for iron sheets and plates could not be met by the time-honored hammering method. Sheets were used extensively in the manufacture of agricultural machinery, and implements and plates were essential for the boilers of locomotives, steamships, and stationary steam engines. For more than two hundred years, iron sheets had been rolled in England. The first American to copy an English rolling mill was Isaac Pennock, who installed a sheet mill at his ironworks, known as the Brandywine Rolling Mill, at Coatesville, Pennsylvania, in 1810. Two years later, his son-in-law, Charles Lukens, who succeeded him in the management of the plant, rolled boiler plates of wrought iron for the first time in the United States. The example set by the Brandywine Rolling Mill was soon followed by others and the rolling of sheets and boiler plates became a large and flourishing business.

By the second quarter of the century, the rolling industry was fairly well established in America. It expanded rapidly, lessening dependence on British imports. In 1830, domestic production of hammered and rolled iron products amounted to 113,000 tons.[1] Just before the Civil War, it was more than 500,000 tons. Production was over 856,000 tons in the last year of the conflict.[2] The bulk of rolled iron was in the form of boiler plate and rails, and more than half of these products were manufactured in Pennyslvania, where the chief center was Pittsburgh. The rise of the rolling mill industry in the several decades before the Civil War was of major importance in the American Industrial Revolution.[3]

The earliest rolling mills were what today would be called extremely crude. They were incapable of being turned in a reverse direction. Consequently, after a red-hot sheet passed between the rolls, it was seized in long-handled tongs by a "catcher" or "tongman" who lifted it and let it slide back over the top roll to the other side for another "pass." Several passes through the rolls were required to compact and reduce the iron to the proper dimensions. Between each pass the rolls were "screwed down" by sheer human power a little closer together. In this manner, the metal was reduced by degrees in thickness and at the same time was elongated. To roll round bars, a number of parallel grooves encircled both rolls; each groove was shaped progressively more like the finished bar. A roughly-shaped bar, at red heat, was passed through one groove after another, each time being returned overhead in the same manner as a sheet. From the last groove a perfectly-shaped rod issued forth.

Three-High and Reversing Mill

The first important innovation in rolling mills eliminated the need of the "idle pass," as the return of the metal over the top of the rolls was called. A third roll was added giving what was termed a three-high mill. In such a mill, the iron being rolled was passed from one side between the top and middle rolls and was returned between the bottom and center rolls. Thus there was no waste motion. The center roll was in a fixed position while the upper and lower rolls could be adjusted according to the thickness of the rolled product desired. Visitors to Henry Cort's mill in 1823 described a three-high mill for rolling bars and another for rolling angle iron.[4] Others in addition to Cort were experimenting with it, and in 1853 a three-high mill was built for the Abersychern Iron Works to roll heavy metal sections. A steam-operated lift table raised and lowered the object being rolled. In the United States, Bernard Lauth in 1864 introduced a new rolling principle into the three-high mill by using a middle roll of smaller diameter than the other two. His purpose was not only to dispense with the idle pass but also for greater ease of reduction with less power. But the most successful three-high mill is generally attributed to John Fritz who erected such a mill at the Cambria Iron Works in Johnstown, Pennsylvania, in 1855-1857 for rolling rails. It greatly accelerated rail output and was widely used in place of two-high mills.

Another important step came with the invention of the "reversing" mill. Various attempts had been made to find a way to reverse the movement of the rolls but without success until it was accomplished at the Parkgate Works in England in 1854 for rolling plates. How the mill was reversed is not explained, but in 1866 a reversing engine was attached to a rail mill at the Ransbottom Crewe Works in England. The same principle was given its initial application in the United States at a blooming mill of the Schoenberger Works in Pittsburgh in 1877. The reversing mill was another triumph of the iron industry in its drive for greater productivity.

Continuous Rolling Mill

We now come to a revolutionary principle in rolling — the continuous mill. Early in the nineteenth century the English iron industry began the practice of placing two or three stands of rolls in tandem, for producing rods. After being worked in one set of rolls, the material was reheated and carried to the second stand where it was further rolled, then reheated and passed through the third stand, if one existed. Men began to think of ways to circumvent the reheating of the iron and to have it pass from stand to stand without interruption. As one of the experimenters described it, his purpose was to roll iron with "as many pairs of rolls as can conveniently operate on the material in one heat."[5] Continuous rolling was first successfully applied to rods.

An intermediate step between the three-high rod mill and the continuous rod mill was the semi-continuous mill. As steam power made it possible for the rolls to turn faster, it became a problem of how to handle the long, fast-moving rod as it issued from the last rolls. In Belgium, it was done by "looping." As the rod issued from the first "roughing" stands, it was grasped by a "catcher" in a pair of tongs, who made a half turn and quickly inserted the rod into the grooves of the first of a series of finishing stands. The rod continued to be "looped" in this fashion from stand to stand, being threaded by hand, so to speak, for each new pass. As the rod came from the last stand it was wound on a hand-turned reel. There were five to seven finishing stands. This type of mill was called the Belgian or looping mill. Although it was a considerable improvement over the three-high mill, it was comparatively inefficient and could not roll rods longer than three hundred feet. The limitation on length was due largely to the time required for looping, during which the rod cooled off too much for further rolling. The Belgian mill underwent marked improvement in the hands of William Garrett, Superintendent of the Cleveland Rolling Mill Company. He quadrupled the cross section of the billet, making it four by four inches square. He also arranged to have the billet mill feed directly into the rod mill, thus dispensing with the need for reheating the billets as was done in the original Belgian mill. The first Garrett mill was errected in 1882 and at once more than doubled the output of the looping mill.

Meanwhile, developments were going forward which were to culminate in a mill which allowed the hot iron to proceed in a continuous process through the entire sequence of stands. A number of men in the United States and Europe contributed to the development of the continuous mill and patented their inventions. The earliest patents were taken out by John Hazeldine of England in 1798 and by J. E. Serrell of New York in 1843.[6] In the Serrell mill, the rod passed continuously through a series of grooved rolls, each set at right angles to the preceding pair. There were guides so arranged that the rod was twisted between certain rolls. In the Serrell mill, as in modern mills, each pair of rolls, beginning with the second, turned faster than the preceding rolls. This was necessary in order to take up the increased length of the rod as it became smaller in diameter in its progress through the mill. The revolutionary nature of Serrell's invention was not fully recognized at that time and was lost sight of for many years, even in the Patent Office, where it was accidently discovered long after the patent had expired.

Another American, H. B. Comer, of Philadelphia, also patented a continuous rod mill with twist guides. This was in 1859.

Experiments along similar lines were going on in Europe. At St. Dizier, France, a Frenchman by the name of Levy patented a continuous rod mill in 1854. The mill was incapable of producing rods in quantity, but it sparked an idea in the mind of George Bedson of England during a visit to Levy's mill. Back in England, Bedson put his ideas into execution and took out a patent in 1862. Although he owed his basic concepts to

Levy, Bedson is credited with having built the first really successful continuous mill. It contained sixteen pairs of rolls in line and could roll rods much longer than was heretofore possible and vastly increased the tonnage output.

Bedson's results were at first discouraging. This not due to shortcomings of the mill but to the charcoal or puddled iron which he used. Since each stand of rolls, after the first, turned faster than the preceding pair, it was necessary to keep a certain tension in the rod between successive passes. The hot iron rods could not always stand the strain and frequently ruptured. Bedson tried steel with gratifying results and from then on steel began to replace iron in rods and in wire, greatly extending the uses of wire. The first continuous mill in the United States was installed by Ichabod Washburn in Worcester, Massachusetts, in 1869.

STRUCTURAL IRON AND STEEL

About the middle of the eighteenth century in England, advances in the techniques of coke blast furnaces resulted in cast and wrought iron of improved quality and lower price. These competitive advantages considerably enlarged the market for both forms of iron and was very likely the compelling reason why builders began making exploratory uses of iron to support wood and masonry and also to replace them. The desirability of a stronger, more enduring material than wood had long been evident, but the relatively high cost of charcoal iron had limited its use.

In France, some bold experiments were made with iron to form structural members of roof framework and in a crude form of reinforced masonry. Ceilings of imbedded iron bars, made in Paris around the 1830s, may be regarded as the precursors of reinforced concrete. G. Soufflot, in Paris, planned an iron frame of fifteen feet eight inches in span to carry a mansard roof and skylight. The framework consisted of wrought iron bars with forged ends pinned together and was completed in 1781. Soufflot also imbedded a framework of wrought iron bars in the masonry of the churches of St. Genevieve and St. Sulpice in Paris.[7]

Over in England, men first gave thought to extending the use of iron in buildings to lessen the hazards of fire. Many valuable factories, built of wood, had burned down with loss of life. Men reasoned that if the upright columns were of iron and the floors were not of wood, the damage by fire would be reduced. An archwork of brick supported a flagstone floor. The columns, beams, and window frames were of cast iron. The exterior walls were of brick or stone. Such structures became standard in fireproof factories in England. In the 1850s, many shops and office buildings were constructed with the interiors similar to the factories, but with the facades entirely of cast iron and glass. Cast iron lent itself to ornamentation in any style. Masonry in fanciful design was most commonly imitated, but even Gothic exteriors for churches were indulged in.

Iron and Steel Bridges

About the time that the construction of fireproof buildings was going forward in England, many bridges of stone and wood were being erected to accommodate the increased flow of trade and commerce across her streams and rivers. In the first application of iron, builders attempted to imitate stone construction. Such was the method employed by Abraham Darby, originator of the coke blast furnace, in designing and building the Coalbrookdale Bridge over the Severn River in England, completed in 1779. He used separate wedge-shaped cast-iron sections to form the arch. The 100-foot span is still standing.

The first American bridge entirely of cast iron was built in 1840, crossing the Erie Canal at Frankfurt, New York. The first all-iron railroad bridge in America was constructed near Manayunk, Pennsylvania in 1845. The rapid extension of railroads in both the United States and Europe was accompanied by the erection of many cast-iron bridges. These bridges collapsed at an alarming rate. Bridge builders next turned to wrought iron, which has greater elasticity under strain than cast iron. But wrought iron proved to be inadequate for the heavier "iron horses" and cars appearing on the rails.

In 1868, the first bridge with its main arch members made of steel was errected at Kuelenberg, Holland, over the Rhine.[8] There was some hesitation to follow the example in England, where a prejudice existed in some quarters against the use of steel in bridges. In 1877, steel was specified in errection of the giant Firth of Forth Bridge in Scotland. The success of the bridge proved to doubters the fitness and reliability of steel for bridge construction. The first specification of steel for a bridge in America was for the ach of the Eads Bridge, errected over the Mississippi at St. Louis in 1874. The rest of the bridge was composed of wrought iron. Five years later the first all-steel span, the Glasgow Bridge, was thrown across the Missouri River.

Structural Rolling Mill

Toward the middle of the nineteenth century, while cast-iron building construction was in vogue, there was a considerable extension in the use of wrought iron, and it appears that this movement led to the first design and rolling of structural iron. Wrought iron was originally used in buildings to strengthen wood. A sheet of wrought iron was sandwiched between two wooden beams or rafters, or a timber beam was placed between two iron sheets. In both cases, the combination was bolted together. The next step was to rivet angular sections of iron to the ends of an iron plate into the shape of a beam with flanged edges. The idea of a flanged beam was born. It is said that Ferdinand Zores of Paris attempted without success to persuade mill owners to roll an iron beam. Finally, in 1847 or 1849, Zores succeeded in rolling I-beams, which were installed as roof girders in a house in Paris.[9]

Wrought-iron I-beams were first rolled in the United States on a three-high mill by Peter Cooper at the Trenton Iron Works, Trenton, New Jersey, in 1854. At that time and for some years, iron beams were quite small. Their size was limited to the mass and weight of a bloom which could be puddled in a furnace at one time. To roll a long, heavy beam, it was necessary to hammer several blooms together, a slow and expensive process. The economic production of large beams in quantity waited upon the availability of Bessemer steel in large ingots. Until such sections were produced, large beams for bridges and buildings were made by riveting plates and angles together. A big step forward was taken in 1876 by Joseph de Buigne of France, who designed rolls for producing wide flange H-beams.[10] The modern era of rolling large structural steel sections dates from 1887, when H. Sack patented a universal reversing mill for rolling flanged beams.[11] The term "universal" refers to small vertical rolls for rolling the edges of a product while its upper and lower surfaces are being worked on by the larger horizontal rolls.

Iron Beams in Buildings

When Peter Cooper rolled the first wrought-iron beams in the United States, he intended them for the Cooper Union Building on which work had already started; but he waived the first lots for restoration of the building of the publishers, Harper & Brothers, which had burned to the ground in 1853. The Harper Building thus became the first in the United States to employ wrought-iron beams in masonry walls as a lateral support. The building had a cast-iron front and was six stories high. The Cooper Union Building, erected shortly after the Harper Building, is still standing. A later fine example of a building with wrought-iron beams and a cast-iron front was the A. T. Stewart Department Store, which was subsequently purchased by John Wanamaker. It was destroyed by fire in 1956. Similar buildings enjoyed a vogue in a number of American cities during the second half of the last century.

Before the invention of elevators, six stories was the practical limit of a commercial building. Taller masonry structures could have been built, but no one would climb any higher. This opposition was overcome by the invention of an elevator safety device by Elisha Otis in 1854. Builders began to erect "elevator buildings" of nine and ten stories. The interiors were constructed of cast-iron columns and wrought-iron beams, but the exterior walls of masonry still carried the weight of the upper floors. The masonry walls in the lower stories had to be very thick, thus occupying a great deal of floor space. Since the walls supported the weight of the upper floors, the walls could not afford to be weakened by allowing much space for windows.

Chicago took the lead in a revolutionary type of building construction. William Le Baron Jenney was commissioned in 1883 by the Home Insurance Company of that city to build a twelve-story block of offices that would be fireproof and admit as much sunlight as possible into every room. He took the dead weight from the walls and placed it on a skeleton iron framework that carried the weight into the foundations, thus establishing the principle of the modern skyscraper. When the structure reached the sixth floor, Andrew Carnegie asked permission to install Bessemer steel beams in the remaining floors. This was granted. The building was completed in the fall of 1885. Two floors were added later.[12] Jenney's skeleton framework, in taking the weight from the walls, permitted them to serve merely as a face for the building to protect the interior and its occupants. He was also able to allow more space for windows and to let in additional sunlight.

The second building of skeleton construction was the Rookery, a twelve-story structure, erected in Chicago in 1886. Other tall buildings followed in Chicago, in which cast iron, wrought iron, and steel were used in construction, often all three in the same building. The first wholly steel frame building was probably the second Rand McNally Building, completed in Chicago in 1890. New York soon wrested leadership from Chicago and became the skyscraper city.

THE BLOOMING MILL

For many centuries, the semi-finished mass of iron to be forged or rolled into finished form was called a bloom. After the Englishman, Benjamin Huntsman, rediscovered the crucible steelmaking process in 1740, the cast steel that he produced in molds became known as an ingot, a term which arose much earlier among non-ferrous metalworkers, chiefly to describe small bars of gold and silver. Huntsman's ingots varied in weight from 80 to 124 pounds, but when a larger ingot was desired, several pots of molten steel were poured into molds of appropriate size.

The steel ingots were reheated to forging temperature and then forged or "cogged" under a hammer into small billets, which were again heated and either forged or rolled into desired finished shapes. Hammer cogging was satisfactory for small crucible ingots, but it had to be discarded after the introduction of the Bessemer process which made it possible to teem much larger ingots. Bessemer ingots at first were small enough to be rolled into finished products in one operation, but as the ingots grew in size a separate mill was required to roll them into a smaller semi-finished form — now designated a bloom. In England, the new equipment was initially called a cogging mill and later a blooming mill. The first mill designed to roll ingots into blooms went into operation at Dowlais, Wales, in 1866.[13] In the 1870s, the blooming mill was generally adopted outside of England.[14] In 1867, George Fritz built the first successful blooming mill in the United States at the Cambria Iron Works in Johnstown, Pennsylvania.

THE CASTING AND FORGING INDUSTRIES

The Industrial Revolution precipitated a demand for iron products, such as parts of locomotives, manufacturing machinery, sewing machines, and iron ranges, which were either too irregular in shape to be rolled, or were more economically produced by casting or forging. The need for cast and forged products in greater variety and quantity, and often of larger size, brought about technological advances in the casting and forging industries second only in importance to that of the rolling mills.

Casting

The cupola, as constructed by John Wilkinson of England to melt pig iron for casting purposes (see page 32), appeared in the United States around 1815. Wider adoption of the cupola made it possible for the foundry industry in America to exist apart from the blast furnace, and once it was firmly established it grew rapidly as a separate branch of its own. New techniques in casting were introduced, and extensive improvements were realized in the construction and operation of the cupola.

The foundryman bought his iron in the form of pigs from a blast furnace operator. The pigs were melted in the cupola. For such cast products as ranges and heating stoves, which were not subject to impact, ordinary grades of pig iron were satisfactory, and the metal was poured directly into molds. But wherever the iron was subject to wear, or impact—as in machinery, railroad wheels, tools, and hundreds of other applications—the brittle nature of pig iron made it unsuitable. Such uses called for malleable iron castings. (See page 32). The foundryman poured the molten pig iron from his cupola into molds to make castings of the shape desired. After the castings cooled, they were imbedded in oxidizing agents and placed in annealing boxes. These were shoved into an annealing furnace which was kept at an elevated temperature from three to five days. The excess carbon, silicon, phosphorous, and other elements that give pig iron its brittle character were oxidized out, rendering the iron malleable. Malleable iron castings were first produced in Europe and were called European, or "whiteheart," castings because of the white or gray color of the fracture. Seth Boyden, of Newark, New Jersey, was the founder of the native malleable iron industry. In 1820, he attempted to reproduce whiteheart castings for harness hardware, but his castings had a black fracture and became known as American or "blackheart" castings.[15]

After Boyden's pioneering work, small malleable iron foundries began to spring up all over the East. They received their initial impulse from the harness trade followed soon by the carriage industry, which together were the largest consumers of malleable iron. Second in importance during the early days of the industry was the market for agricultural machinery.

Forging

The water-driven tilt hammer, which filled the immediate countryside with its rhythmic blows for some five centuries, underwent little change except for larger hammers, but in the nascent industrial age of the nineteenth century, machinery and its accessory parts became larger, and forgemen were asked to shape larger masses of iron than could be done by water power. In 1838, James Nasmyth, a Scotsman, employed at an ironworks in Manchester, England, was assigned the task of forging a large crankshaft for the steamer, "Great Eastern." Dissatisfied with the results of the tilt hammer, he designed a hammer powered by steam to raise the tup, or head of the hammer. His initial patent was taken out in 1842. The Nasmyth hammer opportunely brought the forging industry into step with the industrial age. The hammer obtained the force of its blow from the falling weight of the tup on an anvil, or die, but eventually this force was found to be inadequate to forge the still larger products which customers were ordering. This fault was corrected by the double-acting hammer, in which steam power drove the downward stroke of the tup, greatly increasing the impact of the blow. The first double-acting hammer in the United States was built at Midvale, Pennsylvania, in 1888.

After the open-hearth furnace made possible the casting of more massive ingots, the steam hammer could no longer forge larger blocks of steel. The answer was provided by the hydraulic press which shapes hot metal in a die by the tremendous pressure of a ram, rather than by hammering. It was invented in England about 1861 and was introduced into the United States around 1887. The face of the ram carries the upper forging die, and below it on a stationary block is the lower die. Under strong hydraulic pressure, the hot metal is squeezed into shape between the two dies. In England, as forgings increased in size, principally for marine work, hydraulic presses grew in proportion, from 2,000 to 4,000 tons total pressure in the 1880s to 10,000 tons in the 1890s.

Although ingots grew in size in the present century—some weighing up to 600,000 pounds—they have not necessitated appreciably more powerful presses than many already in existence. There were a greater number of the larger open-die presses, ranging from 10,000- to 12,000-ton pressure in the leading industrial countries. Japan, Germany, England, and Russia could boast of 15,000-ton presses. The largest open-die presses for forging steel in the United States, with a capacity of 14,000 tons, are government-owned.

New uses for large forgings have come into being since 1900. The growth of electrical industries and the development of steam turbines called for the forging of massive shafts. Some of these were for propeller shafts in ships. With the advent of the Atomic Age, heavy forgings have been made for cyclotrons, or "atom smashers," and for nuclear reactors; some of the forged steel sections are thirty-six inches thick.

COKE BLAST FURNACES ESTABLISHED IN AMERICA

It was approximately 125 years after Abraham Darby first smelted iron with coke in England that success was achieved with the fuel in the United States. It was accomplished at the Mary Ann Furnace in Huntingdon County, Pennsylvania, in 1835.[16] There were several reasons for tardiness in adopting coke in America. While large stands of charcoal timber still remained, there was no incentive to resort to other fuels. Furthermore, a strong preference persisted for charcoal pig iron and for bar iron hammered in charcoal forges. But America could not long postpone its discontinuance of charcoal. Great as were the stands of forests, the day was finally reached when those easily available to ironmaking centers were pretty well exhausted, and, as the ironmasters were compelled to reach farther and farther away for their source of charcoal, the cost of transportation to the furnaces became a formidable factor. Lastly, and perhaps most important of all, imported English coke iron considerably undersold the domestic product. In the first quarter of the nineteenth century, these stern realities caused some ironmasters to experiment with mineral fuel.

An enterprising Lutheran clergyman, Frederick W. Geissenhainer, claimed in a patent application that in 1830 and again in 1831 he had successfully smelted iron with anthracite coal in a small experimental furnace in New York City, using hot air as well as atmospheric air. The clergyman-ironmaster next built a furnace for a practical application of his invention. Named the Lucy Furnace, it was located near Pottsville, Pennsylvania. There, in 1836, Dr. Geissenhainer, blowing his furnace with heated air, made pig iron with anthracite as an exclusive fuel for the first time in the United States. He planned to improve his furnace but was prevented by illness which soon proved fatal. Similar results were obtained in 1838-1839 at Mauch Chunk, Pennsylvania, and again in 1839 at Pioneer Furnace in Pottsville. In the latter furnace, the air was blown in by steam power.

Other blast furnace operators were quick to follow suit. By 1842, the use of antracite as a fuel was well established in the American iron industry and continued in use for approximately eighty years, either exclusively or in combination with coke or bituminous coal. (Further references here to ironmaking by anthracite include the fuel alone and as a mixture with coke or bituminous coal.) In 1855, the production of 381,866 tons of pig iron by anthracite first exceeded that of charcoal, which then amounted to 339,922 tons. Anthracite remained the chief furnace fuel for the next twenty years, being finally outdistanced in 1875 by coke-produced iron. Production by anthracite-fueled furnaces continued to rise, as did that of coke and charcoal furnaces, and attained a peak of 2,448,781 tons in 1890, compared to 7,154,725 tons of coke pig iron and 703,522 tons of charcoal pig iron. It fell off in succeeding years, but as late as 1907 anthracite furnaces produced 1,536,140 tons of pig iron. Thereafter smelting by anthracite declined rapidly and in 1914 was used for the last time exclusively as a fuel.

In England during the early seventeenth century, determined efforts were made to smelt iron with bituminous coal, but they all came to naught. The fact that bituminous coal becomes plastic when heated caused the furnaces to "choke up"; this condition was especially serious because of the weak blast that the blowing equipment of those days could produce. Initial trials with bituminous coal in the United States also met with failure. Some later trials met with qualified success. Iron ore was reduced with raw bituminous coal at the Clay Furnace, Mercer County, Pennsylvania, in 1845, and a year later, at the Mahoning Furnace in Lowell, Ohio, built expressly for that purpose.

Meanwhile, some ironmasters were not neglecting coke. The first American experiments appear to have been made in regular charcoal furnaces, in which coke was mixed with charcoal. The weak furnace blast, together with inexperience of the operators, are given as the reasons why all the early efforts with coke met with dismal failure. It was not until 1835 that pig iron was successfully smelted with coke in the United States at the Mary Ann Furnace, as mentioned earlier. Further trials at smelting with coke in the next few years were all unsuccessful. Several attempts at the Lonaconing Furnace in Allegany County, Maryland, in 1839 were variously reported as failures and complete success.[17] Coke furnaces gained headway slowly until 1859, a date generally agreed upon as marking the "real initiation of coke as a blast furnace fuel."[18] In that year it was found that bituminous coal in the Connellsville seam near Pittsburgh made superior coke, and from then on the fuel rapidly took hold in Pennsylvania. From there it spread to other parts of the country.

By 1865, coke furnaces were well established in the United States and in 1869 produced more than charcoal furnaces, the output of pig iron by the two fuels in that year being 553,341 and 392,150 tons, respectively. In the next decade, coke became king of the blast furnace fuels, and in 1883 the production of 2,689,650 tons of coke pig iron for the first time exceeded the combined yield of 571,726 tons of charcoal iron and 1,885,596 tons of anthracite iron. Charcoal furnaces hung on tenaciously in some parts of the country and in 1890 set their record of 703,522 tons, of which 258,000 tons were produced in Michigan. Charcoal pig iron production did not fall off abruptly at that date as might have been expected, but declined slowly to 430,620 tons in 1900 and actually picked up again in 1903 to 566,366 tons. It tapered off gradually thereafter, and finally, in 1945, it may be said that the once great charcoal pig iron industry officially expired.

Beehive Coke Ovens

Coal was first converted into coke by heating it slowly in large mounds covered with turf in the open air, after the manner of charring wood into charcoal. Part of the coal was burned to supply the heat for converting the remaining coal to coke. This method was highly wasteful and various attempts were made to improve it. One of the first steps toward an oven was the construction of a rectangular masonry enclosure, about 5 to 8 feet tall, with an open top and apertures in the side for the admission of air. Shortly afterwards, the oven was capped with a dome-shaped top, giving it the shape of a beehive, from which the name beehive oven was derived. The oven had an opening in the top for charging the coal and a door on the side for the admission of air and withdrawal of the coke. The first enclosed oven was built at or near Connellsville, Pennsylvania, in 1833. With the rapid growth of coke smelting in the 1860s, there was a need to standardize the coke oven. As it finally evolved, the beehive oven was about 12½ feet in diameter at the floor and 7 feet high at the crown, constructed of masonry, firebrick, and tile. The ovens were arranged in single rows, or in double rows with doors opening on opposite sides. Coal was fed to the ovens by cars mounted on tracks above the ovens, drawn by horses or mules. The standard charge was about 5 tons of coal which yielded approximately 3.1 tons of coke from Pittsburgh-seam coals.

Beehive ovens were extremely wasteful, losing all of the valuable coal chemicals, which are now recovered by the by-product ovens. Beehive coke ovens, nevertheless, were important in the growth of the iron and steel industry. From 1871 to 1919, when beehive ovens lost their leadership to by-product ovens, about 88 per cent of all iron produced in the United States was made with beehive coke as a fuel. The abnormal demands for coke in World War II brought beehive ovens back into production again. They reached their peak output in 1942 with a production of 8,275,000 tons, or 11.7 per cent of the total amount. With the war's end, beehive ovens resumed their former minor role in coke production.

IMPROVEMENTS IN THE BLAST FURNACE

In England, coke replaced charcoal as a blast furnace fuel before the steam-powered hot blast came into general use about 1835. It was the reverse in the United States, where the hot blast was introduced about fifteen years before successful smelting with coke and nearly half a century before coke became a major furnace fuel. Hot blast was first used in the United States in 1834 at the Oxford Furnace in New Jersey, where it raised the temperature to 250°F. and increased production by about 10 per cent. After 1840, blast furnaces were generally improved, but it was not until the middle of the century that any furnace was capable of producing 150 tons of pig iron a week. During the Civil War, a blast furnace at Scranton, Pennsylvania, produced 375½ tons of iron in one week, a record up to that time. Twenty-five years earlier, twenty-eight tons a week was considered to be exceptionally good.

Following the Civil War, the productivity of the blast furnace was greatly increased through the famous battle of production between the Lucy and Isabella furnaces, which began in 1872. The Lucy Furnace, owned by Kloman & Carnegie Brothers, was built near Pittsburgh, and the Isabella Furnace, located across the Allegheny River, was owned by the Isabella Furnace Company. Both furnaces were 75 feet tall. A vertical pneumatic lift raised a platform loaded with barrows of raw materials which were dumped into the top of the furnace stack.

At the start of the epic battle between the two furnaces, the output of each was about 350 tons a week. By the end of the year, the Lucy was producing an average of nearly 500 tons a week, with the Isabella close behind with 498 tons in a single week. The weekly crown wavered back and forth between the two as the crews of each labored mightily to outdo the other, while the Pittsburgh newspapers kept the public posted on the scores. In 1874, the Lucy smelted over 100 tons in a single day, an achievement that was greeted with loud hurrahs by the workmen and with incredulity by the iron trade. And so the battle of the titans went on. The mark of 800 tons a week was not reached until 1878 when the Lucy forged ahead with the output of 804 tons. Finally in 1881, the Isabella was the first American blast furnace in history to pour 1,000 tons of pig iron in one week.

THE CRUCIBLE PROCESS REACHES AMERICA

Steel made by the colonists was produced by the cementation process whereby alternate layers of iron bars and charcoal were placed in two long cementation pots inside a furnace. After being sealed and kept at cherry-red heat for about ten days, the bars absorbed enough carbon from the charcoal to form steel. Only scant quantities of steel were produced in this way and it was often uneven in quality.

After the Revolutionary War, progress in steelmaking was slow. In 1810, production was only 917 tons. In 1831, there were but fourteen steel furnaces in the United States, with an annual capacity of about 1,600 tons, equal to the total steel imports.[19] It was nearly a century after Benjamin Huntsman rediscovered the crucible process in 1740 that crucible steel manufacture began to gain a foothold in America. The secrets of successful crucible steel manufacture, which the Sheffield cutlers jealously guarded, had to be learned anew in the United States. The entire operation was performed according to precise specifications, one of the most important being the quality of clay used in the crucibles. The early failures in America were due, says Swank, to the poor quality of clays and the "want of the best quality blister steel at a reasonable price,"[20] that is, below that of British imports. Blister (cementation) steel, with certain purifying materials, was melted in crucibles to form cast steel.

The first fully successful production of crucible steel in the United States was achieved by William and John Garrard at Cincinnati in 1832. The Garrard brothers were natives of England. Their firm prospered for a few years and one of its notable triumphs was the supply of steel for the blades of the first McCormick reapers. This steel sold for eighteen to twenty-five cents a pound. During the administration of Andrew Jackson, a law was passed gradually reducing import duties on all goods for a decade. Imports rose sharply and many manufacturing plants were closed down, culminating in the panic of 1837, which ruined the Garrard Brothers as well as many other industries all over the nation.

Following the demise of the Garrard Brothers' enterprise, experiments in crucible steelmaking continued, some failures, others crowned with success. The manufacture of the "best grades" of crucible cast steel "of uniform quality as a regular product," according to Swank, was not established on a firm basis until the Civil War period.[21]

AMERICAN TIN PLATE—STRUGGLES AND TRIUMPHS

Tin and steel make an ideal combination as a food preserver. A coating of tin about 1/40th the thickness of a human hair prevents oxidation of the outside of the can, keeps a bright finish, resists attack of food acids within, is non-poisonous to the contents, and is easily soldered. Steel conveys heat quickly for sterilization and when rolled to about 1/100th of an inch in thickness, makes a can that is light in weight, yet strong enough to withstand rough usage. Actually, a tin can is about 98½ per cent steel and 1½ per cent tin. It can be produced so cheaply that you throw it away after use, just as you do with wrapping paper.

In the first two decades of the last century, two men who had been preserving food in glass jars, separately went into business to manufacture tin cans, using imported Welsh tin plate. Both firms were moderately successful. The first tin plate in America, specifically manufactured for cans came from Hussey's Copper Works in Pittsburgh in 1858-1859. No further attempts appear to have been made for about fifteen years chiefly because native producers could not compete against duty-free Welsh tin plate, either in quality or price. The unprotected American industry meanwhile had to bide its time. In 1862, a duty of 0.5 of a cent a pound was imposed, and in 1864 was raised to 2.5 cents a pound, but this increase was never put into effect. After the tariff was fixed at 1.1 cents a pound in 1875, a few entrepreneurs took heart and built rolling mills and tinning equipment. Immediately, the British reduced their price of tin-plate exports to the United States 60 per cent and held the price there until existing American companies were forced to the wall and then the British prices returned to their former high level. In 1879-1880, the same mills attempted to resume operations and again were forced to give up for the same reasons as before.

As a result, the American tin-plate industry struggled fitfully and futilely to establish itself. The Welsh trade had the American market entirely to itself.

It was William McKinley who released American tin-plate producers from the stranglehold of the Welsh industry. When he was a Congressman from Ohio, he was chiefly responsible for writing the Tariff Act of 1890 which was named after him. This hotly debated Act increased the duty on imported tin plate from 1 cent to 2.2 cents a pound.

Large portions of the electorate disliked the Act, but it permitted the prostrate tin-plate industry to get on its feet. It did not go into effect until 1891, but already in 1890 a number of sheet-rolling mills installed tinning equipment and other combined rolling and tinning mills were built. In 1891-1892, the first fully-equipped tin mill in this country was constructed at Elwood, Indiana, by the American Tin Plate Company, which formerly operated a plant at Wellsville, Ohio. Altogether, about twenty mills went into operation in 1891, and ten more were being built. In the next fifteen years, the growth of the industry was spectacular. Production increased from 1,118 tons in 1891 to more than 287,000 tons in 1897. In the same period, imports from Wales fell from 516,766 tons to 114,604 tons.

During the late 1890s, tariff protection of the young tin-plate industry was an intermittent storm center of politics. The McKinley Act was superseded by the Wilson tariff, which lowered the import duty on tin-plate to 1.2 cents a pound. The Dingley Tariff Act of 1897 set the duty at 1.5 cents a pound which seemed adequate protection, and from then on politics no longer played a decisive role in the industry. By 1911, tin-plate production in this country passed the million-ton mark for the first time and in the following year equaled that of Great Britain, while imports had practically ceased.

Iron was used as the base for tin plate in the United States until 1875, when steel was introduced.

In the early days, the sheets for tin-plating were rolled on hand sheet mills. The coating was applied by immersing the sheets in a tank of molten tin. This process became known as the hot-dip method. Basically, the process was simple, but there were many tricks to the trade which had been learned much earlier though the trial and error method by the tinners in Europe.

The hot-dip method remained in force until the next grade advance in tin-plating—the electrolytic process—was introduced opportunely before World War II.

11

Invention of the Bessemer Process

> *The invention of printing, the construction of the magnetic compass, the discovery of America and the introduction of the steam engine, are the only capital events in modern history which belong to the same category as the Bessemer process. They are all examples of the era of progress which evolves moral and social results from material developments. . . . Its influence can now be traced, although future results are still beyond the reach of the imagination.*
>
> —*Abram S. Hewitt*

Within a relatively short time—about a quarter of a century—the reign of iron which had lasted three thousand years came to an end and was superseded by that of steel. Three men were responsible for the great metallurgical revolution which made this possible. Each had a hand in giving to the world the Bessemer process which ushered in the modern Steel Age. They were William Kelly, an Irish-American; Sir Henry Bessemer, an Englishman; and Robert F. Mushet, a Scotsman. Bessemer's name was immortalized and from his royalties he reaped over $5 million. Kelly was vilified as an imposter by some of his countrymen who did not want to pay him royalties, and his name is not associated with a process which he was the first to invent. Mushet, without whose contribution neither Kelly nor Bessemer could make steel with their processes, realized only a few hundred English pounds for his indispensable part and died a relatively poor man.

Henry Bessemer was the son of a distinguished English-born scientist of French extraction, who emigrated to Paris and returned to England during the French Revolution. Henry was a mechanical genius and an inventor of the first rank. His steelmaking process was only one of at least 110 inventions, many of which were remarkably brilliant.

114

THE ROLE OF HENRY BESSEMER

Bessemer and Napoleon III

It was pure chance which first directed Bessemer's attention to ferrous metallurgy. Great Britain and France were then allied with Turkey against Russia in the Crimean War. Artillery experts on both sides of the Channel were giving intensive study to the problem of hurling "elongated projectiles" a greater distance than was then possible with smooth bore guns. For a shell to travel a long distance with any accuracy, it must rotate, an effect which the gunmakers were unable to produce. Bessemer went to work and in short order designed a shell which could be given rotation in a smooth bore gun. Experiments with a small cast-iron cannon convinced him that his idea was sound. When he brought his device to the attention of the British War Department, the generals "pooh-poohed" it.[1] Then chance intervened.

Late in 1854, Bessemer, who was then forty-one and already a well-known inventor, attended a house party in Paris given in honor of some French officers about to depart for the Crimea. Among the guests was Prince Napoleon, to whom Bessemer was introduced as the inventor of a new system for firing an elongated projectile from a smooth bore gun. Bessemer "just happened" to have with him in his pocket a model of his projectile carved in mahogany which he showed to Prince Napoleon. The Prince was fascinated by the toy shell and assured Bessemer that his cousin, the Emperor (Napoleon III) would be much interested in the invention and in a few days arranged an audience for Bessemer. At a "most interesting interview" the Emperor gave Bessemer *carte blanche* to conduct experiments at the Vincennes testing grounds. Bessemer found that he could not obtain the necessary materials at Vincennes and returned to his English workshop at Baxter House to carry on his research. Three weeks later, he was back at Vincennes with his new projectiles. There, on a cold December day in 1854, Bessemer satisfactorily demonstrated that an elongated projectile could be given rotation in a smooth bore gun. But, asked Commandant Minié, who was in charge of the experiments, would it be safe to fire a thirty-pound shot from a twelve-pound cast iron gun? "This simple observation," wrote Bessemer in his autobiography, "was the spark which kindled one of the greatest industrial revolutions that the present century has to record."[2]

He determined to study the whole question of metals suitable for guns, then made almost exclusively of cast iron. He considered that iron or "some of its combinations," would be the most likely metal for heavy ordnance. "It was consequently to the improvement of cast iron that I first directed my attention," he wrote.[3] Within three weeks, on January 10, he applied for a patent.

Bessemer Begins His Experiments

Bessemer's aim was to make a short cut in the production of iron and steel. Most steel was then made by the crucible process. Originally, the charging material was cementation or "blister" steel, but in Bessemer's day it was wrought iron. This was refined from pig iron in a puddling furnace and then rolled into bars. These were broken up and heated in clay crucibles, each holding not more than forty to fifty pounds of metal. About ten days were consumed in converting the iron into steel, requiring large quantities of fuel. Consequently crucible steel was expensive, selling for £50 to £60 a ton. Bessemer, in a word, hoped to jump over these involved and cost-consuming steps and convert pig iron directly into molten wrought iron or steel.

Bessemer began with a reverberatory furnace, in which flames from a fuel are drawn over a bath of molten metal residing in an open hearth, whereas in the Bessemer process no fuel is used. Air alone does the trick. Sometime in 1855, Bessemer suddenly dropped his experiments with a reverberatory furnace and conceived the idea of blowing air on molten pig iron.

Bessemer's new theory was in principle very simple. Pig iron as produced in the blast furnace, contains an excessive amount of carbon—about 4 per cent—and certain other elements, such as silicon, phosphorous, and sulphur, all of which tend to make iron brittle. To convert the iron into steel, the carbon content is reduced through oxidation usually to less than 1 per cent, and the other elements are at the same time largely burned out. Bessemer knew that carbon in molten iron unites very readily with oxygen. Why not reduce the carbon content in pig iron and remove the other elements by means of oxygen from a strong blast of air? When he first attempted to do this in what he called a converter, it erupted into a "veritable volcano," sending off flames, sparks, and smoke beyond his control. After ten or more minutes, the flames died down; he tapped the converter into a ladle and found the metal to be wholly malleable. The converter was somewhat egg-shaped with many small holes in the bottom for admission of the air blast.

Bessemer labored many months to improve his converter. Here his mechanical genius manifested itself to advantage. He designed the machinery necessary for the successful mechanical operation of the Bessemer process—a blowing engine, and an "hydraulic apparatus" by which a "lad at a safe distance" could operate the converter, starting the air blast, regulating it, stopping it, and tilting the converter to pour out the contents.[4] This machinery became indispensable for the successful operation of the process everywhere.

Bessemer had not brought his process to the state of perfection he desired when a friend who was given a demonstration of it prevailed upon him to read a paper describing it at the forthcoming meeting of the British Association for the Advancement of Science. This historic paper was delivered on August 12, 1856, and was published verbatim on the fourteenth in the London *Times*.

The import of Bessemer's address burst like a bombshell in British iron and steel circles. The premature disclosure of his process, he said, "brought down upon me a wild pack of hungry wolves, fighting with me and with each other, for a share of what was to be made of this new discovery."[5] The great steel citadel of Sheffield, however, remained haughtily aloof, "believing that it could afford to laugh at the absurd notion of making 5 tons of cast steel from pig iron in 20 or 30 minutes, when by its own system 14 or 15 days and nights were required to obtain a 40-pound or 50-pound crucible of cast steel from pig iron."[6]

All efforts to imitate or circumvent his patent, Bessemer said, failed ignominiously and the leading ironmasters came around one by one, hat in hand, asking for his licensing terms. The ironmasters choked at his fee of ten shillings per ton of metal produced by the process, but they swallowed it and within a month after reading his paper Bessemer had sold royalties amounting to £27,000.

Success Turns to Failure

Then the bubble burst. Every effort by Bessemer's licensees to utilize his process failed disastrously. The reason was, Bessemer explained, that the domestic iron used by his licensees contained so much phosphorus as to make it unfit for his process. Bessemer, without realizing it, had used imported Swedish iron which was virtually free from phosphorus. This startling revelation came upon him "like a bolt from the blue; its effect was absolutely overwhelming. The transition from what appeared to be a crowning success to one of utter failure well nigh paralysed all my energies." As daily reports of fresh failures poured in, the press took up the cry, denouncing Bessemer as a wild enthusiast whose invention, like a brilliant meteor, flitted across the "metallurgical horizon" only to "vanish in total darkness."[7]

Bessemer's faith in his invention was unshaken. Through chemical analysis, he found that all British pig iron abounded "with this fatal enemy, phosphorus, and I could not dislodge it." For more than a year, he toiled night and day to get around the obstacle. One heartbreaking failure succeeded another, as he poured large sums of capital into his experiments, pulling down one furnace after another. The steel men still sneered at him. His best friends urged him "to desist from a pursuit that the whole world proclaimed to be utterly futile . . . those most near and dear to me grieved over my obstinate persistence."[8]

Success Smiles Again

Meanwhile, Göran Fredrik Göransson, of Sweden, visited England in 1857 and obtained from Bessemer one-fifth interest in the first Swedish patent issued for the new process. He bought a stationary Bessemer converster and a steam blast engine and had them set up in Sweden by an English engineer. Göransson was totally inexperienced in iron and steel technology and his initial trials met with failure. Fortunately, he was using a pig iron made from high-grade Swedish ores, low in phosphorus and high in manganese, an ideal ore for his purpose. Finally, in July 1858, he produced a high quality mild steel.[9]

Bessemer could not help but hear of his Swedish licensee's success, but the English inventor makes no mention of it in his autobiography. He simply says that he abandoned his efforts to dislodge phosphorus from domestic ores and decided to prove to the world the merit of his process by ordering some phosphorus-free ore from Sweden. With this, he claimed, he produced soft, pure malleable iron and also steel. He announced his success to the iron and steel trade, but not "one iron or steel master in Britain could be induced to adopt the process."[10] He then resolved to force his scoffers to accept his process by manufacturing the metal himself and underselling the market. With a number of partners, he organized Henry Bessemer and Company Ltd. and built a steel works right in the heart of enemy territory—Sheffield. He offered his steel for sale at £10 to £15 a ton below the current price. This was the kind of language the Sheffield steelmasters understood, and after one large company capitulated the others followed suit.

ENTER ROBERT F. MUSHET

We now come to Robert F. Mushet and our story takes on conflicting elements. Leading iron and steel authorities in Bessemer's day and since, are virtually unanimous that his process could not produce steel without the aid of Mushet's contribution. An editorial on the death of Bessemer, appearing in *The Bulletin* of the American Iron and Steel Association, April 1, 1898, after acknowledging the greatness of Bessemer's invention, said: "But he did not perfect his invention. That was the work of Robert F. Mushet without whose triple compound of iron, carbon and manganese, it would have been a failure. . . . It must be admitted that Mushet brought all Bessemer's experiments to a successful issue."[11]

Robert Mushet had a thorough understanding of ferrous metallurgy as it was then known, and in his lifetime took out fifty-four patents related to steelmaking. What follows is the Mushet side of the story. His experience enabled him, on hearing of Bessemer's repeated and anguished failures, to know at once that Bessemer was trying to solve his problem mechanically, whereas it was a chemical and metallurgical problem. Mushet had learned from his own experiments that Bessemer was producing "burnt iron," which had been overexposed to heat and air, with the result that it contained what Mushet called "occluded oxygen." Furthermore, Bessemer eliminated all the carbon and did know how to put back the small necessary amount to change the iron into steel.[12]

Mushet had earlier discovered that "burnt iron" could be remedied simply by adding a charcoal and manganese oxide, then employed in making crucible steel. Later he learned of a German compound containing iron, carbon, and manganese, called in German, *spiegeleisen*. Mushet found that the addition of spiegeleisen to molten iron was superior to previously used compounds in steelmaking. Manganese, having an affinity for oxygen, withdrew it from the iron in the form of manganese oxide, which passed into the slag. The carbon in the spiegeleisen, meanwhile, remained in the molten iron converting it into steel.

Mushet experimented with some "blown" metal produced by the Ebbw Vale Iron Company of Wales and proved to his satisfaction that spiegeleisen did exactly what he expected it would do. He produced excellent steel. "I saw then that the Bessemer process," he wrote, "was perfected and that with fair play untold wealth would reward Mr. Bessemer and myself."[13]

According to Mushet, Bessemer on hearing of the former's success paid him several visits at Coleford and wanted to know "what my process was, and asked me to confide in him." Mushet refused to divulge his secret and Bessemer on his last visit said: "Well, I shall spend 20,000 pounds this year in experiments, which ought to guide me to success."[14]

Mushet applied for a preliminary patent on September 22, 1856. He also took out patents for France and the United States. He sold shares in his English patent to two men and set up a converter at the Forest Steel Works, where he successfully produced steel in 1857. This is generally acknowledged to be the first Bessemer steel made with the addition of spiegeleisen. In that year, he applied for a final patent.[15]

Through careless neglect or bad memory, the two trustees of Mushet's patent failed to pay the third year's stamp duty of £50, nor did they tell Mushet of their omission, and his patent lapsed before he was able to reap any money from it. In consequence, Mushet's process became public property, and Bessemer had a legal right to use it. "His prosperity," Mushet said, "dated from that period." Mushet estimated that his rightful share in the Bessemer process was worth half a million pounds but all he realized was a few hundred.[16]

Bessemer, on his part, refused to acknowledge that he was indebted to Mushet for the use of spiegeleisen and never recognized the latter's patent. By 1862, the Bessemer process was firmly established in England, and in 1865 on the Continent, where about 100,000 tons of Bessemer steel were produced in that year.[17]

MEANWHILE, IN AMERICA, WILLIAM KELLY...

Now let us cross the Atlantic and see what was happening meanwhile in America. This brings up our third personality, William Kelly, born in Pittsburgh. In his youth he was inclined to "scientific research" and for some years studied metallurgy to prepare himself for the manufacture of iron. With his brother, John, he purchased an ironworks near Eddyville, Kentucky, where they produced pig iron and refined it into wrought iron. Their blast furnace and finery consumed large quantities of charcoal which they produced from their own woodland. After a year or so, they had cut down all the timber near the works. The nearest available source was seven miles away and to haul the charcoal that distance would seriously increase their operating costs.

William began to think of ways to save fuel. One day as he sat watching his finery, he noticed that the molten iron directly under the air blast was whiter and apparently hotter than the rest. In a flash, he realized that the cold air instead of chilling the iron, as everyone before him believed, actually made it hotter. His knowledge of chemistry and metallurgy told him that oxygen was combining with carbon to produce heat. He saw the possibility of refining pig iron into wrought iron by means of air alone. This was in 1847, eight years before the same idea crossed the mind of Bessemer.[18]

Kelly's plan was to force a powerful blast of air on molten pig iron in a specially constructed furnace by what he called his "pneumatic process." He appears to have been interrupted in his initial experiments of 1847 and did not resume them until 1851, when he built his first converter. When he expounded his theory to his friends and neighbors, he was greeted with ridicule and became known as "Kelly, that crazy Irishman." He devoted so much time to his experiments that he seriously neglected his regular business and this began to disturb his father-in-law, Mr. Gracey, and a number of others, who had earlier loaned Kelly money to expand his ironworks.[19]

Finally, William's creditors told him that he must quit giving time to what they contemptuously referred to as his "air boiling process" or settle his debt. He could not afford to ignore this ultimatum, but he was sure he was on the right track and continued his experiments at a secret location in the forest where he built and tore down seven converters.

The secret may have leaked out to Kelly's creditors, for we find that Mr. Gracy, in despair, decided, that his son-in-law was demented and called in Dr. Alfred H. Champion of Eddyville, to examine him. When Kelly explained his pneumatic theory to the physician the latter decided that both his patient's mind and theory were sound and became one of his stanchest supporters.

Kelly continued to experiment with his process and in 1857-1858 trans-

"Metal from Heaven"—Cape York meteorite, named Ahnighito by the Eskimos. Weighing 34 tons, it is 99 per cent nickel-iron. From meteorites man first obtained iron, which he called "metal from heaven." (*Courtesy of the American Museum of Natural History*)

Iron Age Implements—Typical implements of the later Iron Age, derived chiefly from graves and habitations of the Baltic and Alpine areas. Most of the objects are iron, but some are bronze, bone, and other materials. (*Courtesy of the American Museum of Natural History*)

Water-driven bellows, the ends of which protrude from the housing, supplied the air blast. Horses bring in loads of charcoal. A pig iron casting is weighed, while a clerk notes the weight and number. A good week's production was six to seven tons of pig iron. (*Diderot, L'Encyclopédie, 1751*)

Hand Sheet Mill—An iron sheet has just passed between the rolls and fallen on a platform, where it is grasped in tongs by "catchers" who will return it over the top of the stand for another pass. Meanwhile, the workman, turning the wheel, brings the rolls closer together for the next pass, which will further reduce the thickness of the sheet and elongate it. (*Harper's New Monthly, 1894*)

Pouring Crucible Steel—Glowing-white crucibles of molten crucible steel are emptied into an ingot mold. The crucible and other early processes were slow and laborious and steel output was measured in pounds until the Bessemer converter made it possible to produce steel by the ton in a few minutes, ushering in the Age of Steel. (*Scientific American, Nov. 6, 1857*)

An American First—The building of Harper & Brothers, erected in 1854 to replace one that burned to the ground in 1853, was the first in America to use wrought iron beams. The front of the building was faced with cast iron plates and cast iron columns. (*Courtesy of the Museum of the City of New York*)

From Ingot to Rail—Intermediate stages in rolling an ingot into rails. The steel moves up and down the three lines, becoming progressively narrower, longer, and more rail-shaped.

Bessemer in Blow

The pyrotechnic Bessemer converter ended the 3,000-year reign of iron and introduced the Age of Steel in the 1850s.

An open pit iron ore mine on the Mesabi range in Minnesota, part of the Lake Superior iron ore region.

Blast Furnace and Stock Yards

In the background are four blast furnaces, their charging hoists on the far side, out of view. Traveling ore bridges, in the middle distance, transfer raw materials from the dock to stock piles; the darker is iron ore, the lighter is limestone. At the dock, electric unloaders unload the ore vessels.

Open Hearth Furnaces

The charging side of a row of open hearth furnaces. The suspended ladle in the background is adding molten iron to a furnace. In the foreground, the charging machine, which runs on tracks, charges scrap, iron ore, and other materials into the furnace.

ferred his operations to the Cambria Iron Works at Johnstown, Pennsylvania. The converter that he used is still at the Johnstown plant, now a part of the Bethlehem Steel Corporation.

Kelly finally succeeded in producing soft steel by his pneumatic process and sold his product on a fairly extensive scale, as already noted. He was in no hurry to patent his invention because he wanted first to make further improvements in it. But when he learned that Bessemer had obtained an American patent in November 1856, he applied for one. The matter of an interference between Bessemer's American patent and Kelly's application came before the Commissioner of Patents in April 1857. On the thirteenth, Acting Commissioner, S. T. Shugert signed an order stating: "It appears, that by the concurrent testimony of numerous witnesses Kelly made the invention and showed it by drawings and experiments as early as 1847 and this testimony appears to be reliable in every respect. . . . Priority of invention in this case is awarded to said Kelly and it is ordered that a patent be issued accordingly, unless an appeal be taken within sixty days from this date."[20]

No appeal was made and Kelly was given a patent on July 23, 1857. One of the witnesses referred to by Commissioner Shugert was Dr. Champion.

BESSEMER PROCESS LAUNCHED IN AMERICA

In the same year that Kelly received his patent, the nation was gripped in a panic and he was among the many victims who went bankrupt. After the general revival of business, he sold control of his patent in 1861 to two ironmasters—Captain Eben B. Ward of Detroit and Z. S. Durfee of New Bedford, Massachusetts, who were joined in 1863 by Daniel J. Morrell and others in forming the Kelly Pneumatic Process Company, in which Kelly retained an interest. Meanwhile, Captain Ward persuaded William F. Durfee, cousin of Z. S. Durfee, to build an experimental plant at Wyandotte, Michigan, for the manufacture of steel by the Kelly process. The Kelly Company decided that to produce steel it would need the benefit of the Mushet process for adding spiegeleisen, and the American rights to that patent were accordingly obtained. In September 1864, W. F. Durfee succeeded in making steel at the Wyandotte plant in a 2½-ton converter. This was the first steel made in the United States by the Bessemer process. The Kelly Company found also that it could not get along without the accessory machinery invented by Bessemer, and in using it the company was infringing on Bessemer's patent.

The Bessemer machinery patent, obtained in 1864, was controlled by the Albany and Rensselaer Iron & Steel Company, headed by Alexander L. Holley, one of the great steel masters of the last century. His partners were John A. Griswold and John F. Winslow. The company's plant was at Troy, New York. The Holley group, meanwhile, was infringing on the

Mushet patent held by the Kelly Company. Neither company could work successfully with the patent it controlled. Lawsuits followed, and in the end the two groups consolidated their patents and their forces, and in 1866 formed a new company, the Pneumatic Steel Association, of which the Holley group held 70 per cent interest and the Kelly Company, 30 per cent.

In 1870, Bessemer was refused an extension of his American patent on the grounds that he had no right to one in the first place. When Kelly at the same time applied for a seven-year extension of his patent, the steel and railroad interests protested to the Patent Office, claiming that Kelly was an imposter and that Bessemer was the sole inventor of the process. Since Bessemer had no patent rights, if Kelly's extension were disallowed, no royalties would have to be paid for the use of the Bessemer process. All efforts to thwart a renewal of Kelly's patent were unavailing and from 1870 on he reaped $450,000 in royalties which indicates the extent to which his process was used. Out of this opposition arose the glorification of Bessemer and the belittling of Kelly, which all but submerged the American inventor's name. However, there was another factor. The first Bessemer steel, chiefly in the form of rails, which was sold in America in any appreciable quantity, was imported from England and labeled "Bessemer Steel." The product, having established customer acceptance, was easier to sell under that label. For all these reasons the steel tended to become identified with the name of Bessemer while Kelly's faded away.

Americans had a great deal to learn in the operation of the Bessemer process, and many of the pioneer efforts met with failure. The repeated failures dampened for a time the ardor of American ironmasters to invest money in constructing Bessemer steel plants. It was these failures, no doubt, that prompted Andrew Carnegie to make his famous quip, "experimenting does not pay" when he was being importuned in the 1860s to go into the steel business. The name of Alexander Holley deserves to shine brightly among the luminaries of the American steel industry. Through many improvements in the Bessemer process itself and in the design of plants, he made the Bessemer process a practical succes in the United States. He was recognized as the foremost technical authority on the process in the nation. His type of Bessemer plant became the accepted type in America and unquestionably accelerated the establishment of the Bessemer steel industry in this country. In 1867, a year after the basic patents were consolidated, production was 3,000 tons. Within thirteen years, production had reached 1 million tons, surpassing that of Great Britain for the first time, and in 1899 totaled 8.5 million tons.

The Steel Age Begins

The consumption of iron is a social barometer by which to estimate the relative height of civilization among nations.
—*Abram S. Hewitt*

The invention of the Bessemer process in the middle of the nineteenth century launched the Steel Age in Europe and the United States. For the remainder of the century the chief use of Bessemer steel was in the manufacture of rails.

Robert Mushet, who produced the first Bessemer steel by the addition of spiegeleisen in 1857, sold that steel to the Ebbw Vale Iron Company of Dowlais, Wales, where it was rolled into a double-headed rail the same year. This was the first steel rail ever made. It was laid at the Derby Station where wrought iron rails were "turned" every six months and occasionally every three months. Mushet also supplied steel for the second steel rail, which was rolled for the Great Western Railway.[1] Although these two pioneer steel rails proved their durability over wrought iron, there was considerable skepticism over the reliability and safety of steel rails. Bessemer reported that when he proposed the use of steel rails to a high official of a British railway, the latter replied, almost in anger, "Mr. Bessemer, do you wish to see me tried for manslaughter?" The remark was due, Bessemer explained, to the fact that the steel then being used was crucible steel, employed largely for manufacturing sharp-cutting implements and which was, in fact, too hard for rails. The official in the end agreed to try a Bessemer rail. This was in 1862. After two years of heavy use the steel rail had not been turned and had "outlasted the seventeenth and eighteenth face of the wrought iron rails adjoining it."[2]

These demonstrations of Bessemer steel's superiority over wrought iron for rails dispelled any lingering doubt that the answer had been found to the greatest need of the carriers. By the early 1860s, the Bessemer process was being adopted successfully in England, France, Sweden, and other European states. In those areas, Bessemer steel was used very largely at the start in the manufacture of rails and was responsible for the rapid extension of rail systems in Britain and on the Continent.

The United States was one of Britain's leading markets for steel rails. Domestic producers suffered in the beginning from this competition. Some railroads were reluctant to buy the American product, believing that native mills could not match the British in quality. American producers of Bessemer steel rails also had to contend with the traditional British policy of lowering the price of its exported articles to stifle the growth of a home industry.

In spite of the short life of the wrought iron rail, the heavy cost of frequent replacement and the far greater durability of the steel rail, the manufacture of wrought iron rails in the United States continued on a large scale for fifteen years after Bessemer rail production was begun in appreciable tonnages. In 1867, 2,550 tons of Bessemer rails and 459,558 tons of wrought iron rails were manufactured. Wrought iron rails continued to hold a strong lead, reaching their maximum production of 905,000 tons in 1872, trailed by 94,000 tons of Bessemer rails. The gap between the two began to narrow swiftly and in 1877 Bessemer rail production of 432,000 tons for the first time exceeded that of wrought iron which amounted to 332,500 tons. The death knell for wrought iron rails had not yet sounded and production held up to more than 225,000 tons annually as late as 1882. From then on it dropped off precipitously.[3]

One explanation for the high level of wrought iron rail production during this period was the preference of western railroads for wrought iron rails. Bessemer steel rails were largely confined to the eastern half of the United States. It was said that the western lines chose to lay wrought iron rails over the plains and other sparsely populated areas because if a wrought iron rail became bent it could be straightened, but this could not be done with a Bessemer rail, which might take days to replace. Wrought iron rail mills sprouted all over the West, even as far west as Laramie, Wyoming. During the decade of greatest railroad expansion, 1880-1890, the proportion of Bessemer steel manufactured into rails was at its highest. The peak was 86 per cent in 1881. By 1890, it had dropped to 50 per cent and in 1900 had fallen to 35 per cent. The average proportion of Bessemer steel output that went into rails from 1867 to 1890 inclusive was 67 per cent.

Table 2 shows the relationship between the production of Bessemer steel, Bessemer steel rails, the growth of the railroads, and the percentages of steel rails in the United States at selected periods from 1867 to 1900 inclusive.

TABLE 2

RELATIONSHIP BETWEEN THE PRODUCTION OF BESSEMER STEEL, BESSEMER STEEL RAILS,
THE GROWTH OF RAILROADS, AND PERCENTAGES OF STEEL RAILS IN THE
UNITED STATES:
SELECTED PERIODS, 1867–1900

| | BESSEMER STEEL | | | RAILROADS | |
Year	Production Net Tons	Rails Net Tons	Per Cent of Total	Mileage	Percentage of Steel Rails
1867	3,000	2,550	85	39,000	—
1870	42,000	34,000	80	52,922	—
1880	1,200,000	954,000	79	115,600	29
1890	4,000,000	2,000,000	50	200,000	80
1900	7,500,000	2,500,000	35	258,000	93

SOURCES: Bessemer steel: James M. Swank, *History of the Manufacture of Iron in All Ages*, Philadelphia, 2nd ed., 1892, pp. 415, 440. Railroads: *Chronology of American Railroads*, Association of American Railroads, Washington, D. C.

THE OPEN HEARTH FURNACE

The Bessemer process did not have the field to itself for long. In the 1860s, a rival appeared on the scene: the open hearth process. This process, as its name implies, converts iron into steel in an open hearth and owes its commercial development to two pairs of brothers, the Siemens in England and the Martins in France. The idea of melting steel in an open hearth did not originate with these men. It had undergone experimentation many years earlier by a number of others, notably by an Englishman, Josiah M. Heath, in 1839.[4]

Dr. Charles William Siemens and his brother, Frederick, were natives of Germany and naturalized English citizens. In 1856, Dr. Siemens, the leader of the two, developed a regenerative gas furnace which remains the distinguishing feature of the open hearth process. A regenerative furnace transfers the heat from burnt gases to chambers called regenerators, through which air is subsequently passed. This heated air, in turn, is united with the flaming gases, causing them to burn with more intense heat. Such a furnace provides a higher temperature than from natural flames and for that reason became an invaluable adjunct to the open hearth process. In 1861, Dr. Siemens, for the first time applied the regenerative principle to an open hearth and patented his invention that year. He experienced great difficulty with his furnace and appears not to have been successful. Meanwhile, Emile and Pierre Martin, at Sireuil, France, were experimenting unsuccessfully with an open hearth furnace. When Dr. Siemens came to France in 1864 and added his regenerative device to the Martin furnace, the combination proved to be successful. A new type of furnace was developed, combining the best features of the English and French inventions and became known as the Siemens-Martin furnace, but in the United States it is more commonly called the open hearth furnace. The steelmaking process carried out in such furnaces was called the Siemens-Martin process.

An open hearth furnace using the Siemens-Martin process was installed by Abram S. Hewitt at the New Jersey Steel & Iron Company of Trenton in 1868, but it never worked with any regularity. A small five-ton capacity open hearth furnace, built for the Bay State Works of South Boston two years later, is said to have been the first "put regularly to work" in America.[5] Other companies began adopting the new steelmaking furnace, and by 1800 open hearth steel attained an output of 112,950 tons. Production had quintupled by 1890 and in 1900 stood at 3,805,900 tons, or more than half that of Bessemer steel.

Bessemer vs. Open Hearths

The Bessemer process, having been established ahead of the open hearth, maintained its leadership during the nineteenth century. The big jump in open hearth steel production from 1890 to 1900 is largely attributed to a wider adoption of the basic process and greater utilization of Lake Superior ores. During the first five years of this century, Bessemers continued to hold an appreciable lead over open hearths, but in 1906 the lead began to shorten, and in 1908 open hearth production for the first time exceeded that of Bessemer. From then on, the open hearth furnace became the major producer of steel and now accounts for about 86 per cent of all steel produced in the United States, while Bessemer output has dwindled to 0.8 per cent.

The Bessemer process began to lose its once proud position as a pre-eminent steel producer primarily because of the numerous advantages offered by the open hearth furnace after introduction of the basic process. The shift from Bessemers to open hearths was also accentuated by metallurgical advances and the need for furnaces of greater capacity. The Bessemer converter makes steel in one volcanic rush, permitting little opportunity for control of the operation and hence of the steel's chemical composition. When Bessemer steel first appeared on the market it answered virtually all needs for steel, except those for which crucible steel was indispensable. With the beginning of the present century, the requirements for steel became more severe. The steelmaker called more and more on science to aid him in meeting the exacting standards demanded by modern industry. Each batch of steel was manufactured according to a customer's precise specifications for chemical composition and mechanical properties. The production of these steels called for furnaces susceptible to better control than could be exercised over the Bessemer converter. The slower steelmaking processes carried on in the open hearth and electric furnaces, by allowing periodic laboratory testing of molten steel samples, answered these needs. It was also found that both furnaces could make greater use of the steel scrap which was being returned to the mills in increasing quantities. Whereas the Bessemer converters produced five to ten tons at a time, the open hearth furnace could produce fifteen to sixty-five tons at a heat. This was around the turn of the century when the average open hearth capacity was about forty-eight tons. In a word, steel companies turned increasingly from the Bessemer to the open hearth because of the latter's greater flexibility, larger capacity, and the generally higher and more uniform quality of its products.

An important reversal in the uses of Bessemer and open hearth steel took place in rails. In 1902, practically all rails continued to be manufactured of Bessemer steel, but open hearth rails were edging in with a production of 6,000 tons. The first large-scale production of basic open hearth rails was begun in 1904 at Ensley, Alabama. Since then, rail production has been given over entirely to the open hearth process.

SLOW GROWTH OF THE STEEL AGE

Just as steel rails displaced those of wrought iron slowly, steel made inroads gradually into other products traditionally made of iron. Once a few manufacturers began to advertise horseshoes, nails, and wire fence made of steel, it did not mean that the change from iron to steel in these products was immediate and thoroughgoing. Because some enterprising mill owners undertook to roll beams and plates of steel, it did not follow that the production of these products from wrought iron was quickly discontinued by others. It was not until 1886, when the Steel Age was nearly twenty years old, that the output of hot rolled steel products was greater than that of iron. The figures for that year were 2,568,922 and 2,283,622 tons, respectively. The production of hot rolled iron actually increased in the next few years and in 1890 was nearly 3 million tons, but hot rolled steel production went ahead at a slightly faster rate and was nearly 4 million tons.

Despite the very great increase in steel production by the Bessemer and open hearth processes, iron continued to be a major industrial metal until the middle 1890s. This is borne out in Table 3, in which the figures for columns 3, 4, and 5 were estimated. Rounded figures were used. The year 1880 was selected as a starting date because it was then that the open hearth began to be of commercial importance.

The table was prepared in the following way: Both the Bessemer converter and the open hearth furnace use a certain amount of scrap, together with pig iron, in the production of steel. The proportion of scrap varies with its availability, price, and other factors. To arrive at an estimate of the quantities consumed in the period under review, it was assumed that the Bessemer converters used 10 per cent and the open hearth furnace, 40

TABLE 3

RELATIVE GROWTH OF IRON AND STEEL PRODUCTION IN THE UNITED STATES:
SELECTED PERIODS, 1880–1904, INCLUSIVE

1	2	3	4	5	6	7
				Cast,		*Increase*
				Wrought and		*or Decrease*
		Scrap	*Pig Iron*	*Malleable*	*Total*	*Column 6*
	Pig Iron	*Consumed in*	*Converted*	*Iron*	*Steel*	*vs. Col-*
Year	*Production*	*Steelmaking*	*into Steel*	*Production*	*Production*	*umn 5*
		(Thousands of Net Tons)				
1880	4,295.4	185.0	1,212.0	3,083.4	1,397.0	1,686.4
1890	10,307.0	643.1	4,147.2	6,159.8	4,790.3	1,369.5
1892	10,256.0	767.0	4,711.8	5,544.2	5,478.8	65.4
1893	7,979.4	690.7	3,811.7	4,167.7	4,502.4	334.7
1895	10,580.0	1,059.0	5,789.6	4,790.4	6,848.6	2,058.2
1900	15,444.0	2,271.0	9,139.9	6,304.1	11,410.9	5,106.8

SOURCE: Figures in Columns 2 and 6 from *Historical Statistics of the United States,
1789–1945,* U. S. Department of Commerce, Washington, D. C., 1949.

per cent scrap in their charges. (Today the proportion in the open hearth
is fifty-fifty.) Applying this rule-of-thumb to Bessemer and open hearth
production, the scrap consumption for each year was estimated. In 1880,
for example, it was estimated to be 185,000 tons. If this is subtracted
from the 1,397,000 tons of steel produced, it leaves 1,212,000 tons of pig
iron which was consumed in the production of steel. The remainder of
the 4,295,000 tons of pig iron produced, or 3,083,000 tons, was therefore
used for industrial purposes in the form of wrought iron, ordinary cast
iron, and malleable castings. The difference between columns 5 and 6 is
1,686,000 tons—the amount that industrial iron production exceeded steel
production.

The most important reason for the slow ascendancy of steel over iron
had to do with the nature of our iron ores. An early difficulty encountered
in both the Bessemer converter and the open hearth furnace was due to a
lining of sandstone for converters and silica sand for open hearths, both of
which are acid materials.

In an acid Bessemer furnace, phosphorus, which had been the "fatal
enemy" of Henry Bessemer, is not eliminated from the pig iron and goes
over into the steel, since no slag-making materials are added to catch and
hold the phosphorus. As a consequence, the acid Bessemer process was
restricted at first to the use of pig iron smelted from low phosphorus ores,
which were not abundant. This limitation was overcome by two English
metallurgists, Sidney Thomas, and his cousin, P. C. Gilchrist, who found
that by lining a Bessemer-type converter with some chemically basic material, such as limestone and dolomite, basic slag-making materials could
be used and the phosphorus could be absorbed from the pig iron and

passed into the slag. The Thomas-Gilchrist process was patented in 1877, but it was never adopted in Bessemer converters in the United States.

The use of a basic open hearth furnace was introduced into the United States about 1885. Its effects were revolutionary, because it made possible the utilization of immense deposits of Lake Superior ores which would otherwise have been unsuitable because of their high phosphorus content.

The basic process produced a number of profound changes in the American iron and steel industry, and it was the primary cause for starting a trend from the Bessemer converter to the more adaptable and productive open hearth process. From 1890 to 1900, while Bessemer steel output increased less than two times, open hearth production was multiplied more than six and a half times. The impetus given by the basic process to open hearth steel production was the principal reason for the final dethronement of iron in the middle 1890s as America's chief industrial metal and the crowning of a new sovereign metal—steel.

A number of technological changes also speeded up the advance of the Steel Age in the United States. One of these was the Jones Mixer, invented in 1889 by the famous Captain Bill Jones, Superintendent of Carnegie's Edgar Thomson Works. Formerly, molten iron was run from a blast furnace into molds where the iron solidified into "pigs." It was necessary to remelt the pigs into liquid iron for conversion into steel in the Bessemer converter or open hearth furnace. The Jones Mixer was a vessel that kept the iron molten from the time it was tapped from the blast furnace until it was charged into a steelmaking furnace. This dispensed with the remelting stage and represented a saving of $1 a ton in the manufacture of steel.

In the late 1880s, the substitution of electrical power for steam produced a minor revolution, and all plants wishing to keep abreast of developments had to be largely rebuilt to accommodate themselves to the new source of power. The installation of steelmaking facilities and their frequent modification to take advantage of technological changes, was expensive. The manufacturer of wrought iron who could not afford to change over to the manufacture of steel tended to fall by the wayside. Many of the independent plants were so small that for them to have attempted to "modernize" would have been, in the words of an eminent steelmaker of the period, "an economical absurdity." Processes in the iron industry were disconnected. One company mined the ore, another smelted it, a third puddled it into wrought iron, and a fourth operated rolling mills. In the 1890s, some steel companies began to integrate their operations to include several stages of the process. In sum, by 1895 steel was king over a rapidly expanding domain.

GERMANY TAKES THE LEAD IN EUROPE

After the Steel Age began in England, the manufacturers of wrought iron, there as in America, fought stubbornly to hold their position against the inroads of steel, especially in rails. In 1883, 70 per cent of British pig iron was converted into puddled iron bars.[6] In the worldwide era of railroad building, England dominated export markets, and the makers of iron rails confidently expected their trade to hold up and greatly expanded their plants. In the struggle between wrought iron and steel rails, steel finally won, and in 1876 it was recognized that the iron rail business was dead.[7] Other markets for iron also shrank, and in 1897 not more than 5 per cent of England's pig iron was converted into puddled iron.[8] The Age of Steel was firmly established in Great Britain.

As steelmaking became more scientific, British ironmasters, after their many technological innovations of the past, were largely content to carry on in the old routine way and were "resting somewhat on their oars."[9] Britain did little to improve the Bessemer process which she had introduced in England and Europe, and the most important technical advances were accomplished elsewhere. She greeted the Thomas-Gilchrist basic process for eliminating phosphorus, invented by her own sons, with "patronising skepticism," but Germany and Belgium adopted it eagerly, and Germany soon took the lead in its technical perfection.[10] Britain hesitated to invest money in by-product coke ovens while Germany was forging ahead to a position of world leadership.

Other technological innovations were pioneered outside of Great Britain in the last decades of the century to a greater extent than in the 1870's. The reasons for technological weakness in the British iron and steel industry were the same as in an earlier period—attachment to routine and the employment of but few, if any, trained technicians at plants, while they were being engaged increasingly by other advanced steelmaking nations.

After a domination of world iron markets by Great Britain for over a century, the period from 1878 to 1914 was marked by a relative decline in her position and the emergence of Germany as the leading iron and steel producer of Europe and the premier exporter of the world. It saw the entrance of the United States into the ranks of major steel exporters.

In 1878, Great Britain accounted for 69 per cent and Germany for 22 per cent of sales in major international markets. In 1895, Great Britain's share dropped to 57 per cent, Germany's climbed to 31 per cent, and the United States was nosing into world trade with less than 2 per cent. In 1910, Germany moved into first place as a steel exporter, with 38 per cent of major markets, compared to Britain's 36 per cent and America's 12 per cent. On the eve of World War I, in 1913, Germany's share of world markets was 39 per cent, Britain's had slipped to 30 per cent and America's had risen to 18 per cent. In the space of thirty-five years, Britain's proportion of sales in international iron and steel markets had been cut more than half—from 70 to 30 per cent. In the early years of the new century the English iron and steel industry, as the *Economist* pointed out, was "dancing in increasing measure to the tune of foreign producers, not of foreign buyers: and the tune was uncomfortably syncopated."[11]

LAKE SUPERIOR IRON ORES

After the advent of the Bessemer and open hearth processes, the relatively small known bodies of iron ore in the United States were totally inadequate to meet the needs of a rapidly expanding steel industry. Demands from the dynamic steel center of Pittsburgh were particularly insistent. Discovery of large, rich ore deposits in the Lake Superior region was made at a most propitious time.

In 1844, the federal government sent a group of surveyors into upper Michigan to chart the region and mark it into rectangular sections for future townships. In charge of the group was William A. Burt. He knew that minerals existed in the Lake Superior country but they were of secondary interest to him. As the party wandered through the forest, they noticed at one point that their compass needle behaved irregularly. Searching for the cause, they found outcroppings of iron ore. Burt marked the word "iron" on that area of the map, and for all we know, never suspected that in that remote wilderness the ore would ever be of commercial importance.[12]

Apparently, Burt and his men talked of the discovery to Indians and later to white men. One of the persons who heard of these rumors was Philo M. Everett, who had left his Connecticut farm some years earlier to prospect for gold and copper around Lake Superior. He hired an Indian guide to prospect for iron ore in the upper peninsula of Michigan, and in Everett's own words he came to "a mountain of solid iron ore, 150 feet high. The ore looks as bright as a bar of iron just broken."[13] Everett acted quickly and formed the Jackson Mining Company with title to one square mile of land near Negaunee. The ore proved to be 60 per cent iron, but this first mining venture, for one reason or another, was not a financial success. In 1849, the town of Marquette was founded about sixty miles from the Jackson mine. In the same year, R. J. Graveraet leased part of Everett's property and formed the Marquette Iron Company. Six barrels of the ore were shipped from the Marquette Range on July 7, 1852 to New Castle, Pennsylvania. This was the first shipment of Lake Superior ore down the Great Lakes.

Other companies became active on the Marquette Range and ore shipments down the Great Lakes continued to mount, swollen further by the first shipments from the Menominee Range in 1877 and from the Gogebic and Vermilion Ranges in 1884. In the latter year, shipments from the Lake Superior district totaled 2.5 million tons. (Iron ore shipments are in gross tons unless otherwise indicated.) Within five years ore shipments had climbed to more than 7 million tons.

Opening Up the Vermilion Range

We now come to the first large scale entrepreneur in Lake Superior ores, Charlemagne Tower. He had already made a fortune in coal lands and railroads when at sixty-six years of age he embarked on the greatest financial venture of his life. Iron mining may have been the thought farthest from his mind one day in 1875 when he was visited at his eastern office by George C. Stone, who had journeyed from Duluth to try to interest Tower financially in a Minnesota "iron mountain." It lay, said Stone, about sixty miles northeast of Duluth and was twelve miles long and one mile wide. This was the Mesabi Range, the name being derived from the word for "giant" in the language of the Chippewa Indians. Tower's interest was fired sufficiently to engage A. H. Chester, a mineralogist of Hamilton College, New York, to go on an exploration trip to the ore range. Chester's party was misdirected and struck the one-hundred-mile-long Mesabi belt at its lean end. He was discouraged in the low-grade ore which he found there and decided to move on to the Vermilion Range where he discovered beds of ore averaging over 65 per cent iron. In his report to Tower, he condemned the Mesabi ore as unworthy of development but strongly recommended the Vermilion. Thus Tower, misled by Chester's report, dismissed as a poor investment the world's greatest single iron ore field.[14]

As further favorable reports concerning the Vermilion Range reached Tower he decided to plunge into its exploitation and in 1882 organized the Minnesota Iron Company with himself as president. His first projects were to construct an eighty-mile railroad to the ore fields at Tower, Minnesota, and to build ore docks at what is now Two Harbors on Lake Superior. Costs proved to be far beyond his estimates. By 1884, he had sunk three and a half million into the enterprise and still the railroad was short of its goal. He was in despair. He had but one million dollars left. But there was no withdrawing now and in a desperate gamble he threw in another half million dollars. Within a few months the first carloads of ore trundled down to Two Harbors.

Tower's ore bed became famous as the Soudan Mine. The ore was not only rich in iron but low in phosphorus and was ideal for making Bessemer steel. For a period, his sales were limited only by the amount of ore that could be produced. One of his largest customers was Andrew Carnegie who, it was said, "hardly knew at that time where to look for Bessemer ore."[15] The success of the Minnesota Iron Company drew the attention of a syndicate headed by Henry H. Porter of Chicago and including among others, John D. and William Rockefeller. Tower sold out to the syndicate for roughly $6.4 million, netting himself a good profit on his original investment, plus the earnings of the company from the sale of ore up to that time.

The Great Mesabi Range

The second entrepreneur of large stature to enter upon the scene was Henry W. Oliver. It was he who opened up the Mesabi Range. Various persons had explored the range without tangible results until the Merritt brothers began their famous trek through the Mesabi territory. Four Merritt brothers were joined by their three nephews in the venture, but the seven men became known through the North country as the Merritt brothers, and also as The Seven Iron Men. Originally woodsmen, they had accumulated a considerable fortune in buying and selling timber. In 1890, they encountered a body of soft hematite ore at a site which was later called Iron Mountain. This was the first discovery of soft ore on the Mesabi Range.[16] After removing the overburden the ores could easily be scooped up by shovels. This led to the development of open pit mining.

When news of the Merritts' discovery reached the outer world, excited prospectors poured into Duluth and from there fanned out over the range. In 1892, the first shipments of Mesabi ore were begun—4,245 tons. Before another year was out, they rose to more than 600,000 tons, and from then on exploitation of the great Mesabi belt was in full swing, and in 1902 shipments amounted to 13,342,840 tons, more than half of the ore transported from all the Lake Superior ranges.

Now let us return to the Merritt brothers after their momentous discovery. Leonidas, the oldest and leader of the group, traveled to Pittsburgh to try to interest the Carnegie Steel Company in the ore. He was received by Henry Clay Frick, then Chairman of the Carnegie Company. According to Leonidas' story, Frick showed no interest in the preposterous location or its inconsequential ore and heaped "ridicule" on the idea.[17]

Meanwhile Henry W. Oliver, in Pittsburgh, pricked up his ears when he heard of the Merritt brothers' rich strike in the Mesabi ore fields. Oliver's life alternated between startling successes and crashing failures and during his ups and downs he was associated with some of the leading industrial and financial Titans of his day. He was second to none in realizing that the booming steel industry needed still larger sources of iron ore, and in 1892 he betook himself to Duluth with the intention of visiting the Merritt brothers. The city's hotels were so crowded with prospectors that he had to content himself with sleeping on a billiard table. The next day he bought a horse and rode through the wilderness to the Merritt headquarters. It has been said that his horseback journey later netted him $13 million.[18] When Oliver was shown the loose ore that could be shoveled like sand, he saw in a flash that he had found what he was looking for. The Merritt brothers were in need of cash to develop their claims and particularly to complete their railroad, the Duluth, Missabi & Northern Railroad, which was to connect with another line running to Duluth.

Oliver gave Leonidas Merritt a check for $5,000 in return for certain rights on the Mesabi Range and in the same year organized the Oliver Iron Mining Company.

On his return to Pittsburgh, Oliver, as an eye witness of the Mesabi ores, had little difficulty in convincing Frick of their possibilities. Frick now completely reversed his attitude and in 1892 proposed to Oliver that the Carnegie Company be given one-half interest in Oliver's properties in return for a $500,000 loan to develop the mines. Oliver readily agreed, but when Carnegie was approached for his approval he shied away, saying that ventures in ore would result "in less profit than in almost any branch of our business," and that "the Messaba is not the last great deposit the Lake Superior is to reveal."[19]

For nearly two years, while in Frick's opinion, valuable time was being lost, Carnegie withheld his approval. It was what Carnegie considered to be an outside threat which induced him to agree to the Oliver deal. The threat was in the person of John D. Rockefeller. Having secured a monopoly in oil, he was quietly buying up Lake Superior ore properties. His big opportunity came during the panic of 1893 when mining companies on the Mesabi Range, including that of the Merritt brothers, were failing or in dire financial straits. Rockefeller bought up vast tracts, including the mines and railroads of the Merritt brothers, and formed the Lake Superior Consolidated Iron Mines. In this one coup he became master of the range.

Carnegie did not want to clash with Rockefeller, but he wanted to be assured of a supply of ore for an indefinite period. Let Rockefeller own the property, the more the better, Carnegie reasoned, so long as he, Carnegie, had access to them. So he entered into an arrangement with Rockefeller whereby he leased the ore properties for fifty years on a royalty basis of twenty-five cents a ton against the then current rate of sixty-five cents, with a guaranteed output of 600,000 tons a year, the ores to be shipped over the Rockefeller railroad and steamship lines. This deal, commented *Iron Age* in the issue of December 17, 1896, gave the Carnegie Company "a position unequalled by any producer in the world.[20]

Carnegie was not one to be content with less than a controlling interest in any of his enterprises, and in 1897 he insisted upon buying five-sixths interest in the Oliver Iron Mining Company. Oliver agreed. By this time the Carnegie-Oliver interests between them controlled a large portion of the Mesabi iron ore.

Mining and Transportation

When iron ore was first mined in the Lake Superior region it was shoveled into horse-drawn wagons and hauled to Marquette on Lake Superior where it was transferred by wheelbarrows onto a sailing vessel. When the ship reached the rapids on the St. Mary's River between Lake

Superior and Lake Huron, the cargo was unloaded and carted in wagons past the rapids and put aboard another vessel. Construction of the first Sault Ste. Marie lock was begun in 1853 and completed in 1855. This vital waterway link between the upper and lower Great Lakes, popularly known as the "Soo," now has five locks and handles a greater tonnage annually than all other locks in the world, nearly twice as much as the Panama and Suez canals combined.

Prior to the building of the Soo, four to five days were required to unload and reload small vessels at the rapids. With the coming of steam-powered vessels in 1882, faster ore handling methods became imperative to speed the flow of iron ore down the lakes. Loading was made more expeditious by having railroad ore cars run out on a trestle beside the docked vessel and letting the ore flow down chutes into the holds. The mechanical unloader invented by George H. Hulett in 1898 shortened the "turn around" time at lower lake ports. Now powered by electricity, the Hulett unloader can dip its clam-shaped bucket into the hold of a ship and come up with nineteen tons of ore in one bite. In 1905, it took twenty-one hours to load an ore vessel and thirty-three hours to unload. By the mid-twentieth century, the time for each operation was reduced to four or five hours.

About 60 per cent of all the iron ore mined in America is done by the open-pit method in the Lake Superior region. Hand shovels were thrown aside after steam power in 1885 began to drive large scoops, superseded later by electrically-operated shovels capable of gouging out twenty tons of ore in their steel jaws and dumping the contents into railway cars. The world's largest open-pit mine, the Hull-Rust-Mahoning mine, was begun in 1895 on the Mesabi Range and by the middle of the present century was probably the largest excavation in the world, about three miles long, one-half to one mile wide, more than 350 feet deep, and containing more than seventy miles of railroad tracks.

A special type of ore vessel was developed to transport ore on the Great Lakes. As the hungry mouths of the blast furnaces devoured more and more iron ore, larger and swifter vessels appeared on the lakes. A typical ore vessel of the mid-twentieth century is about 600 feet long and 60 to 65 feet wide, with a capacity of 11,000 to 14,000 gross tons of ore. Some of the giants on the lakes are nearly 650 feet in length, with a breadth of 70 feet and a capacity of more than 21,000 gross tons of iron ore. Because parts of the water route freeze in winter, the vessels operate only about seven and a half months a year.

From the opening of the first Lake Superior iron ore range in 1855 through 1960, more than 3.3 billion gross tons of ore have been shipped. Of that total, more than 2 billion tons, or roughly two-thirds, came from the Mesabi Range. The figure of 62,738,000 tons, reached in World War I, was not surpassed until the boom year of 1929. The lowest shipments of the century were in the 1932 depression year, when 3,589,000 tons were shipped. The peak shipment of World War II was 92,950,000 tons in 1942, exceeded in 1953, with a record of 96,207,000 tons.

Lake Superior iron ores have comprised about 85 per cent of all the ore mined in the United States in the present century; they have supplied the substance for the economic vertebrae of America, and on two occasions enabled the United States to become the Arsenal of Democracy in world-wide conflicts. As the higher-grade natural ores of the Lake Superior district are mined out, the steel industry is making increasing use of lower grade ores, including taconite, which exist in great abundance in the Lake Superior region and which, by beneficiation of one type or another, can be converted into an ore of even better quality than direct-shipping ores. Steel plants far removed from Lake Superior, particularly those located at or near the Atlantic seaboard, are meeting their growing requirements from other sources, principally Canada, South America, and Africa.

13

Enter Automobiles, Exit Horses

Some day, Charlie, we'll be making sheets in long strips like they make paper.

—John Butler Tytus

When the American people removed the last leaf from the calendar of 1900, they could look forward to the brave new world of the twentieth century with confidence and optimism. Their past accomplishments entitled them to do so. In the 101 years since the Father of His Country had been laid to rest, the United States had come from a frontier nation to a position of world leadership in steel and manufacturing. In every decade since the Civil War, new wonders had emerged from the brains of scientists and inventors. One of the latest was the horseless carriage, which tore along at fifteen to twenty miles an hour, endangering human life and limb and frightening horses into a panic.

The early automobiles were quite literally "horseless carriages," with an internal combustion engine installed in a specially constructed buggy. Such was the one-cylinder automobile built by Charles E. and J. Frank Duryea, the first American-made car to be driven on the streets of America. The date was 1893. In the first decade or so of the century, men with modest amounts of capital and little or no knowledge of manufacturing rushed to enter the automobile business. The ephemeral life of most of the early models tells the story of this period in the evolution of the automobile, the path of which was strewn with mechanical "freaks" that could not survive competitive conditions. The man who paced the field as a manufacturer, and who more than any other person established the modern American automobile industry, was Henry Ford. While employed as an engineer in an electric plant in Detroit, he built his first car in 1896 during his spare hours. In 1908, he turned out his first Model T and in 1913 put in his first assembly line.

137

The first job of the car makers was to build a motor that did not break down on nearly every journey, and could be relied on to propel the vehicle and passengers up a moderately steep hill. Since the body was literally a horse buggy, it was natural that it was built by carriage makers, who continued to carry on the new business in their customary factories. The wooden bodies were given several coats of varnish. Counting the time consumed between coats, it took ten to fifteen days for the painting operation alone. Carriage makers could conceive of the automobile only in terms of a carriage and they persisted in designing a body that was suitable to be drawn by horses but not propelled by an engine. The early motors produced a great deal of heat, which warped the wood and weakened the glue. The roads being what they were, it is small wonder that the joints gave way, dreadful creaking developed, and the panels sometimes split. The body makers at first tried to meet the situation by fastening sheet steel over the wooden dashboards and hood, then over the doors, and later around the rear of the car. They added steel, little by little, to the door jambs, sills, roof, and elsewhere until the wooden frame was completely covered by steel.

From this point on, our story follows two separate but closely related paths. The first concerns the development of the all-steel automobile, and the second, the evolution from hand-sheet mills to continuous hot-strip and cold-reduction mills in the steel industry.

THE ALL-STEEL AUTOMOBILE

The story of the all-steel automobile is also the story of one of America's great industrial pioneers, Edward G. Budd. His interest in the automobile grew out of his work in shaping steel sheets, in a cold condition, in stamping presses. Up to the last decades of the nineteenth century, iron and steel were shaped chiefly by rolling, forging, casting, and wire drawing. Relatively little shaping was done on a commercial scale by the means of dies in stamping presses. The stamping of sheet metal in the United States arose from a movement to produce steel products of lighter weight than castings and forgings. There is meager information on its origin, but it appears to have taken place in the lock, clock, and hardware industry of New England which had long been the center of the trade in the United States. In the late 1880s, the substitution of pressed steel for castings and forgings took hold in the light metal industries of Connecticut and Rhode Island. By 1900, the changeover there was well established.[1]

Edward Budd, a young Philadelphia engineer, gained his first experience with stamping presses in the closing years of the last century while partner in a small firm that introduced the substitution of pressed steel for castings or wood in the manufacture of belt pulleys. After joining Hale & Kilburn Manufacturing Company of Philadelphia in 1902, Budd enjoyed a wider latitude in exploring the potentialities of pressed steel fabrication and while with the firm made his first contact with the automobile industry. The company was asked by the Hupp Motor Car Company to manufacture pressed steel sheets to cover the wooden framework of their car bodies. While occupied with this contract Budd is said to have conceived of the all-steel automobile. He believed that the motor car industry was destined to grow, but the management of Hale & Kilburn took a dimmer view. Budd was not to be deterred from pursuing his vision of an all-steel car, and he left his employer in 1912 to form the Edward G. Budd Manufacturing Company, setting himself up in a shop with thirteen employees.

When Budd approached the problem of manufacturing a steel car, he conceived of steel not as a surface covering laid on a wooden frame but as a structural material which would provide both skin and framework in itself. The flexibility of the steel body would permit it to absorb the shocks from the chassis. Greater strength would be realized with less weight. This original conception conflicted with established ideas, and Budd's proposed models were not welcomed by the great majority of automobile manufacturers, and the young company experienced difficulty in keeping alive.

The first all-steel body frames were made by Budd for Oakland and Hupmobile cars and were introduced in 1912. There were the open touring models with cloth tops. Budd's first really large contract for an all-steel body frame was made with the Dodge brothers, John and Horace, in 1913. The car appeared in 1914 and was also the open touring type. By 1916, all-steel open touring models were in substantial production. Authorities differ when the first all-steel closed automobile was put on sale. One says that "as early as 1919 Budd entered the field with a sedan body constructed wholly of steel, and in 1922 commenced large scale production while other companies were still using wood."[2] Others give 1923 as the date when the all-steel sedan was put on the market.[3]

The all-steel body frame eliminated the long tedious job of varnish painting. It was possible to bake enamel on the steel frames, which gave a black finish of pleasing appearance and of greater durability than varnish.

At an early stage in the development of the all-steel body Budd sought to reduce the number of panels. In 1915, a complete side panel was pressed from steel for an Oakland open four-seater. Eventually, closed bodies were made of eight main sections—two one-piece side panels, a roof, a floor, and four doors complete with window frames.

Some ex-carriage makers denounced the all-steel car as "ridiculous" and "cheap" and maintained that thin sheet steel construction would not be strong enough. In spite of the many advantages of the all-steel automobile, it was adopted slowly by the automobile industry and did not become universal until the middle 1930s.

HAND-SHEET MILLS TO CONTINUOUS MILLS

Slowness in adoption of the all-steel car is not to be charged entirely to the resistance of ex-carriage makers. The steel industry was technologically unprepared to produce sheets on a volume basis of the quality desired by the automotive world. There was no shortage of sheets. Production had risen from 1,101,449 tons in 1905 to 2,839,880 tons in 1912, and to 3,232,769 tons in 1920. The principal complaint of car makers concerned the surface defects of sheets and their lack of uniformity in gauge and ductility. These deficiencies were the result of the hand-sheet mills, then universally used. Each lot of sheets varied from the others in dimensions and temper. As late as 1926, some 1,200 hand mills, each producing in small quantity of variable quality, were struggling to supply a mass production industry where uniformity of component parts was a prime requisite.

"Give us sheets in long lengths of uniform quality," was the cry of automobile makers. Budd reported that in cutting the pattern for stampings from sheets, there was always a waste at the ends and the corners. "If it were possible," he said, "to buy these sheets as the dressmaker buys cloth in long pieces, much saving in waste would result."[4] The same thought was shared by many men at that time. John Butler Tytus, of the American Rolling Mill Company, who had once worked in a paper mill and had seen wood pulp transformed into rolls of paper, predicted that the steel industry would one day roll steel "in long strips like they make paper."[5]

The continuous process for rolling wide, thin, flat steel in long sections represents the convergence of two different lines of development—strip mills and sheet mills. To the outsider, the terms "strip" and "sheet," which appear to be used interchangeably for the same product, are confusing. The confusion in terminology is due to the origin of the terms, sheet and strip. Originally each was a distinctly different product, produced on a different type of mill. Strip was the narrower and longer of the two and was produced from billets and slabs and was always rolled "single." Sheets were wider and shorter than strip and were produced from sheet bars and were generally rolled in "packs." The continuous wide strip mill gave a product having the dimensional characteristics of both strip and sheet—that is, it was both wide and long—hence the resulting confusion in nomenclature.

Hand Mills—Operation and Deficiencies

Since the sheet mills are the older of the two, we shall consider them first. Hand-sheet mills had undergone little fundamental improvement since Major Hanbury introduced them to the Welsh tin-plate trade early in the eighteenth century. (See Chapter 5.) As developed in this country, there were two kinds: "jobbing" mills and "pack" mills. The former rolled heavier sheets, about 1/16-inch thick or thicker. The latter rolled light sheets, less than 1/16-inch thick, and as thin as 1/100 of an inch or less. The principal use of light gauge sheets was for tin-plating. In both mills, the operation began with a semi-finished product known as a "sheet bar," which was generally 8 inches wide and varied in thickness and length according to the width and length desired in the finished sheet. The sheet bar commonly weighted from 8 to 60 pounds per lineal foot. For pack mills, it was about ¼ inch thick and 30 inches long, with the usual width of 8 inches.

A hand mill consisted either of a single stand of rolls, on which all the rolling was done from bar to finished sheet, or of two stands, one for roughing down the bar and the other for finishing the sheet. The rolls varied in size, according to the dimensions of the sheets to be rolled, and ranged from 22 to 32 inches in diameter and from 30 inches to 60 inches in length.

A man called a "roller" was in charge of all the rolling operations. According to his judgment, he directed the setting of the screws that diminished the space between the rolls after each pass of the sheet bar or sheet through the rolls, thereby both reducing the thickness of the bar or sheet and elongating it. He was generally assisted by nine men, each with a specialized task, and a varying number of helpers.

The following description is of a two-stand mill. After the sheet bars were heated in a furnace to a uniform rolling temperature, a helper deposited two bars before the roughing stand. Its purpose, as the name implies, was to thin down and elongate the bar into the rough form of a sheet. A "rougher" grasped a bar with tongs and inserted it sideways between the rolls. As the bar emerged on the other side, it was grasped in tongs by a "catcher." While he was lifting the bar to return it over the top roll, the rougher fed a second bar into the mill and then grasped, for a second pass, the first bar which the catcher was steadying on the top roll. One of the helpers, meanwhile, used a steel bar, called a "spanner bar," that actuated the screw mechanism which brought the rolls closer together. These movements were repeated in rapid succession until the bars were near the desired gauge. The two roughed-down bars were then "matched," that is, one was placed on the other and the pair was given two or three more roughing passes, generally until the bars were elongated to one-half the length intended for the finished sheets. Afterwards the bars were placed on the floor and separated by sheer human brawn with the aid of tongs, or, if necessary, with "sticker-opener-swords." The roughed-down sheets were then heated in pairs in preparation for finishing.

On the finishing stand, the roughed-down bars were passed back and forth, between and above the rolls, as in the roughing stand, until the desired gauge of the sheets was reached. If a heavy gauge was desired, the sheets were rolled singly, one at a time. Lighter gauges were produced by pack rolling. The practice originated in Wales as a means of producing very thin sheets for tin plate. Pack rolling was taken over directly from the hammering method. Before the introduction of the rolling mill, it was found that sheets could be made thinner by hammering two or three at a time than one at a time. Rolling multiple layers had additional advantages because a pack of several sheets retained its heat longer than a single sheet and also resulted in a more evenly distributed pressure from the rolls.

The number of sheets in a pack varied from two to eight, according to the gauge desired, the more in a pack, the lighter the gauge. Packs of four and six sheets were made by doubling over single packs of two and three sheets. Packs of eight sheets were made by twice doubling single packs of two sheets. For extremely light gauges, two packs of eight sheets were matched to make a pack of sixteen sheets.

The finished pack of sheets had rough, irregular edges. After cooling, the pack was sheared along all edges to the length and width of sheets desired. The pack was separated in the same manner as a pair of rougheddown bars. A crew of ten men could produce one ton of sheets an hour.

The surface of hand-rolled sheets was uneven and was also frequently marred by small pits caused by a scaly oxide which forms on red-hot metal when worked in contact with the air. If sheets with a high finish were desired, they were pickled in acid to detach the scale, box-annealed to remove the brittleness imparted by hot rolling, then pickled again in acid to remove any oxides that might have formed during annealing, and cold rolled. Afterwards they were again annealed to lessen the hardening effect of cold rolling.

Up until about 1876, all sheets were made of iron. In that year, the first Bessemer steel sheet bars were produced at the Edgar Thomson Works of Andrew Carnegie and were rolled into sheets at the plant of the United States Iron and Tin Plate Company at McKeesport.[6] Bessemer steel afforded a smoother, brighter finish than common grades of iron, and its use became almost universal until open hearth steel also began to be used in the period from 1900 to 1910.

Hand-rolled sheets, by the very nature of the process, were not only of irregular surface finish, but also varied in dimensions. In no other rolling operation of the steel industry did the human factor enter so extensively as in hand mills. At appropriate stages of the process, the roller adjusted the distance between the rolls, which determined the thickness of the sheets, and he did it according to his own judgment. There could not possibly be the same precision and accuracy in the manual rolling of sheets as in other mills where the machinery was subject to greater mechanical control. No two lots of hand-rolled sheets were exactly the same in thickness and temper, and it was these variations which the automobile makers complained most loudly about. Lack of uniformity in steel sheets became a serious impediment in stamping body parts, where nothing caused more failures and rejections than variation in gauge and stiffness.

Efforts to roll sheets by a continous process were attempted by Henry F. Mann in Pittsburgh in 1865 and by Samuel R. Wilmot in Bridgeport, Connecticut, in 1875, but both were given up as unsuccessful. In 1892, a continuous mill for "rolling of sheet in multiple lengths" was built in Teplitz, Germany. It rolled sheets as wide as 50 inches and in lengths up to 60 feet, but it experienced great difficulty due to "non-uniformity of gauge" and was abandoned in 1907.[7]

Early in the present century, two American ventures in the continous rolling of wide sheets were made by the American Sheet and Tin Plate Company, a subsidiary of the United States Steel Corporation. The first mill was built in 1902 at the Monongahela Works in Pennsylvania and consisted of eight stands of two-high mills, arranged in tandem, through which the steel passed continuously. Due to the number of faulty sheets which had to be rejected, the breakage of rolls, and other difficulties, the plant was shut down in 1905. The second mill, built in 1905 on a more ambitious scale at the Mercer Works in South Sharon, Pennsylvania, was also unsatisfactory and was dismantled in 1910.

Evolution of Continuous Hot-Strip Mill

It is now time to return to the strip mill and trace its development to the point where it and the sheet mill converged into a mill producing a product with the characteristics of both strip and sheet—the continuous wide hot-strip mill.

Strip steel was originally a specialty product of the merchant bar mill. The latter term arose in the early days of bar mills, which carried a selection of their products in stock for the convenience of merchants. Bar mills ordinarily turned out round or rectangular bars, but it was also possible to roll light, narrow, flat sections which were used for such purposes as barrel hoops, cotton ties, and skelp, the stock for making welded pipe. From 1890 to 1900, the demand for narrow, thin, flat sections increased to such an extent that separate mills were built for their production, and it was but natural that their designers copied, in principle, the merchant bar mills with which they were familiar. Thus, the strip mill was an offshoot of the bar mill.

The first strip mill, as such, was for the production of narrower sizes, from 3 inches down to ⅝ inch, and the product was known as hoop. Beginning in 1890, there was a rapid development of the narrow mill and by 1896 the evolution from a bar-type mill to a distinctly different mill was complete. The next departure from the parent stem was a skelp mill which rolled strip 4 inches wide and over. From then on there was a succession of hot-strip mills, each embodying some new feature, and producing wider and longer strip, from a maximum width of 7 inches and a maximum length of 100 feet in 1890 to a maximum width of 24 inches and lengths from 500 to 1000 feet in 1925.

The ribbon of strip, 500 to 1,000 feet in length, produced in the most advanced of these mills, was run out on a cooling table where it was either sheared into sheets or was wound on an automatic coiler. The problem was to produce light, flat steel in equally long lengths but still wider. Earlier attempts in Germany and this country had resulted in failure because they were based on the erroneous belief that the sheet in each pass through the rolls should be perfectly flat. Discovery of the principle that the rolls should be slightly convex and that those in each successive stand should be less convex, made it possible to roll flat steel of much greater width in proportion to thickness than had previously been thought attainable. Convexity of the rolls provided a guide for the wide sheet, preventing its lateral movement which would have destroyed uniformity of shape or resulted in the sheet running into the neck of the rolls.

JOHN BUTLER TYTUS

The man who first discovered and successfully applied this principle was John Butler Tytus. He came from a well-to-do family of Middletown, Ohio. Upon graduation from Yale University in 1897 with a B. S. degree, he worked for a few years in his father's paper manufacturing business which he was expected to take over eventually. But John became restless, and fate took him by the hand one day in 1904 and led him on a visit to the hand-sheet mill of the American Rolling Mill Company, where he watched with puzzlement and fascination the slow, hot, heavy work of producing sheets by the time-honored process. He counted twenty-two different times that the sheets were handled and concluded that a "business which had so much lost motion had plenty of future for a young man." He applied for a job. The superintendent, Charles R. Hook, tried to discourage this frail-looking young gentleman, warning him, "It will break your back."[8]

"Perhaps. But I want to try it."

Tytus was hired as a "spare hand," the lowest rung on the ladder. By the end of eighteen months, he was skilled in every operation, and in another year he was appointed Superintendent of the company's Zanesville plant. He was not with Armco, as the company is now called, very long before he began searching for ways to improve hand-sheet mills, which from the start he considered antiquated. When he made his prediction to Hook, "Some day Charlie, we'll be making sheets in long strips like they make paper," he struck a responsive chord in the older man; for Hook had witnessed earlier attempts to roll sheets continuously, and although it and other similar trials had not been entirely successful, he believed it was feasible. Hook encouraged his young protégé to pursue his ideas.

An opportunity for Tytus to translate his vision into reality came in World War I. The company was concentrating on forgings and other heavy material and the sheet mills were virtually idle. Tytus was allowed to use one of the mills as a technological laboratory. By the end of the war, he was convinced that he had progressed far enough to construct a continuous sheet mill, but he did not have an opportunity to give his ideas practical form until 1921, when Armco purchased the idle plant of the Ashland Iron and Mining Company of Ashland, Kentucky. The properties contained steelmaking facilities and a blooming mill but no finishing department. Why not let Tytus install his experimental plant there? Thither he went, armed with blueprints and about one hundred skilled workers from Middletown, all pledged to withhold the secrets of their experiments from the outside world.

The years 1922-1923 were spent by the band of co-inventors in experimentation. Rolls broke, housings snapped, and the sheets buckled. More millions were poured into the venture. In January 1924, a completed wide-sheet mill was put together, but it proved to be full of "bugs," and it was another six months before they were removed. The mill produced sheets up to 36 inches wide and as thin as 0.065 inch.

The Tytus mill was the first to demonstrate the commercial practicality of hot-rolling wide, thin, flat material in multiples of ordered lengths by a semi-continuous process. The mill operated on the principle of what is termed "intermediate heating." The metal cooled to such an extent between successive stages that it had to be reheated four times in special furnaces. There were nineteen rolls in all—seven in the bar plate mill, seven in the rough sheet mill, and five in the finishing mill. The Ashland mill was anything but a continuous mill. The great contribution of Tytus was the discovery that slightly convex rolls are necessary to roll wide flat material. His mill had a number of serious defects. He had difficulty in preventing the sheet from slipping from side to side and in maintaining proper tension between the rolls. These handicaps were overcome in a mill designed and constructed by A. J. Townsend and H. M. Naugle for the Columbia Steel Company at Butler, Pennsylvania. It began operation in 1926. The Butler mill produced strip up to 36 inches wide and was the first in the world to roll long lengths of wide strip on the continuous principle. It was the prototype of the modern continuous wide hot-strip mill. Uninterrupted rolling was made possible by the installation of four-high mills in the finishing stands.

The question of conflicting patents arose between Armco and the Columbia Steel Company. It was resolved by the former purchasing the latter. Thus, Armco controlled all the basic patents on the continuous wide hot-strip mill. The company decided to share the process with the rest of the industry by licensing the use of its patents. Within a decade after the Ashland plant rolled its first sheets, an estimated half billion dollars had been invested in twenty-seven continuous wide strip mills with a combined annual capacity of fourteen million tons.

The finest engineering brains of the steel industry were devoted to improving this wonderful creation—giving it greater power, speed, productivity, and range in the dimensions of its product. Each mill varies slightly from the others in the size of its finished products, but as a group wide strip mills roll flat steel from 0.04 inch to 1.25 inches in thickness, from 26 to 96 inches in width and in lengths up to 2,000 feet.

The continuous hot-strip mill should be regarded as one gigantic machine, stretching some 2,000 feet in length, in which the component parts of heating furnaces, roller tables, and massive rolling stands are synchronized to heat and roll a slab of steel into a long thin ribbon, racing at a speed of more than 2,000 feet a minute from the delivery end. The entire rolling operation is performed in about two minutes.

Products of the continuous hot-strip mill were welcomed by the trade, because sheet and strip in greater widths and lengths, with a more even surface, and of more uniform dimensions than hand-rolled sheets, were at last available in mass quantities. Further improvements in the quality and properties of sheets and strip were made in response to demands of customers, who no sooner had a taste of one improvement than they asked for others. Improvements were of two kinds—metallurgical and technological. These advances had to do with the cold reduction mill. In hearings before the Temporary National Economic Committee in 1940, Charles R. Hook, President of the American Rolling Mill Company, exhibited a fender from a model T Ford and another from a 1939 Buick. Holding up the first fender, which he said was made from two welded hand-rolled sheets, he showed that it was possible to see right through its many coats of paint and detect the imperfections on the surface. By the hand-mill process, he explained, "You couldn't get a surface fine enough, smooth enough, that the imperfections wouldn't show through on three or four operations." The larger Buick fender, on the other hand, was the product of the continuous mill and was stamped from one sheet. "There wasn't any process that the steel industry knew anything about," Hook said, "there wasn't any way, under the old hand mill process, by which we could produce a sheet to make that part." Changes in the quality and properties of sheets made by the new process (continuous mills), he said, "are so great as to amount practically to the introduction of an entirely new product in the steel industry."[9]

The development of the cold reduction mill culminated the long evolutionary path from Major Hanbury's hand-sheet mills of the early eighteenth century to contemporary metallurgical practices and rolling facilities which resulted, as Charles Hook said, in "an entirely new product." The primary purpose of cold rolling is to impart a smooth, polished surface to the steel, with only a slight reduction in thickness.

Cold reduction, on the other hand, drastically reduces the thickness of the steel and at the same time gives it a smooth lustrous surface.

COLD ROLLING AND COLD REDUCTION

Cold rolling for the purpose of polishing iron sheets was known as early as 1747, but little more is heard of it until 1783, when John Westwood of England took out a patent for cold rolling iron to improve its surface finish. Cold rolling as an industry originated in Germany around 1830 with weavers who manufactured and used steel "reeds" in their trade. The reeds were made by cold rolling round wire into flat form. The reeds, and flattened wire for clock and watch springs, were the principal products of cold rolling in this period. The German process was afterwards copied in the United States.

Bernard Lauth extended the cold rolling process to iron bars. The idea is said to have occurred to him after his tongs were caught in a rolling mill one day, and he was fascinated by the high luster given to them. He undertook experiments which led to the issuance in 1859 of a patent for cold rolling.

The cold rolling of strip as an industry was begun some time before 1859 by Ichabod Washburn of Worcester, Massachusetts, to produce flat wire for the support of crinoline or hoop skirts. When the fashion died out after ten years, the vanished market for crinoline wire was replaced by a still larger demand for corset wire which was also cold-rolled in a flat form.

The earliest known cold rolling of soft steel strip in America was done experimentally about 1871 by the Stanley Works of New Britain, Connecticut, using crucible steel. About two years later, tests were made of open-hearth steel imported from England. The tests demonstrated the suitability of cold-rolled steel for the requirements of the hardware trade, which became one of the chief outlets for this product. Shortly afterwards, several companies in Pennsylvania began cold rolling high carbon strip steel for clock springs, steel pens, and corset bones, and still later for shoe shanks. The strip at that time was cold-rolled in narrow widths—probably not more than 3 inches—and in short lengths.

In 1877, S. R. Wilmot of the American Belt-Tin and Tube Company of Bridgeport, Connecticut, cold-rolled flat steel in long lengths and in widths up to 6 inches. His product found a receptive market among manufacturers of small hardware and related industries in Connecticut. The movement to replace small castings by pressed and stamped steel products began about 1888. By 1900, the replacement of cast parts by stampings was well under way and from 1900 on increased by leaps and bounds.

The function of the cold-rolling mills, just described, was to give strip a smooth and lustrous finish, with little reduction in thickness. Very thin sheets, especially those destined for tin-plating, were still produced on hand mills by the old pack-rolling method, because the continuous hot-strip mill did not reduce steel to the thinner gauges. The lower limit of the hot-strip mill is 0.0449 inch in thickness, while tin plate stock may range from 0.014 to 0.008 inch thick. The need for volume production of thinner material was met by the cold reduction mill. Companies possessing continuous wide hot-strip mills began to install cold reduction equipment in order to produce the thinner sheets under one roof instead of sending the hot-rolled strip to hand mills for further reduction. The cold reduction mill developed quickly from single-stand mills up to the high-speed tandem four-high mills of today, some of which have as many as five stands. The evolution was even more rapid than that of the continuous hot strip mill. In 1936, only 24 per cent of tin plate stock was cold-reduced, the remainder being made by the hand-rolling pack method. By 1939, 75 per cent of all tin plate was cold-reduced, and in 1943 the figure reached 100 per cent.

So far, discussion of the cold reduction mill has emphasized the heavy reduction in the thickness of sheets and the lustrous finish imparted to their surface. What made the cold-reduced sheet an "entirely new product," was its more uniform physical and mechanical properties. The cold-reduced sheet, after appropriate heat treatment, possesses deep-drawing properties far in excess of any previously attainable. Therein lies the unique value of this product. Today a sheet of cold-reduced steel will yield in a press to form an automobile top or the rounded curves of an automatic toaster. Thirty years ago, to have attempted such deformation would have cracked the steel. Deep-drawing steel literally opened up a whole new world of manufacturing possibilities. It lent itself to the improvement of existing products and encouraged the invention and manufacture of new products, especially for the home, never before attainable with the old sheets. But it should not be forgotten that the continuous hot-strip mill made the cold reduction mill possible. The two mills, by facilitating the expansion of existing industries and the founding of many new mass production industries, have had profound economic and social consequences in the United States and throughout the civilized world.

SOME RESULTS OF MASS-PRODUCED STRIP AND SHEET

Lower Costs

The mechanization of hand-sheet mills not only gave a superior product, but by increasing productivity and lowering operating costs, also made it possible to reduce prices steadily for a number of years, to the ultimate benefit of the consumer. Armco charged an average price of $100.15 a ton for iron and steel sheets in 1923, a year before it installed

America's first semi-continuous mill at Ashland, Kentucky. The company's prices dropped from $80.18 a ton in 1926 to $57.31 a ton in 1939, a decline of 31.1 per cent. Industry-wide prices of sheets for those years are not available, but Armco's prices may be taken as fairly typical. In the same period, the average price of electric refrigerators fell from $475 to $169 and standard electric washers from $140 to $68. Automobile prices also dropped in terms of value per dollar. Since the models were rapidly changing in these years, with the introduction of two and four-door, all-steel bodies and the addition of new features as standard equipment, there is no basis for comparing retail prices.

Shift from Heavy to Light Steel Products

The continuous strip and cold reduction mills came in fortuitously at the end of one, and the beginning of another, era in the economic and social life of the United States. In the years following World War I, there began an accelerated shift from the manufacture of capital goods to the mass production of consumer goods, made largely of steel sheets. The all-steel car entered into production in the early 1920s, and a number of home appliances such as the washing machine, vacuum cleaner, electrical refrigerator, and toaster were already appearing on the market.

The change in the economy of the United States began even earlier and was reflected in the relative production of heavy and light steel products, as may be seen in Table 4, for the years 1905 to 1955. In that period, the production of one group of heavy steel products—plates, structural steel, and rails—was a little more than doubled and fell from 42 per cent to 18.4 per cent of all hot-rolled steel products. On the other hand, the output of light, flat products was increased more than twenty-six times and rose from 8.9 per cent to 47.2 per cent of all hot-rolled products. An almost complete reversal took place in the relative position of the two groups, in percentages of hot-rolled products. It will be noticed that in heavy steel products, rails suffered the greatest decline, dropping from 20 per cent to 1.3 per cent of all hot-rolled products.

Between 1925 and 1955, inclusive, a total of 560.7 million tons of sheets, strip, and black plate were produced in the United States, most of which was domestically consumed. More than one-half billion tons of thin flat steel, absorbed by the American economy in thirty years, much of it manufactured into consumer products unknown or known only to a privileged few in 1900, could not help but exert a powerful impact on the American way of life. Predominant in this influence was the automobile, which has become the greatest economic and social force in the nation. Commenting on the motorcar, Lerner says that for the masses it has become "more important even than adequate housing or education or health . . . the car is a house on wheels."[10]

If the automobile provided Americans with "a house on wheels," it may

TABLE 4

RELATIVE PRODUCTION OF HEAVY AND LIGHT STEEL PRODUCTS IN THE UNITED STATES
AND PERCENTAGES OF HOT-ROLLED PRODUCTS: SELECTED PERIODS, 1905-1955

	1905		1920		1940		1955	
	Production	%	Production	%	Production	%	Production	%
HEAVY PRODUCTS								
Plates	2,286,151	12.1	5,325,749	14.7	4,323,408	8.8	8,190,979	9.1
Structural Steel	1,859,781	9.9	3,703,558	10.2	4,232,346	8.7	7,269,653	8.0
Rails	3,781,041	20.0	2,916,610	8.1	1,678,986	3.5	1,227,365	1.3
Totals	7,926,973	42.0	11,945,917	33.0	10,234,740	21.0	16,687,997	18.4
LIGHT PRODUCTS								
Sheets	1,101,449	5.9	3,232,769	8.9	11,705,956	24.0	31,517,276	34.8
Black Plate	568,497	3.0	1,899,683	5.2	521,924	1.1	—	—
Strip	—		656,907	1.8	2,077,744	4.3	3,683,574	4.1
Strip & Sheets for Cold Reduced Black Plate & Tin Plate	—		—		3,103,627	6.4	7,579,400	8.4
Totals	1,699,946	8.9	5,789,359	15.9	17,409,251	35.8	42,780,250	47.2

SOURCE: American Iron and Steel Institute.

also be said that life within the home itself was also revolutionized, thanks again largely to deep-drawing steel sheets. The mechanical refrigerator, which altered the diets of the American people, has become almost as indispensable as the family car, and at the start of 1961 was in 98 per cent of all wired homes. That puts it in first place as a home appliance. The old scrubbing board, with all of its attendant drudgery, belongs to a bygone era for most American families, replaced by the effortless mechanical washer, which was in 95.4 per cent of wired homes in 1961. The remaining part of the laundry operation—ironing—has also been revolutionized. Gone from 88.4 per cent of all wired homes is the old flat iron, superseded by the automatic electric iron, which, in recent years has rapidly lost ground to the all-purpose steam iron.[11]

It would underestimate the importance of steel sheets to confine a discussion of them to the automotive industry and products for the home. Sheets of carbon steel and a wide range of alloy steels find use for mechanical and structural purposes in every branch of the economy. A large portion of the domestic food crops we eat, the dairy products we consume, the cotton cloth we wear or use in sheets, handkerchiefs, table covers, and so on are grown or processed through mechanized equipment in which sheets predominate over other forms of steel. Machines plow the land, throw in the seed, cultivate and harvest the crops, milk cows, pasteurize and bottle the milk. Machines, together with great strides in agricultural research, have made farming a form of industrial enterprise in which productivity has registered tremendous gains. In America, it may be said that the machine "mothers" the crop from seed to the mechanical refrigerator.

Important other uses of steel sheets are in the electrical, drug and chemical manufacturing industries, aircraft, passenger trains, ships, petroleum refining, surgical and medical equipment, furniture, office desks and other business equipment, such as filing cabinets and business machines, restaurant equipment, sporting and camping goods, toys, and finally, in machinery of every description. Given a protective coating of zinc, "galvanized," steel sheets are made into roofing and gutters, highway culverts, garbage pails, and ordinary water pails. Four to six million tons of sheets a year are converted into tin plate for the preservation of food and for other uses such as containers for paint, petroleum products, tobacco, and beer, as well as for bottle caps, baker's hardware, and dairy equipment.

It was the automobile that led the way into the new America which came into being in the present century. The motor vehicle evoked one of the steel industry's most important technological changes, which has been the subject of this chapter. Because of the universality of sheet steel, it has had more to do than any other steel product—than any other manufacturing material—in creating the new America. Sheet steel was the magic carpet on which America rode to new adventures in living.

14

Alloy Steels—I
Historical Development, 1819–1961

Wootz steel, with which we became acquainted in Chapter 3, is of interest to us here because it set off the first systematic, scientific investigation of alloy steels in the early part of the last century. The Indian steel was still being used by some English steelmakers who found it superior to any other for cutting edges, and they were intrigued by the imported steel because they could not account for its unusual properties. One English steelmaster, Josiah Heath, went to India and brought back twenty tons of wootz ore in order to experiment with it. The "steel-iron" and steel which he made from the ore were so well received by the cutlery trade in Sheffield that he erected furnaces in India where a considerable quantity of excellent quality pig iron was smelted and shipped to England for conversion into steel-iron.

The series of events which were to bring about the first scientific inquiry into alloy steels began with Helenus Scott, who, while practicing medicine in India, sent some specimens of wootz steel to Sir Joseph Banks, president of the Royal Society in London. Sir Joseph asked Dr. George Pearson, a Fellow of the Royal Society, to investigate the samples. In 1795, Pearson began his work in association with James Stodart, a well-known manufacturer of surgical instruments and cutlery. Stodart forged a penknife from a wootz sample and in the process became convinced that the steel was better for many purposes than any then used in England. He was so won over to the merits of the imported metal that he used it in his business, and by 1820 his trade card annouced that his products were made from "(wootz) a steel from India, preferred by Mr. S. to the best steel in Europe after years of comparative trial."[1]

152

FARADAY PIONEERS IN ALLOY STEELS

The investigation of Pearson and Stodart intensified the interest in wootz steel. Stodart wanted to learn its secrets and showed one of Sir Joseph's original wootz specimens to Michael Faraday. The great scientist brought to bear the full power of his genius on a study of alloy steels and the results of his researches entitle him, says Hadfield, to be "termed the Pioneer of Alloy Steels."[2] Faraday and Stodart worked together, the former leaning heavily on the latter for practical advice and for forging and finishing trial knives, razors, and other cutting instruments from alloy steel specimens. Faraday began his researches in 1819 and terminated them in 1824.

He analyzed the wootz steel sample given to him by Stodart and found that it contained aluminum and silicon. He concluded that it was an aluminum alloy and succeeded with the help of Stodart in producing artificial wootz steel. Faraday and Stodart next attempted to reproduce meteoric iron. By fusing horseshoe nails with 3 to 10 per cent pure nickel they succeeded in producing a metal closely akin to meteoric iron. These two experiments were apparently what stirred the scientist in Faraday to undertake a study of the whole field of alloy steels in which his twofold objective, he said, was to discover alloy steels that would improve cutting edges and be resistant to oxidation.

Faraday at first devoted attention to alloys of the noble metals, gold, and silver, and to rare metals such as platinum, rhodium, iridium, osmium, and palladium, but he also experimented with titanium, chromium, and nickel. In the later stages of his experiments, Faraday sent samples of his steels to Sheffield where they were manufactured on a small scale into cutlery, razors, and a few other objects. These were the first commercial products made of deliberately prepared alloy steels.

The true significance of his researches was his systematic investigation of twenty different alloying elements which pointed the way, after Bessemer and open-hearth steel replaced iron, to the development of steels alloyed singly with manganese, nickel, chromium, and tungsten and to multiple alloy steels, such as nickel-chromium corrosion- and heat-resistant steels, high-speed tool steels, and still later to steels alloyed with no less than nine elements.

One of the first fruits of Faraday's labors was born in France. M. P. Berthier read one of Faraday's papers and was attracted by the corrosion-resistant properties of iron-chromium alloys. By reducing chromium directly from its ore, he won a historic position by being the first to produce ferrochromium and to use this material in making chromium steel. A group of distinguished metallurgists at the Terre Noire Company in France "set out boldly along the road trodden so laboriously by Faraday"[3]

and made significant advances in the knowledge of alloy steels. One of
their number, M. Pourcel, developed ferromanganese, which was to
become so important, first in the manufacture of Bessemer steel, and later
in all modern steelmaking practices.

In the first quarter of the nineteenth century, the Industrial Revolution
was gaining momentum. To maintain and perpetuate itself, one of the
first requisites was the invention of steam-powered metal-cutting tools.
The human hand was unable to hold a cutting tool with sufficient pressure
against a revolving piece of iron or steel more that a few minutes at a
time. Yet thousands of machine parts were essential for steam engines and
the mechanisms they propelled. The man who rose to the occasion above
all his contemporaries was an Englishman, Henry Maudslay. James
Nasmyth, inventor of the steam hammer and a disciple of Maudslay,
wrote of his master in 1841:

> Up to within the past thirty years, nearly every part of a machine had to be
> made and finished to its required form by mere manual labor. . . . Then a sud-
> den demand of machinery of unwonted accuracy arose . . . and but for the
> introduction of the principle which I am about to describe, we could never have
> attained to one-thousandth part of the bright object . . . which has since been
> so wonderfully realized.
> The principle to which I allude consists of a substitution of a mechanical con-
> trivance in place of the human hand for holding, applying, and directing the
> motions of a cutting tool. . . .[4]

Machine tools required a particularly hard steel with a sharp cutting
edge that would not dull too quickly. Robert Mushet, who first developed
alloy tool steel on a large commercial scale, stands second only to Faraday
in the early history of alloy steels. He did important work in alloying steel
with titanium, chromium, and tungsten. He is generally credited with the
invention of tungsten tool steel which he patented in 1868, but his work
was anticipated thirteen years earlier by an Austrian chemist, Franz
Köller, who invented tungsten steel in 1855. Köller's invention became
widely known in Europe, and it is considered likely that Mushet "obtained
some knowledge of it." Be that as it may, Mushet's air-hardening steel,
containing about 7 per cent tungsten, made possible a 50 per cent faster
cutting speed than could be done with ordinary high carbon steel. The
term air-hardening is applied to steel which does not require quenching
in water or any other liquid to make it hard, but hardens when cooled in
the air. Mushet's tungsten steel within a few years was being used in
almost all the "engineering workshops of the world" and was a forerunner
of modern high-speed tool steels.[5]

Following the success of Mushet's tungsten steel, the machine tool
industry went forward with a great burst of activity. New metal-cutting
devices, driven at a faster rate, depended for their effectiveness on improved steel in their cutting edges. For a period, machine tools shared

with armor plate the center of the stage in metallurgical research, and by 1890 steels with 18 per cent tungsten and 4 per cent chromium had been developed, a proportion identical with that used in most high-speed tools today. Then, in 1895, a long forward leap was taken by Frederick Taylor and Maunsel White of the Bethlehem Iron Company (predecessor of Bethlehem Steel Company) who invented a high temperature method for heat-treating high-speed tool steels by heating them almost to the melting point and then cooling them fairly rapidly. Up to that time, a cutting speed of 30 feet a minute was considered a good rate for carbon tool steels, but the new steels of Taylor and White could cut for hours at 150 feet a minute and continue to cut for some time even after the speed was so much increased that the tip of the tool became red-hot. The Taylor-White process for heat-treating high-speed tool steels revolutionized the machine tool industry and exerted a profound influence on modern industrial development throughout the world.

PROGRESS IN ALLOY STEELS

Hadfield's Manganese Steel

Robert A. Hadfield is the third ranking name, after Faraday and Mushet, in the history of alloy steels. In 1882, when a youth of twenty-two assisting his father in the management of the family steelworks in Sheffield, England, he began experiments with the object of producing a very hard steel for tramway wheels and also as a substitute for emery in grinding wheels. In the course of numerous investigations with manganese-alloyed steel, he made the discovery that whereas 1 per cent to 1.5 per cent manganese made a good grade of ordinary steel and 3 per cent to 7 per cent made the steel too brittle to be of any use, a proportion of 10 to 15 per cent gave an entirely new kind of steel. It was the first malleable, non-magnetic ferrous product discovered and it made available a combination of mechanical properties possessed by no other material. Hadfield manganese steel does not have a particularly hard surface in a raw state, but possesses the peculiar property of acquiring hardness under repeated impact. For this reason, manganese steel has won a unique place for itself. Power shovels, bulldozers, dipper dredges, ore-crushers, and similar earth-moving and mining equipment, which must withstand severe knocks and abrasive action, have their jaws, lips, and teeth made of manganese steel. Castings of manganese steel, for identical reasons, are universally used for railroad crossings, switches, and frogs.

The Taylor Iron Works of High Bridge, New Jersey, obtained a license from Hadfield in 1890 to manufacture manganese steel in the United States. The Taylor company was then producing iron products for railroads and after planning to produce Hadfield steel for car wheels, was reorganized in 1892 as the Taylor Iron and Steel Company. The first heat of Hadfield manganese steel was poured in the United States in the same year.

Silicon Steel

Another accomplishment of Hadfield was the invention of silicon steel, which became of great importance to the electrical industry. Hadfield undertook his researches in silicon steel in his continued search for a hard material to substitute for emery grinding wheels. Experiments were begun in 1883, and within a year he invented and patented a low carbon steel containing from about 1.5 to 5 per cent silicon. In 1886, he patented a silicon steel with a higher carbon content.

Hadfield appears to have been unaware at the time of the electrical properties of silicon steel and first marketed his product as a tool steel to Sheffield firms. His silicon steel was capable of assuming unusual hardness through quenching in oil or water, and by virtue of this property was well received by tool makers.

Dr. John Hopkinson is credited by Hadfield as the first person to study the electrical and magnetic properties of iron alloyed with high percentages of silicon. Hopkinson, who reported his findings in 1885, confined his researches to silicon steels high in carbon, which were proven by Sir William Barrett to be far inferior for electrical purposes to the low carbon silicon steel invented by Hadfield.

These and other investigations were prompted by a desire to improve the material then being used in the cores of transformers and generators of the burgeoning electrical industry. The cores were first made of solid iron, which dissipated large amounts of electrical current through "hysteresis loss and eddy currents," resulting in low efficiency of operation. In consequence, the cost of electricity was high. Later, it was found that laminated cores, built up by stacking thin sheets of iron that were insulated from one another, considerably reduced the energy loss. Then investigators discovered that the excellent magnetic properties and high electrical resistance of steel sheets containing up to 5 per cent silicon reduced the energy losses in laminated cores to a far greater degree than unalloyed iron sheets.

It would be difficult to exaggerate the importance of silicon steel electrical sheets to the growth of the electrical power industry throughout the world, and particularly in the United States after Thomas Edison's first central power station at Pearl Street, New York City, threw its starting switch in 1882. It has been estimated that if electrical energy consumed for illumination alone by Americans in 1939, had been furnished by the power plants of 1900, the additional cost would have exceeded $15 billion.[6] A good part of this saving is attributable to research which has improved the performance of electrical sheets at least 70 per cent since they came into general use.

Another name which deserves a place among the pioneers in alloy steels is Leon Guillet of France. His writings, published in the first decade of the present century, describe alloys of iron with chromium, nickel, silicon, manganese, tungsten, titanium, cobalt, vanadium, tin, aluminum, and other elements, singly and in combinations. Among his many great accomplishments was his study of compositions on which modern stainless steels are based, as shall be pointed out presently.[7]

Chromium and Nickel Steels

Although Faraday, Mushet, and others had investigated chromium steel, it was an American, Julius Baur, who first produced it on a commercial scale. He patented it in 1865—the first patent for an alloy steel in America—and in 1869 opened his Chrome Steel Works in Brooklyn, New York. He produced the steel in a crucible furnace and sold his product to manufacturers of mining tools, grinding equipment, and burglar-proof vaults and cells.

M. Boussingault in France followed up Baur's work with some success and another notable Frenchman, A. Brustlein, put chromium steel out in front of all others by initiating its use for armaments between 1877 and 1886, thereby opening a new phase of military tactics through metallurgy. The arms race became intensified, and steel for ship armor and projectiles absorbed, for a period, a major share of metallurgical research.

Nickel steel, which had been produced commercially by Johann Conrad Fischer in 1824-1825 at his steel works in Schaffhausen, Switzerland, and again by Marbeau in France in 1885, excited the interest of armament makers, particularly in England. Steels alloyed singly with chromium and with nickel were used for guns, armor, and projectiles in Europe during this period, with nickel steel favored in guns of heavy caliber. The United States Navy sent a representative to Europe to investigate nickel steel armor, which was found to be so superior to unalloyed plates that it was adopted in 1891 as standard equipment.

These trials with chromium and nickel in steel brought to metallurgists the realization that a combination of both elements produced a metal superior in many respects to a steel alloyed with only one. The result was the development of nickel-chromium steels in the last decade of the nineteenth century, a period in which the alloy steel industry was passing through its adolescence. It was brought to maturity in the Spanish-American War of 1898 when alloy steel greatly aided Admiral Dewey's victory in Manila Bay. America's first 16-inch guns, of nickel steel, fired chromium-nickel steel projectiles with devastating effect.

In the closing decades of the nineteenth century and the opening years of the twentieth, alloy steels were entering into non-military uses at an increasing rate. Krupp's in Germany forged a nickel steel crankshaft for the steamship "Deutschland" in 1899, and in 1893 the same alloy was applied in parts of the electric generators at Niagara Falls. In 1898, nickel steel entered the bicycle industry in the form of sprocket chains and still later as tubing. Power shovels with manganese steel teeth dug most of the Panama Canal in 1904-1914. The Wright Brothers' plane, the *Kitty Hawk*, which made the world's first power-driven flight in 1903, contained nickel-chromium steel, as did the *Spirit of St. Louis*, which Charles Lindbergh flew from New York to Paris twenty-four years later.

Automobile makers pioneered in the application of practically all of the early constructional alloy steels. By 1905, the automotive industry knew what it wanted in alloy steels and began to write its own specifications, and in 1911 a profusion of proprietary analyses was reduced to seven carbon and eleven alloy steels. In the ensuing years alloy steels continued to proliferate and between 1935 and 1940 some 4,000 steel specifications were reduced by the American Iron and Steel Institute and the Society of Automotive Engineers to about one hundred standard types known as A.I.S.I. and S.A.E. steels. The steels were of great benefit to the automotive industry and were found to be equally applicable to the manufacture of agricultural machinery and equipment. When the aviation industry began its spectacular growth, most of its alloy steel needs were already worked out for it in the alloy series. The same may be said of the petroleum industry.

Stainless Steel, the Glamor Metal

For a great many years men have searched for a metal as rustless as gold with the strength of iron and steel. In lieu of such a metal they have protected iron and steel with various coatings, such as tin, zinc, enamel, and paint. All these coatings have a serious drawback, because the protection is superficial and is of little, if any, value if the material is subjected to rubbing or wearing, or if a cutting edge is desired. For iron and steel to resist corrosion satisfactorily under such circumstances the protection must be embodied in the metal itself so that as the outer surface wears away the newly exposed area will be equally resistant to corrosion. Such resistance can only be attained by altering the properties of the steel by alloying it with elements which render the steel impervious to attacking agents. Steel of this kind which surpasses all others in resistance to corrosion is stainless steel.

Stainless steel has become known as the "glamor metal," because of its beautiful polished surface which gives it a decorative as well as a utilitarian value, whether in automobile trim, a coffee maker, or the façade of a building. The superior corrosion resistance of stainless steel is due to the presence of chromium which on contact with oxygen in the air forms a transparent microscopic film on the steel's surface. This film acts as a protective barrier against the attack of corrosive agents. Nickel is used in combination with chromium in some grades of stainless steel, but chromium excells all other elements in conferring corrosion resistance to steel.

WHO DISCOVERED STAINLESS STEEL?

Harry Brearley of England and Benno Strauss and Edward Maurer of Germany, have long been regarded as the men who discovered stainless steel some time between 1912 and 1915.[8] The Iron and Steel Institute of England awarded the Bessemer Gold Medal to Brearley in 1920 in recognition of his great "discovery,"[9] and he himself wrote, "When I am asked if I discovered stainless steel I say, 'Yes.'"[10] Carl A. Zapffe, writing in the October 14, 1948, issue of *Iron Age*, says that published records prove that the exact steels promoted by Messrs. Brearley, Strauss and Maurer, as well as numerous other grades of stainless steel which have since become standard, were produced, tested and described in detail by Leon Guillet and A. M. Portevin of France, and by P. Monnartz in Germany and W. Giesen in England in the years between 1903 and 1910. Zapffe acknowledges that Brearley and Maurer discovered the industrial usefulness of these steels and "certainly unfolded their vast commercial aspects," but claims that they did not discover the "primary metallurgical attributes" of stainless steels.

Investigators of chromium and chromium-nickel steels in the last century unwittingly made a number of near misses in the discovery of stainless steel, according to Zapffe. In the first half of the century experiments were confined to steels either too low or too high in chromium and failed to include the intermediate ranges where the stainless steels are found. Futhermore, these steels were too high in carbon. As early as 1821, M. P. Berthier found that chromium increased the hardness and corrosion resistance of steel and recommended such steel for cutlery. In 1872, Woods and Clark applied for a British patent on an acid and weather resisting alloy containing 30 to 35 per cent chromium and 1.5 to 2.0 per cent carbon. Zapffe has found no record that the patent was ever issued or put into practice but he considers the claim important in view of those made forty years later concerning the discovery of stainless steel.

In 1886, Boussingault made a special point of the corrosion resistance imparted to steel by chromium and, at last, in 1898, Carnot and Goutal reported that the resistance of iron-chromium alloys to corrosion was being obscured by their consistently high carbon content. In reading these records, says Zapffe, "one cannot resist expressing some surprise that 'stainless steel' was not discovered before the turn of the century."

Leon Guillet, mentioned earlier as one of the great pioneers in alloy steels, stands at the head of the list of the true discoverers of stainless steel, in the opinion of Zapffe. Guillet was the first to explore chromium steels with a low carbon content. He began his work no later than 1902 and between 1904 and 1906 published detailed studies of iron-chromium alloys in the stainless range. His steel with 14.5 per cent chromium and 0.38 per cent carbon is identical to that patented by Brearley more than ten years later. It should be noted that Guillet made no point of the corrosion resistance of his chromium steels. His primary interest was to establish their metallurgical and mechanical features.

In 1909, A. M. Portevin of France published a study of Guillet's chromium alloys, including at least seven not listed by Guillet, but which fall within the modern classification of stainless steels. Portevin also confined his studies to the mechanical and electrical properties of his steels and made no issue of corrosion resistance.

In the same year that Portevin published his findings, W. Giesen in England was the author of a "monumental article," says Zapffe, in which he discussed steels with 8 to 18 per cent chromium and 0.3 per cent carbon, which were "exactly Brearley's analyses."

A fourth great pioneer in the discovery of stainless steel was P. Monnartz of France. In 1908, he began his work with low carbon steels, giving particular attention to their corrosion resistance and the relationships of the chromium and carbon contents. In 1910, he patented a stainless composition and in 1911 published a paper which proves, says Zapffe, "his priority in discovering the stainlessness of stainless steel," along with other phenomena "discovered" by others decades later.

Zapffe lists the discoverers of stainless steel in what he considers to be their proper order. Top honors go to L. Guillet, A. M. Portevin and W. Geisen for having discovered the "compositions and primary metallurgical characteristics of the stainless steels." In fourth place is P. Monnartz for his discovery of the "stainlessness" of stainless steel. H. Brearley, who formerly headed the list, is in fifth position, but still recognized as the first person to discover the "commercial utility" of stainless steel, followed by E. Maurer. Zapffe accords prominent roles in the early development of stainless steels to Benno Strauss, E. Haynes, F. M. Becket, C. Dantsizen, P. A. E. Armstrong, E. C. Bain, and C. M. Johnson.

DEVELOPMENT AND USES OF STAINLESS STEEL

Commercially, stainless steel was born and reared in the cutlery trade of Sheffield. The ability of the steel to withstand oxidation at high temperature was recognized at an early date, resulting in its application in steam turbine blades in 1914. The first large commercial order for stainless steel in the United States was placed in 1924 by E. I. du Pont de Nemours for tanking and piping nitric acid. The successful commercial production of these steels made possible the economical development of chemical processes that had depended earlier on other more expensive materials. Eventually, the use of stainless steel spread throughout the chemical and drug industries and to other industrial operations, where severe corrosive conditions exist—petroleum refining, manufacture of pulp and paper, textiles, dyes, varnish, lacquers, and rayon. Stainless steel drums are used for shipment of acids, foods, and products of the beverage industry. Bulk shipments of acids and many food products are made in stainless tank cars. In 1929, stainless steel trim first appeared on automobiles. The beautiful finish and non-tarnishing properties of the steel took hold with the public and today the automobile industry is the largest purchaser of stainless steel.

Stainless steel is not only corrosion-resistant, it is also remarkably strong. In the early 1930s, Edward G. Budd, whom we met in the last chapter as the originator of the all-steel automobile body, became interested in the structural possibilities and weight-saving economy of stainless steel. He sought to beautify railroad cars and to introduce a new design in which all the stainless steel members would serve a structural purpose, even in the roof. The greater strength of stainless steel over plain carbon steel permitted the use of smaller stainless steel members with considerable saving in weight. The longer life service expected from stainless steel also represented investment savings. The result was the appearance in 1934 of the first streamlined train in the United States—beautiful in appearance, with more luxurious fittings, lighter in weight and hence capable of greater speeds. Since then, a large number of streamlined cars have been built of stainless steel and many of them have given economical service for more than twenty-five years. The trucking industry was quick to appreciate these advantages of stainless steel in transportation—greater payloads and longer life service—and thousands of trailer trucks designed in stainless steel are rendering economical service through lighter weight and longer wear.

A smooth, polished surface can be imparted to stainless steel that contains no tiny pits in which contaminating matter may reside and it can therefore be easily cleaned and rendered aseptic. This characteristic, combined with its "stainlessness" and its strength and resistance to oxidation at high temperature, make stainless steel the premier metal for hygienic and sanitary purposes. The last two properties are essential in a metal for sterilizers in hospitals, doctors' and dentists' offices, which are subjected repeatedly to heat and the oxidizing influence of steam. It is also essential that the implements being sterilized be made of a metal that retains its strength under frequent heating at high temperature. There can be no risk of a surgeon's scalpel, a doctor's probe, or a nurse's hypodermic needle losing its strength or becoming deformed by the heat in a sterilizer. In a hospital operating room, gleaming stainless steel is everywhere—the operating table, basins, sinks, cabinets, and implements. Elsewhere in the hospital we encounter stainless steel in autoclaves, refrigerators for storing serums and blood, oxygen therapy equipment, incubators for premature infants, elevators, and furniture. It is of special importance in maternity and contagious wards.

For identical reasons, stainless steel has no peer as a metal for food handling and processing equipment, which must be kept scrupulously clean so that food passing through at any given moment is not subject to contamination. The polished surface of stainless steel equipment can be easily flushed and cleaned of any adhering matter. No other ferrous metal is as resistant to fruit, vegetable and organic acids. For processed foods to retain their original flavor and color, the equipment must be made of a metal which is neither affected by the foods nor affects them in turn. Such a metal is stainless steel. In many food-processing plants, from the time the raw products are received until they are canned and ready for shipment, they encounter only stainless steel equipment—sorting tables, transfer boxes, cooking vats, canning sinks, conveyor belts and so on. The dairy industry was an early user of stainless steel. The laws of many states require that milk and milk products be processed in stainless steel equipment. The purity and taste of milk are protected in the same way by the use of stainless steel in milking machines, tanks, piping systems, pasteurizers, bottling and packaging equipment. Stainless steel also stands as a loyal sentinels for our health by serving many sanitary purposes in restaurant kitchens, ship galleys, lunch rooms, and drugstore counters.

Stainless steel is widely used in the brewing industry. Because the metal does not affect the taste or purity of brewer's products, tanks, piping, and bottling equipment are constructed of stainless steel. Stainless steel tanks are also used in wineries and distilleries.

Stainless steel has made possible rapid advances in harnessing nuclear power. Power generating equipment and maritime propulsion systems also make use of stainless steel.

In the textile industry, stainless steel has permitted rapid changes from color to color in dyeing operations. Formerly, other materials required costly maintenance and a long shut-down of operations in which to make the changes.

Stainless steel, in addition to its remarkable resistance to corrosion, also possesses superior resitance to oxidation at relatively high temperatures. For this reason, stainless steel is unexcelled for aircraft exhaust systems and combustion chambers, and in space-heating equipment. The same properties make stainless steel suitable for certain applications in rockets and missiles.

Stainless steel is also effectively used in extremely low temperatures, and finds many applications where temperatures as low as —425° F. are encountered. Processing equipment and storage vessels for handling liquid gases in this temperature range are made of stainless steel.

Stainless steel first entered the home in the form of cutlery and it is still prized in knives, carving sets, and table ware. Next to automotive trim, the second largest use of cold-rolled stainless steel strip is for the manufacture of cutlery and household products such as coffee makers, electric grills, cooking utensils, sinks, dishwashers, drainboards, refrigerator shelves, stoves, washing machines, and other appliances.

The beautiful appearance of stainless steel, and its non-tarnishing property which permits economy of maintenance, have won a favored place for the metal as an architectural material, both as curtain wall construction on the exterior of buildings and as interior decorative panels, many of which are cast in beautiful designs.

HIGH-STRENGTH LOW-ALLOY STEELS

Prior to 1900, mild carbon steel with an ultimate tensile strength of 60,000 pounds per square inch was generally used in buildings and bridges. A chromium steel, for greater strength, had been specified for the arch of the Eads Bridge, the first span in America utilizing steel in part of its structure, erected over the Mississippi River in 1874. In 1902, designers of the Queensboro Bridge in New York City requested a stronger steel in order that fewer and smaller structural members could conform to the limitations in space and weight of the bridge design. The Carnegie Steel Company supplied a nickel steel for this purpose. The results were so satisfactory that the same steel was specified for the stiffening trusses of the Manhattan Bridge built over the East River in 1906. This steel, however, was too expensive for ordinary structures where a decrease in weight or size of members was not a necessity.

Engineers and metallurgists continued their search for ways to obtain less weight in structures by specifying steels of greater strength. In Great Britain, economies were attempted in ocean freight and handling charges by reducing the dead weight of structures built of stronger steels generously alloyed with silicon and manganese. In 1933, the Germans completed construction of *The Flying Dutchman*, the first light-weight streamlined train built of high-strength low-alloy steel. It contained silicon, manganese and copper. One of the main preoccupations of engineers was to develop a money-saving, high-strength structural steel. Around 1930, they began to realize that the new steel must have enhanced resistance to corrosion if the thickness of a structural member was to be reduced without sacrifice of serviceability. Accordingly, elements were added to the steels for the express purpose of improving their resistance to atmospheric corrosion.

The men who were engaged in the development of high-strength steels had their eyes primarily on the transportation industry, particularly the railroads. Thinner sections of steel with increased strength could eliminate the hauling of excess dead weight. The search for these physical desiderata in steel resulted in the development of "high-strength low-alloy steels." For the sake of brevity, they are hereafter referred to as high-strength steels. The earliest of contemporary high-strength steels was introduced by United States Steel Corporation in 1934 under the brand name of COR-TEN. It proved to have a corrosion resistance four to six times that of plain carbon steel and two to three times that of carbon steel containing copper.

The application of COR-TEN steel made it feasible to reduce the weight of freight cars as much as 10,000 pounds without any sacrifice in strength. COR-TEN steel has likewise been applied to passenger coaches, especially to streamlined trains, with savings in weight up to 30 per cent. By judicious use of this steel, manufacturers have been able to trim as much as 40,000 pounds from the dead weight of a passenger car without sacrificing safety or strength. This permits the more extensive use of luxury accessories.

Following the lead of United States Steel Corporation, other steel producers in this country and abroad developed their own compositions of high-strength steels. The new steels were adopted extensively by railroads and car builders in the United States and Canada for the construction of many types of freight cars. Railroads in Mexico, Central and South America, Europe, Africa, and Australia ordered freight cars built of high-strength steels. The automotive industry uses appreciable quantities of high-strength steels in passenger car bumpers, truck bodies, and frames, gasoline tank trucks, garbage trucks and trailers. They are also widely applied in heavy earth-moving equipment such as bulldozers, power shovels, ditchers, scrapers, and graders, all of which are subjected to rough usage. The steels are also of value in mine cars and mine equipment. Bridge designers are giving increasing recognition to the weight-saving advantages of high-strength steels, especially in long spans where a reduction in dead load at the center permits further saving of weight in the supporting members. High-strength steels lend themselves to economical tower construction where small sections lessen wind resistance, a factor of importance in television towers.

ALLOY STEELS IN TWO WORLD WARS

World War I came at a time when many varieties of alloy steel were in laboratory and experimental stages. There were no startling new developments in alloy steels. Perhaps the most important was a new composition worked out in the laboratory of the Ford Motor Company: a chromium-nickel-vanadium steel alloyed with fractional percentages of molybdenum, which opened up a new era in molybdenum steels. The new steel rendered outstanding service in Liberty motors and baby tanks. The Union Carbide and Carbon Corporation introduced a new element to the alloy steel industry in this period—zirconium. Nickel-chromium-zirconium steels were tried out in plates for light tanks. If the war did not signalize any revolutionary metallurgical developments, it did affect the commercial status of alloy steels by bringing into production many varieties whose compositions were known but had been manufactured previously only in moderate amounts. By the end of the war, the steel industry was in a position to produce a wide variety of alloy steels in quality and quantity unavailable on the market before the conflict. As a result, World War I left a rich legacy of established alloy steels to the automobile industry which standardized them as S.A.E. steels, previously mentioned.

The demands put upon steel in World War I were as nothing compared with those of World War II. In the Age of Steel, warfare had caught up with the machine. Infantry, artillery, and supplies rolled to battle on motor-driven wheels. The war, moreover, became global. The steel in mechanized equipment had to stand up and perform in climatic conditions that varied from the dripping humidity of the tropics to sub-zero arctic weather. Armor had to be tougher for defense and more powerful armor-piercing shells were needed to penetrate the enemy's own tougher armor. *In World War II, nearly every major and minor part of military equipment required alloy steel.* It was not merely a War of Steel; it was more particularly a War of Alloy Steel.[11]

The demands upon the steel industry of the United States for alloy steel were enormous. While total steel production in 1944, the peak year of the war, was 70 per cent over 1939, total alloy steel output was 309 per cent over 1939. Before that scale of alloy-steel production was attained, a critical situation confronted the steel industry. In normal times, the United States depends on foreign sources for all of the chief alloying elements except molybdenum and vanadium. Stockpiles of alloying metals were dwindling with alarming rapidity under the pressure of war needs. Germany overran regions of Russia from which the United States had obtained 25 per cent of its manganese imports. Japanese conquests in 1941 and 1942 cut off the source of 88 per cent of tungsten imports, the chief metal used in the manufacture of alloy steel for armor-piercing shells.

Stockpiles of strategic alloying metals were sufficient if consumed in conventional proportions, to make only a portion of the tonnage of alloy steels required for the American war production program. The Alloy Technical Committee of the American Iron and Steel Institute was charged by the War Production Board to find a way to stretch out America's reserves of scarce alloying elements. The committee took advantage of the knowledge gained in earlier studies of the effect of alloys on the response to heat treatment, namely, that small percentages of several alloying elements can be as effective as, and even more effective than, a high percentage of only one. By combining two, three, or even four, of the most plentiful alloys, in place of a single critical alloy such as manganese, tungsten and nickel, the committee found that steels could be produced to serve the purpose of former alloy steels. The new steels were called National Emergency Steels. By 1943, they constituted one-third of total alloy-steel production in the United States. Without this timely contribution by metallurgists, it is doubtful if the United States could have built up its tremendous fighting power for a new kind of war on a global scale.

POSTWAR YEARS

The National Emergency Steels were so successful that after the war many of them were adapted to peacetime use and altogether these steels represented from 30 to 40 per cent of total alloy steel production. The leaner alloy content of National Emergency Steels was a wartime acceleration of metallurgical practices which had begun early in the century in the use of nickel and chromium. In 1900 the average nickel content was about 3.5 per cent, the chromium 1.50 per cent; molybdenum was not yet being used. Just before World War II, the nickel content had declined to 1.90 per cent, the chromium to 1.05 per cent and molybdenum had risen to 0.18 per cent. During the war the percentages of nickel and chromium were reduced still further—to an average of 1.25 per cent and 0.90 per cent respectively, while that of molybdenum rose to 0.24 per cent.

Once the war was over, the United States was not allowed to breathe easily very long because the Iron Curtain descended over Europe and the hot war was exchanged for the cold war. In order not to be caught short again, the American government began to stockpile strategic alloying elements. Then in mid-1950, the Communists launched an offensive in Korea. The production of war material and the stockpiling of strategic elements put a squeeze on the amount of alloy steels available for civilian uses. To insure equitable distribution to steel producers, the government instituted controls over a number of strategic and critical alloys. By 1953, the National Production Authority faced the necessity of conserving still further all strategic alloying elements, particularly nickel and molybdenum. It faced an abnormal demand for nickel in military applications such as jet engines and also for the atomic energy program, and, in addition, a further drainage on nickel and molybdenum supplies to replace even more critical elements such as cobalt, tungsten and columbium, indispensable for the applications just mentioned.

Once again the Alloy Technical Committee of the American Iron and Steel Institute was called on for assistance. The committee, in collaboration with the Society of Automotive Engineers, succeeded in pushing down the average nickel content to 0.90 per cent, the chromium to 0.85 per cent and the molybdenum to 0.18 per cent. As a result of these joint labors, 80 new alloy steels were devised. In some cases, the drastic reduction in critical elements was effected by the addition of boron. Boron is used in steel for one purpose only—to increase the depth to which steel will harden when quenched.

The progressive mechanization of life in industrial society, the manufacture of worldwide commercial fleets of supersonic aircraft, the outfitting of vehicles for space travel, and military missiles—all can be expected to put extraordinary demands upon alloy steels and cause their production to increase at a faster rate than carbon steels. After several thousand years in the Iron Age, man passed into the Steel Age about a century ago. It was largely a "carbon steel" civilization. For the past half century we have been moving, at a pace greatly accelerated since World War II, into an "alloy steel" civilization, not so much from a quantitative as from a qualitative standpoint.

With the expected increase in alloy steel as well as carbon steel production, there will be a vastly increased consumption of alloying elements. At this point, it may be fitting to take up the alloying elements, consider what each one adds to the properties of steel, and give some information on the reserves, production, consumption, and other salient features of these materials so indispensable to the future of steel throughout the world.

Alloy Steels—II
Alloying Elements

CHARACTERISTICS, DEPOSITS, PRODUCTION, CONSUMPTION

Almost 90 per cent of all steels produced in the United States are plain carbon steels. They are so called because they contain only those elements which are carried over from the original charge of pig iron and steel scrap during their refinement into steel, or are deliberately added, like manganese, as a part of normal steelmaking procedure. Carbon, even in small amounts has a profound effect upon iron. Up to a point, the greater the amount of carbon iron contains, the stronger and harder it will be. Iron containing 0.02 per cent carbon, as in wrought iron, is tough but lacks the hardness and strength required for most industrial uses. When the carbon content goes up 2.5 to 3.5 per cent, as in iron castings, the iron is hard but excessively brittle. The majority of plain carbon steels (excluding lower carbon steels for sheets, etc.) falls within the range of 0.08 to 1.7 per cent carbon content. Generally the carbon is well under 1.00 per cent. All carbon steels also contain manganese, phosphorus, and sulphur, and frequently silicon and aluminum. The manganese, which enters carbon steel through the molten iron and steel scrap in the charge and through the addition of ferromanganese as a deoxidizer, ranges from 0.25 to 1.65 per cent. Phosphorus and sulphur, the former carried over mostly from the ore and the latter mostly from the coke, can be all but eliminated in basic steelmaking processes, being reduced generally to less than 0.040 per cent and 0.050 per cent, respectively.

Within these chemical limitations, carbon steels can be made possessing a wide range of properties, which can be modified by various forms of heat treatment and other processing methods. But there is a limit to what carbon can do for a steel. Many service requirements arose in the evolution of modern industrial society for which carbon steel reached the limits of its performance. By the admixture of one or more alloying elements with carbon steel, its well-known properties of strength and hardness can be realized in larger sections than in carbon steel, and new properties can be imparted, such as toughness and resistance to corrosion and high temperatures, virtually transforming it into a new metal.

ALLOYING ELEMENTS AND THE FREE WORLD

The principal alloying elements are chromium, manganese, molybdenum, nickel, silicon, tungsten, and vanadium. Aluminum, boron, cobalt, columbium, copper, selenium, titanium, and zirconium are also used in some alloy steels.

The seven elements in the first group are by far the most important used by the steel industry. Each element makes its own unique contribution toward improving one or more of the characteristics of steel: machinability, magnetic properties, ductility at high strength, hardenability, and resistance to corrosion and heat. Of the seven major alloying elements, the United States is self-sufficient only in molybdenum and vanadium, of which it is the world's largest producer. Nickel may be had from neighboring Canada, world's leading exporter of the metal, but the other four elements must be waterborne. In times of peace, adequate imports of alloying elements flow freely into the United States, but if the water lanes were severed for a considerable period the nation would be seriously handicapped in its struggle for survival.

The report of the President's Policy Commission, *Resources for Freedom,* popularly known as the Paley Report, after William S. Paley, commission chairman, informed the American people that in the decade of World War II the United States changed from a net exporter to a net importer of materials and that it would become increasingly dependent on imports.[1] Published in 1952, the report estimated the resource needs of the United States in 1975, based on consumption figures of 1950. Foreseeing an increase of 55 per cent in steel requirements in 1975, the report predicted a still higher rate of increase in the demand for strategic alloys, due to a greater proportionate rise in demand for alloy steels than for carbon steels during the twenty-five year period. On this basis, the peacetime demand for nickel and chromium may be multiplied about two times, that for tungsten and molybdenum more than two and a half times, and that for cobalt four times. The greater relative consumption of cobalt will be due to its use in rockets, guided missiles, and atomic energy developments. The same rates of increase are expected to prevail in other free nations. No estimate was made for columbium, whose future was viewed as "too uncertain." Domestic supplies of molybdenum and vanadium were considered to be sufficient for domestic needs until 1975.

The reserves of all these metals, except possibly tungsten and columbium, are adequate for the peacetime needs of the Free World, the report said, but in case of war, "supplies of many of these metals are likely to be short of wartime needs." The report strongly urged that steps be taken "to assure emergency supplies" through stockpiling strategic materials, exploration and development of new deposits.

In 1951, the Secretary of the Interior announced that the Defense Production Administration had allocated $10 million for stimulating exploration for strategic and critical metals and minerals needed by the defense program. The program was supervised by the Defense Minerals Exploration Administration. Under the DMEA plan, the government advanced up to 50 per cent of the exploration cost of an approved project, with repayment to the government from income on future production. The DMEA on June 30, 1958, was succeeded by the Office of Minerals Exploration which continued to grant assistance for mineral exploration under much the same terms as those of the DMEA.

Aluminum

Symbol	Atomic Number	Atomic Weight	Melt.Pt. (°F)
Al	13	26.98	1220.4 ± 0.2

Aluminum is used in steelmaking furnaces as an alloying element and as a deoxidizer and degasifier. It is added in the form of secondary aluminum, 85 per cent pure or better, derived from scrap. A fair amount of aluminum is also used by the steel industry as a coating for wire, strip and sheet. In such cases, virgin aluminum of relatively high purity is applied.

In 1960, the steel industry of the United States consumed 3,032 tons of aluminum for alloying in steel, 41,976 tons for deoxidizing and degasifying purposes, 2,645 tons for coating purposes, and 790 tons for all other purposes. Aluminum consumed by the domestic steel industry represents but a fraction of total production. The United States is the world's leading aluminum producer, followed by Russia, Canada, West Germany, and Norway.

Chromium

Symbol	Atomic Number	Atomic Weight	Melt. Pt. (°F)
Cr	24	25.01	3430 ± 20

Chromium is one of the most important alloying elements. It surpasses all others in conferring corrosion resistance to steel. It also fortifies the strength of steel at high temperatures and is present in all heat-resisting steels. Generally speaking, small amounts of chromium (about 1.0 to 3.5 per cent) improve the hardening and wearing properties imparted to steel by heat treatment. In smaller amounts (up to 1 per cent) it is used in combination with other elements to improve corrosion resistance and impart greater strength for structural purposes. Larger amounts of chromium (above 5 per cent) impart corrosion and heat resistance. Chromium is an important element in high-speed tool steels, in armor plate, and other military equipment and in a long list of steels for components of machinery. Chromium is added to steel in the form of ferrochromium containing 65 to 72 per cent chromium. Its most common ore is chromite.

CONSUMPTION

The consumption of chromium has been expanding throughout the world for a good many years. Perhaps nowhere has the rise been as spectacular as in the United States where annual chromite consumption increased from 175,000 tons in 1940 to a record of 1.847 million tons in 1956. Consumption in 1960 was 1.22 million tons.

The striking rise in chromite consumption in the United States since 1940 is due to a greater use of chromium for metallurgical purposes than for its other two chief purposes—refractories and chemicals. In the 1947-1951 period, the consumption of chromite for metallurgical purposes averaged 46 per cent of total consumption, refractory uses averaged 37 per cent and chemicals 17 per cent. In 1960, the proportions were 55 per cent, 32 per cent, and 13 per cent, respectively.

Of the 252,112 tons of chromium ferroalloys (containing 150,709 tons of chromium) consumed in the United States in 1960, stainless steels took the lion's share, with 101,272 tons; high-speed steels and other tool and alloy steels absorbed 40,298 tons, and 2,787 tons went into making gray and malleable iron castings. High-temperature, nickel-base and other alloys, presumably super-alloys, accounted for 6,352 tons.

PRODUCTION AND IMPORTS

The United States Government included chromite in its Defense Minerals Exploration program. The gain in domestic production from 21,000 tons in 1952 to a record of 207,600 tons in 1956 was made possible by the government purchase of domestic ores at prices considerably above those of imported ores. The 1956 output was 11 per cent of total consumption in the United States. Production in 1960 of 107,000 tons represented 9 per cent of domestic consumption.

In 1959 the General Services Administration offered for sale approximately 1,600 long tons of chromite ore, declared in excess of defense requirements, but no acceptable bids were received. In 1960, the GSA announced plans to dispose of an additional 89,750 long tons of domestic chromite ore and 151,000 long tons of chromium ferro alloys that were declared in excess of stockpile needs.

The chief suppliers of chromite to the United States in 1960 were the Union of South Africa, the Federation of Rhodesia and Nyasaland, the Philippines, and Turkey, in the order named. Smaller supplies came from a number of other nations.

According to a 1956 report of the Bureau of Mines, the United States has 60,000 tons of contained Cr_2O_3 "currently acceptable to most industrial users," but only a part of these resources "will yield usable lump ore."

The world resources of chromite are estimated at 300 million tons of contained Cr_2O_3, about 80 per cent of which are in the Union of South Africa and the Federation of Rhodesia and Nyasaland.

Turkey is considered to contain the world's greatest single source of metallurgical chromium ores. Its reserves, conservatively estimated to be 6 million tons, are not considered to be enough to maintain normal production for more than a generation. New Caledonia is the only other current source of high-grade metallurgical chromite. Data are not available on the actual size of the reserves, but recent exploration indicates that they are substantial and apparently capable of increasing with demand. The Philippines have about 1 million tons of metallurgical ores. The largest potential source of chromium in the Western world is Cuba's lateritic iron ore, but it cannot be considered a reserve until satisfactory methods are devised for utilizing it.

Additional deposits of high-grade metallurgical ore occur in Pakistan, Iran, and Afghanistan. Yugoslavia has about 2 million tons of chromite and Greece an estimated 1 million tons. India, Japan, and Sierra Leone also have substantial reserves. The USSR has extensive reserves of high-grade metallurgical and refractory ores.

A world record production of 5.11 million tons of chromite were produced in 1957. World production in 1960 was 4.92 million tons. The USSR led with 1 million tons. Other leading producers were the Union of South Africa, the Philippines, the Federation of Rhodesia and Nyasaland, and Turkey, in the order named.

Cobalt

Symbol	Atomic Number	Atomic Weight	Melt. Pt. (°F)
Co	27	58.94	2723±2

Cobalt is a comparatively rare element in the earth's crust and is estimated to make up only 0.001 per cent. Its important minerals are sulfides, arsenides, and oxidized compounds. They are seldom found in sufficient quantity to be mined for cobalt alone. Consequently, cobalt is obtained chiefly as a by-product or a co-product of other metals, chiefly copper.

TABLE 5

WORLD PRODUCTION OF CHROMITE, BY COUNTRIES, IN SHORT TONS[1]

Country	1950-1954 (average)	1960
North America:		
Cuba	75,771	32,774[4]
Guatemala	413	200
United States	50,189	107,000
Total	126,373	139,974
South America: Brazil	3,038	5,233
Europe:		
Albania	72,091	330,700[2]
Greece	29,466	110,200[2]
Portugal	46	—
USSR[2][3]	645,000	1,010,000
Yugoslavia	126,334	111,170
Total[2]	893,000	1,590,000
Asia:		
Afghanistan	138	—
Cyprus (exports)	13,668	15,702
India	40,297	110,354
Iran	15,767	55,000[2]
Japan	42,200	74,398
Pakistan	22,027	19,945
Philippines	460,076	809,579
Turkey	723,927	528,690
Total[2]	1,318,100	1,613,668
Africa:		
Egypt	171	—
Rhodesia and Nyasaland, Fed. of		
Southern Rhodesia	483,941	668,401
Sierra Leone	20,205	6,023
Union of South Africa	658,545	850,916
Total	1,162,862	1,525,340
Oceania:		
Australia	2,543	—
New Caledonia	107,551	43,211
Total	110,094	43,211
World Total (estimate)	3,615,000	4,920,000

SOURCE: *Minerals Yearbook,* U. S. Department of the Interior, Washington, D. C., I, 1956, 1960.
[1] This table incorporates some revisions. Data do not add exactly to totals shown because of rounding where estimated figures are included in the detail.
[2] Estimate.
[3] Output from USSR in Asia included with USSR in Europe.
[4] United States imports.

USES AND CONSUMPTION

The greatest use of cobalt is for permanent magnet alloys which used 27 per cent of cobalt consumption in the United States in 1960. The second largest use is for high-temperature, high-strength alloys which used 23 per cent of total consumption in 1960. Cobalt in metallic form (97 to 99 per cent pure) is usually added to the furnace in the form of shot or rondelles in the manufacture of alloy steels.

Before World War I, consumption of cobalt was mainly in the form of cobalt oxide used in the ceramic industry. Scarcely any cobalt metal was produced. During the war, the value of the metal as an alloying element in high-speed and high-temperature steels gained recognition, yet only a few hundred thousand pounds of cobalt in all forms were consumed. In the interval of the 1920s and 1930s, the annual consumption of cobalt rose from around 300,000 pounds to 1.7 million pounds. It was in World War II that cobalt won its stellar role as an element for high-temperature alloys. In 1941, consumption shot up to nearly 3 million pounds and reached a peak of 11 million pounds in 1952 and 1953. In 1960, it was 8.9 million pounds, 10 per cent below 1959.

The greatly increased rate of cobalt consumption in the United States since the beginning of the cold war has been due chiefly to the requirements of the military program, which in 1950 consumed 62 per cent of the total available supply. The main uses of cobalt in the future are expected to be in jet engines, rockets, guided missiles, and the generation of nuclear energy. In view of cobalt's importance in these applications, the Paley Report predicted that consumption of the metal would be quadrupled between 1950 and 1975.

PRODUCTION AND IMPORTS

Because of the vital role of cobalt in high-temperature alloys, the Defense Minerals Exploration Administration vigorously pushed the exploration and development of domestic mines. A goal of 5.3 million pounds annual cobalt-mining capacity was set for 1956. Prior to World War II, the United States was wholly dependent on foreign sources for its supply of cobalt. Average production for the years 1947-1951 was 456,000 pounds of recoverable cobalt, representing 7 per cent of average annual consumption for that period. In 1958, production reached a record of 4 million pounds, equivalent to 54 per cent of consumption. Production in 1959 dropped to 2.33 million pounds, representing 24 per cent of consumption. In that year, however, consumption drew more heavily on imports which rose to 21.2 million pounds, an increase of 6 million pounds over 1958. Production figures for 1960 were withheld by the Bureau of Mines to avoid disclosing individual company confidential data.

The United States obtains most of its cobalt from the Republic of the Congo which in 1960 supplied 39 per cent of imports amounting to 10.8

million pounds of contained metal, 43 per cent less than in 1959. Thirty-five per cent of United States imports came from Belgium, but this metal was processed from Congo Republic white alloy, so that 74 per cent of total American imports originated in the Republic of the Congo. Almost all of remaining foreign supplies came from West Germany, Norway, the Federation of Rhodesia and Nyasaland, and Canada, in the order named.

WORLD RESERVES

Fully 85 per cent of the world's supply of cobalt has been produced as a by-product of copper mining in the Republic of the Congo, where the largest commercial reserves exist. The Congo ores are considered to be sufficient to last forty to fifty years and the possibilities of expansion are held to be excellent. Potential output is estimated at 14 million pounds a year. The oulook for expanded operations in Northern Rhodesia, the second largest cobalt producer, are also described as excellent. Newly discovered deposits in neighboring Uganda may contain considerable cobalt. French Morocco has long been one of the major producers of cobalt, but information on its reserves is not obtainable. A fourth large producer of cobalt is Canada, where the metal is a by-product of nickel-copper mining in the Sudbury district. Canadian cobalt reserves are about the size of those in Northern Rhodesia. The world's largest potential source of cobalt is the laterite ores of Nicaro, Cuba, but it has not been economically feasible so far to recover the metal. If economic recovery of cobalt from lateritic ores ever becomes possible, it would add immense potential resources of cobalt, including not only those in Cuba, but also those in Brazil, New Caledonia, Celebes, Venezuela, and the Philippines.

Altogether, the cobalt reserves in the Free World are considered adequate to support the increased demand expected to materialize in the period 1950-1975

Columbium (Niobium) and Tantalum

Symbol	Atomic Number	Atomic Weight	Melt. Pt. (°F)
Nb	41	92.91	4380±30
Ta	73	180.88	5425±90

Columbium (also called niobium) and tantalum are chemically much alike, are closely associated in nature, and are extracted together from their ores. Both are rare metals and have been described as "important to the United States economy in peacetime and vital in wartime."

OCCURRENCES

Columbium and tantalum are obtained commercially from two groups of complex mineral ores—the columbite and pyrochlore groups. Columbite and tantalite are the two principal minerals of the first group, and were used almost entirely as sources for the two metals until 1953, when a process was developed for extracting columbium from pyrochlore.

TABLE 6

FREE WORLD PRODUCTION OF COBALT, BY COUNTRIES,
IN SHORT TONS OF CONTAINED COBALT[1]

Country	1950-1954 (average)	1960
North America:		
Canada	681	1,665
United States (recoverable cobalt)	438	[3]
Total	1,119	[3]
Africa:		
Congo, Republic of the, (recoverable cobalt)	7,624	9,083
Morocco: Southern zone (content of concentrates)	757	1,401
Rhodesia and Nyasaland, Federation of: Northern Rhodesia (content of white alloy, cathode metal, and other products)	843	2,036
Total	9,224	12,520
Oceania:		
Australia (recoverable cobalt in zinc concentrates)	11	16[2]
New Caledonia (content of concentrates)	—	—
Total	11	16[2]
Free World total (estimate)[1]	11,000	16,700

SOURCE: *Minerals Yearbook,* U. S. Department of the Interior, Washington, D. C., I, 1956, 1960.
[1] This table incorporates some revisions. Data do not add exactly to totals shown because of rounding where estimated figures are included in the detail.
[2] Estimate.
[3] Figures withheld to avoid disclosing individual company confidential data; U. S. figures included in world estimate.

USES

Closely akin as columbium and tantalum may be chemically, they differ enough so that columbium is the more potent for alloying purposes, while tantalum is peculiarly adaptive to the manufacture of electronic equipment.

Columbium is usually added to steel in the form of ferrocolumbium containing from 50 to 60 per cent columbium. Tantalum may be used as a substitute for columbium in some steels, in which case it is added in the form of ferrotantalum-columbium.

The major use of columbium for some years has been to act as a stabilizer in certain grades of stainless steels for service at high temperature, or when they are welded. However, columbium is proving itself to be unsurpassed as an ingredient in super-alloys for high temperature applications, particularly in jet engines and gas turbines, and its consumption for such purposes may eventually exceed its use in stainless steel.

Columbium and tantalum have been recognized as desirable metals for service at temperatures above 2,000° F.

During World War II, the demand for columbium and tantalum greatly exceeded supply and both metals were put on the restricted list in the United States. Restrictions on columbium were lifted in 1945, on tantalum, in 1944. After being valued so highly during the war that they were "rationed," the demand, surprisingly, dropped between 1945 and 1950, at least for columbium, so that little interest was taken in exploration for new sources. No one had paid much attention to pyrochlore as a potential source of columbium until explorations in Norway and Germany during World War II opened the eyes of mineralogists to the possibilities of pyrochlore deposits throughout the world. Then suddenly, in 1950, the Communist aggression in Korea created a tremendous demand for columbium far beyond supply. Once again, columbium and tantalum were controlled, and to stimulate exploration and production of ores, the Defense Materials Procurement Agency in May 1952 began buying domestic and foreign columbium and tantalum ores, paying producers a bonus price of 100 per cent of specified prices. The purchase program was extended to December 31, 1956, for foreign ores and to December 31, 1958, for domestic ores, or until 15 million pounds of contained pentoxides (both Cb_2O_5 and Ta_2O_5) of both domestic and foreign origin had been bought.

WORLD RESERVES

Reserves of columbium throughout the world were reported by the Bureau of Mines in 1956 to be rapidly increasing and known supplies were believed to be "more than adequate for foreseeable future requirements." The indicated Free World-reserves of contained Cb_2O_5 in 1956 were estimated to be at least 4.5 million tons, mostly in low-grade pyrochlore deposits. Brazilian reserves, mostly inferred, were placed at 2.5 million tons of Cb_2O_5. African ores were estimated at 1.3 million tons; those in Canada at 600,000 tons, and American reserves at a mere 80,000 tons; all three in terms of Cb_2O_5.

Discoveries of columbium-bearing ores in the Free World continued to increase and in 1959 were estimated to be more than 7 million tons of contained metal. The pyrochlore ores can, for the most part, be mined and beneficiated at low cost; expanded production waits only on larger markets.

PRODUCTION, CONSUMPTION, IMPORTS

In 1958, American production of columbium-tantalum concentrates was 428,347 pounds, the highest in history. Production in 1959 fell to 189,263 pounds. There was no domestic mine production of tantalum-columbium in 1960. Consmption set a record of 2 million pounds in 1960. World production of 11,540,000 pounds of columbium-tantalum concen-

TABLE 7

FREE WORLD PRODUCTION OF COLUMBIUM AND TANTALUM CONCENTRATES BY COUNTRIES, 1950–1954 (AVERAGE) AND 1960 IN POUNDS[1]

Country	1950–1954 (average) Columbium	Tantalum	1960 Columbium	Tantalum
North America:				
Canada				
United States (mine shipments)	11,001			
South America:				
Argentina		668		
Bolivia (exports)	882			
Brazil (exports)	74,821	45,852	324,076	
British Guiana	5,893			
French Guiana	22,054			
Europe:				
Germany, West (U. S. imports)	267,957	62,865		
Norway	216,393		600,000	
Portugal (U. S. imports)	43,791	55,206	35,383	34,092
Spain (U. S. imports)	2,205	247	976	3,157
Sweden (U. S. imports)	8,357	11,745		
Asia:				
Malaya, Federation of	108,864		208,320	
Africa:				
Congo, Republic of the, and Ruanda-Urundi	465,964		227,724[2]	332,724[2]
French Equatorial Africa	3,391			
Malagasy Republic (Madagascar)	14,826		25,000	
Mozambique	40,747		330,690	
Nigeria	3,633,280	6,720	4,071,115[2]	7,698[2]
Rhodesia and Nyasaland, Federation of	8,093	10,934		108,080
Sierra Leone		8,960		
South-West Africa	12,977		10,390	
Uganda	21,945			
Union of South Africa		20,400	5,040	14,000
Oceania:				
Australia		34,732	10,000	
Free World total (estimate)[1]	5,220,700		6,350,000	

SOURCE: *Minerals Yearbook,* U. S. Department of the Interior, Washington, D. C., I, 1956, 1960.
[1] Data do not add exactly to totals shown because of rounding where estimated figures are included in the detail.
[2] U. S. imports.

trates in 1955 was the highest on record. It was 6.35 million pounds in 1960.

Imports of columbium-mineral concentrates into the United States declined from a high of 9.6 million pounds in 1955 to 5 million pounds in 1960. Nigeria continued to be America's major source of the metal, supplying 80 per cent of total imports in 1960. The Republic of the Congo, Norway, the Federation of Malaya, and Brazil were other major sources of American imports. United States imports of tantalum-mineral concentrates set a record of 1.3 million pounds in 1956, and were 710,000 pounds in 1960. The Republic of the Congo and Ruanda-Urundi furnished 332,424 pounds, or 47 per cent. Other imports came chiefly from Brazil, Mozambique, Portugal, and the Malagasy Republic.

Copper

Symbol	Atomic Number	Atomic Weight	Melt. Pt. (°F)
Cu	29	63.54	1981.4±0.2

Copper, in the amounts used, is the most potent of all common alloying elements in improving the corrosion resistance of steel. It is especially effective in minute doses—as low a 0.10 per cent in regular carbon steels. Copper also increases the strength and hardness of low and medium carbon steels, while at the same time enhancing corrosion resistance, and for these dual characteristics is chosen as an ingredient in most high-strength, low-alloy steels, where it is present in amounts ranging from 0.20 to 1.30 per cent. Copper is also used as a coating for steel wire and other steel products. As an alloying element, copper is added to steel in a pure metallic form or in copper-bearing scrap.

Copper consumption by the steel industry is so small a part of total consumption that it is grouped by the Bureau of Mines with miscellaneous uses, which altogether amount to less than 1 per cent of total consumption.

The United States is the world's leading copper producer, and in 1960 accounted for about 23 per cent of the 4.95 million tons mined and smelted by all countries. Other large copper producers were, in the order named: Federation of Rhodesia and Nyasaland, Chile, USSR, Canada, and the Republic of the Congo.

Manganese

Symbol	Atomic Number	Atomic Weight	Melt. Pt. (°F)
Mn	25	54.93	2273±20

Between 96 and 98 per cent of manganese consumption in the United States goes to the steel industry, where an average of about 13 pounds is used in making every ton of steel produced. Manganese has a powerful attraction for oxygen and sulphur and by virtue of these affinities the metal's primary purpose in steelmaking is to remove these two elements by combining with them. In so doing, all but a minute portion of the manganese passes into the slag. For fulfilling this role there is, in present steelmaking practice, no satisfactory substitute for manganese.

If more manganese is added than is needed for purging action, sufficient quantities of the metal will remain in the steel to act as an alloying element. Small amounts of manganese—from 1 to 2 per cent—appreciably increase the toughness and strength of steel, but if the proportion is raised to 10 to 15 per cent, as Sir Robert Hadfield found out, "an entirely new kind of steel" is produced. Manganese alloy steel becomes tougher and harder under repeated impact and is unexcelled for conditions of hard-wearing and abrasive action, as in rails and earth-moving equipment.

Manganese is generally added to the steel in the form of ferromanganese containing from 78 to 85 per cent manganese. Silicomanganese, silicospiegel, and spiegeleisen, containing various proportions of manganese (16 to 68 per cent) and silicon (1 to 20 per cent) are used to a minor extent in steelmaking. Manganese ore is the principal raw material used in the production of these ferroalloys. Only relatively high-grade manganese ores are mined for conversion into ferromanganese. About 45 per cent manganese content is considered desirable for economical manufacture of the ferroalloy, in which the manganese content is raised to around 80 per cent.

WORLD RESERVES

No major steel-producing nation in the Free World possesses large deposits of high-grade manganese ores. The United States has enormous deposits of low-grade ores, but produces only about 2 per cent of its manganese requirements. The Soviet Union has in her territories over half of the known manganese reserves of the world and produces nearly five times the tonnage of India, the second largest producer. Russia furnished more than one-third of America's manganese requirements up to 1938 and again in 1948, but by 1950 Soviet manganese exports to the Free World had virtually ceased.

Exclusive of the United States, world reserves of high-grade manganese ore are estimated to be approximately one billion tons of which roughly two-thirds lie in the USSR and associated countries. The bulk of the remainder is found in Africa, India, and Brazil. In addition to known resources, there are presumably vast unexplored tonnages of low-grade material, perhaps as much as 10 billion tons containing more than 10 per cent manganese—sufficient to supply the world for at least 1,000 years.

SUPPLIERS AND RESOURCES

In 1960 Brazil was the leading supplier of manganese to the United States, providing 35 per cent of total imports amounting to 1,213,834 tons of contained metal. Brazil, India, and Ghana supplied 67 per cent of American manganese imports in 1960. The remainder came chiefly from the Union of South Africa, the Republic of the Congo, and Ruanda-Urundi, Mexico, and Morocco.

In considering future sources of manganese for the United States and also the rest of the Free World, the Paley Report said that as India and

TABLE 8

WORLD RESERVES OF MANGANESE ORE
(million tons)

Country	Estimated Ore High Grade	Intermediate
USSR	± 550	± 75
India	100	—
Brazil	60	—
Union of South Africa	± 60	—
French Equatorial Africa	50	—
French Morocco	30	20
China	18	11
Gold Coast	12	—
United States	1	11
Hungary	4.5	6
Belgian Congo	10	—
Egypt	—	± 9
Rumania	—	7
Mexico	5	1
Czechoslovakia	—	4.5
Angola	.4	3
Manchuria	—	3
Cuba	1	1.2
Chile	1.2	—
Turkey	± 1	—
All others	2.8	—

SOURCE: *Mineral Facts and Problems,* U. S. Bureau of Mines, Washington, D. C., 1956.

South Africa become industrialized they can be expected to retain a larger proportion of their manganese production, so that the United States cannot count on continuing to receive half of the manganese exports of the Free World as it has since World War II. The Indian reserves promise to hold out the longest in the Free World. Ghana's reserves of high-grade ore may be exhausted by 1975, but other African deposits are large in relation to their present output. In the South American continent, newly discovered deposits at Urcum and Amapa, in Brazil, are described as "very large" and are expected eventually to yield as much as 600,000 tons of high-grade ore annually. Both deposits are being developed by American steel companies with the assistance of loans and purchase guarantees by the United States government.

UNITED STATES DEPOSITS

There are actually immense deposits of manganese ore in the United States, but they are of such low grade—much of them averaging from 5 to 15 per cent manganese—that the cost of mining and beneficiating the ore to make it equal to the imported product would cost two times, and in some cases more than four times, the price of foreign ore delivered

TABLE 9

WORLD PRODUCTION OF MANGANESE ORE, BY COUNTRIES, 1950-1954 (AVERAGE)
AND 1960, IN NET TONS[1]

Country	1950-1954 (average)	1960
North America:		
Cuba	226,328	17,644[3]
Mexico	166,289	171,400[2]
United States (shipments)	143,700	80,021
Total	536,317	269,065
South America:		
Argentina	4,827	16,500[2]
Brazil	229,764	942,205
Chile	48,555	66,100[2]
Peru	2,895	1,905
British Guiana	—	137,454
Total	286,041	1,164,164
Europe:		
Bulgaria	24,582	88,200[2]
Greece	14,825	38,581
Hungary	108,670	132,000
Italy	39,489	51,738
Portugal	9,203	7,700
Rumania	118,575	209,400[2]
Spain	30,165	24,828
USSR	4,657,900	6,393,400
Yugoslavia	6,821	14,700
Total	5,010,230	6,960,600
Asia:		
Burma	4,651	324
China[2]	128,100	1,380,000
India	1,557,447	1,267,657
Indonesia	14,010	12,026
Iran	6,297	2,400
Japan	196,040	355,696
Korea, Republic of	3,176	1,521
Malaya	—	3,222
Philippines	22,871	19,159
Portuguese India	106,631	56,263
Thailand	—	582
Turkey	67,002	31,112
Total[2]	2,106,000	3,130,000
Africa:		
Angola	45,875	25,728
Bechuanaland	—	13,912
Congo, Republic of the	180,231	429,900[2]
Ghana (exports)	788,005	600,261

TABLE 9 (Continued)

WORLD PRODUCTION OF MANGANESE ORE, BY COUNTRIES, 1950–1954 (AVERAGE)
AND 1960, IN NET TONS[1]

Country	1950–1954 (average)	1960
Ethiopia	—	1,683
Ivory Coast	—	68,343
Morocco:		
Northern zone	1,464	—
Southern zone	422,314	532,508
Rhodesia and Nyasaland Federation of:		
Northern Rhodesia	7,839	64,298
Southern Rhodesia	320	1,676
South-West Africa	22,453	67,439
Union of South Africa	871,537	1,316,124
United Arab Republic:		
(Egypt Region)	3,154	104,700[2]
Total	2,343,192	3,226,600
Oceania:		
Australia	20,396	68,300[2]
Fiji	3,289	13,073
New Caledonia	10,550	—
New Zealand	358	110[2]
Papua	23	54
Total	34,616	81,500[2]
World Total (estimate)[1]	10,316,000	14,832,000

SOURCE: *Minerals Yearbook,* U. S. Department of the Interior, Washington, D. C., I, 1956, 1960.
[1] This table incorporates some revisions. Data do not add exactly to totals shown because of rounding where estimated figures are included.
[2] Estimate.
[3] United States Imports.

to the eastern seaboard. The known manganese reserves in the United States contain 84 million tons of metallic manganese.

For a good many years the steel industry and the government of the United States have looked longingly at all the manganese which disappears annually in the slag. About 75 per cent of the manganese charged into the steelmaking furnaces ends up in this waste material, which is estimated to contain more than 700,000 tons of manganese annually. The Bureau of Mines, in cooperation with the American Iron and Steel Institute, has been developing a plan that, it is hoped, will make possible the recovery of up to half of the manganese in the slag. The process does not offer formidable technical problems. It is a question of cost—whether the expense of recovery would be more than the value of the recovered metal.

Molybdenum

Symbol	Atomic Number	Atomic Weight	Melt. Pt. (°F)
Mo	42	95.95	4760±90

HISTORY AND USES

Molybdenum has won a place among the top three or four alloying elements used by the steel industry. It is also one of the two alloying elements in which United States is self-sufficient—producing over 90 per cent of the world output. Self-sufficiency in molybdenum no doubt helps to account for the attention given to this metal in the past thirty to forty years in order to realize the full potential value of a raw material existing in abundant quantities within American borders.

Molybdenum was first added to steel in 1901 and was produced commercially in 1906, but it was not until World War I that it became of any importance. Then it was discovered that fractional amounts of molybdenum—0.10 to 0.50 per cent—added to chromium-nickel-vanadium steel enhanced the hardenability and shock resistance of the alloyed metal which was used with outstanding success as tank armor plate. In the years following the war, the effect of molybdenum in increasing the depth of hardening was utilized with such rewarding results in low-alloy automotive and engineering steels that in the mid-1950s it was said that virtually every automobile on the roads carried molybdenum-bearing steels. In World War II, steels containing molybdenum were in such demand for armor, guns, and armor-piercing shells that production of the metal did not meet demands and it was in critical short supply.

If higher percentages of molybdenum are added to steel—from 5.5 to 9.25 per cent—the steel gains in hardenability, and certain combinations are used for high-speed tool steels. Perhaps the greatest value of molybdenum as an alloying element is the strength which it imparts to steel for service up to 1200° F., and for this reason molybdenum-bearing steels are used in steam pipelines and boilers and in the turbine blades of jet engines. Molybdenum is also present in certain stainless steels and in super-alloys for severe service at high temperatures.

TECHNOLOGY

Because molybdenum melts at 4,700° F. a great deal of effort has been made to utilize this metal for extremely high temperature service. However, molybdenum oxidizes rapidly in the air and other oxidizing atmospheres at temperatures of 1,000° and higher, causing serious problems in the fabrication and use of the metal. In January 1959, the Bureau of Mines announced what may be a major breakthrough in molybdenum technology: the first successful casting of molybdenum in hollow form. One of the potential uses of the hollow casting would be in the nozzles of fuel propellants in jets and rockets.

Molybdenum is usually added to steel in the form of molybdenum trioxide (MoO_3) and sometimes as calcium molybdate ($CaMoO_4$). Ferro-molybdenum containing 55 to 75 per cent molybdenum was formerly the chief form used by the steel industry, but the first two mentioned are preferred today.

PRODUCTION, CONSUMPTION, EXPORTS

American production of molybdenum in 1960 was approximately 68 million pounds, compared to an average of 45.3 million pounds for the years 1950-1954. Most of the domestic ore comes from a mine in Colorado, said to be one of the world's largest underground operations. Almost all of domestic molybdenum is derived from the mineral molybdenite which contains about 60 per cent molybdenum by weight.

American consumption of molybdenum in 1960 was 44.7 million pounds. The 1950-1954 average consumption was 29.7 million pounds. About 27 million pounds of molybdenum, or 84 per cent of total consumption in 1960, was used as an alloying element in steel.

The United States is the world's largest exporter of molybdenum. The 1948-1952 average was 5 million pounds of contained molybdenum. The export of 30.2 million pounds in 1960 was 60 per cent above 1959 and higher than in any past year. The major importing countries of American molybdenum are West Germany, United Kingdom, Canada, Japan, France, and Sweden.

World production of molybdenum in 1960 was 89.4 million pounds of contained metal, of which 76 per cent was produced in the United States. The USSR was second with nearly 11 million pounds, followed by Canada and Chile. Small amounts were produced by several other countries.

Nickel

Symbol	Atomic Number	Atomic Weight	Melt. Pt. (°F)
Ni	28	58.69	2651±2

Ever since the late 1880s, when France showed the world the extraordinary degree of toughness and strength that nickel could add to naval armor plate and guns, no metal has been found to surpass it for imparting these properties, while at the same time rendering the steel ductile and easily worked—a combination of characteristics ideally suited to meet the requirements of an industrial society. Low-alloy steels of 0.70 to 3.75 per cent nickel and also containing, as a rule, small amounts of chromium and/or molybdenum, have been the "shock troop" steels for mechanisms of many kinds that are subjected to repeated stress and strain. Nickel lengthens the life service and increases the dependability of gears, crankshafts, and other vital parts of machines used in transportation, on the farm, in factories, on the sea, and in the air.

That is but half the story of nickel. High percentages of the metal in combination with chromium add to the corrosion resistance of steel and fortify its strength at elevated temperatures. Nickel is present in many grades of stainless steel. At the other end of the temperature range, in sub-zero climates and in artificially created low temperatures, down to —300° F. in liquid air machinery, nickel-bearing steels are able to perform their functions when ordinary steels are apt to become brittle and crack under shock. Lastly, nickel readily forms an alloy with a number of non-ferrous metals. It is an important component in a number of super-alloys for extremely high temperature service beyond the range of alloy steels. Nickel is added to steel in a metal form about 99 per cent pure, or as a sinter containing 75 per cent nickel, or sometimes as an oxide.

LESS NICKEL USED

When nickel first entered into steelmaking it was rather prodigally used, as were most alloying metals. Beginning with the early years of the century, a number of factors—advances in alloy steel metallurgy, desire to economize in alloy steel costs, scarcity of some alloying elements—accounted for a drop in the proportions of elements in most alloy steel compositions. Nickel content in steel declined from an average of 3.5 per cent in 1900 to 1.90 per cent on the eve of America's participation in World War II. During the conflict, it was reduced to 1.25 per cent and afterwards, in the Korean crisis of 1950, the average nickel content in steels was squeezed down to 0.90 per cent.

PRODUCTION, IMPORTS, CONSUMPTION

Nickel mine production in the United States amounted to 11 tons in 1953. As domestic expansion programs began to yield results, production rose from 3,356 tons in 1955 to 14,079 tons of nickel in 1960. In addition, 623 tons were recovered as a by-product of copper refining. The 1960 production represented 13 per cent of domestic consumption.

American imports of nickel climbed steadily upward from 1950 through 1956, reaching an all-time high in the latter year of 143,000 tons. Imports in 1960 were 103,000 tons. Canada and Norway supplied the bulk of the imports. During 1960, the U.S. government-owned plant at Nicaro and the Freeport Nickel Company plant at Moa Bay, Cuba, each with an estimated annual capacity of 25,000 tons of nickel, were closed.

Nickel consumption in the United States was at a record high of 127,500 tons in 1956. Of the 108,000 tons consumed in 1960, 28 per cent was used in making stainless steels, and 14 per cent in other steels.

WORLD NICKEL PRODUCTION

Since 1905, Canada has supplied the bulk of the world's nickel and in 1960 accounted for 59 per cent of the total output, followed by the USSR with an estimated 17 per cent, New Caledonia with 11 per cent, Cuba with 4 per cent, and the United States with 4 per cent. The remainder came from a number of other countries.

TABLE 10

WORLD PRODUCTION OF NICKEL, BY COUNTRIES, 1950-1954 (AVERAGE) AND 1960, IN NET TONS OF CONTAINED NICKEL[1]

Country	1950-1954 (average)	1960
North America:		
Canada	141,419	214,774
Cuba	7,463	14,147
United States:		
By-product of copper refining	706	623
Recovered nickel in domestic ore refined	102	11,907
Total	149,690	241,451
South America:		
Brazil (content of ferronickel)	20[1]	160[1]
Venezuela (content of ore)	—	30[1]
Total	20[1]	190[1]
Europe:		
Albania (content of nickeliferous ore)	—	2,700
Finland	93[1]	2,591
Germany, East (content of ore)	—	110
Poland (content of ore)	915	1,400[1]
USSR[1] (content of ore)	37,800	64,000
Total[1]	38,800	70,800
Asia:		
Burma (content of speiss)	180	81
Africa:		
Morocco: Southern zone (content of cobalt ore)	99	280
Rhodesia and Nyasaland, Federation of:		
Southern Rhodesia (content of ore)	3	24
Union of South Africa (content of matte and refined nickel)	1,526	3,200[1]
Total	1,628	3,504
Oceania:		
New Caledonia (recoverable)	9,411	42,300
World Total (estimate)	200,000	358,000

SOURCE: *Minerals Yearbook*, U. S. Department of the Interior, Washington, D. C., I, 1956, 1960.
[1] Estimate.

Selenium

Symbol	Atomic Number	Atomic Weight	Melt. Pt. (°F)
Se	34	78.96	428 ± 9

The use of selenium by the steel industry is one of the least important of the many applications of this element. A minute portion of selenium— about 0.15 per cent—improves the machinability of stainless steel. It is added in the form of ferroselenium during the tapping of electric furnace steel. Ferroselenium contains from 50 to 60 per cent selenium. An average of 36 tons of ferroselenium was consumed by the steel industry in the period, 1952-1960.

The United States is the world's leading producer of selenium followed, in the order named, by Canada, Japan, Sweden, Belgium-Luxembourg, Northern Rhodesia, Finland, and Mexico.

It is estimated that there are, potentially, 18,750,000 pounds of selenium recoverable from copper reserves in the United States and "tremendous tonnages" of selenium in the rocks and soils of some states. Information on selenium occurrences elsewhere in the world is not available.

Silicon

Symbol	Atomic Number	Atomic Weight	Melt. Pt. (°F)
Si	14	28.09	2,605 ± 35

Silicon up to 5 per cent in steel increases its magnetic permeability and electrical resistance and reduces hysteresis loss. Manufactured mostly in the form of electrical sheets, silicon steel has made possible the development of more powerful and more efficient electrical equipment and has figured importantly in the growth of the electrical industry as the chief source of power in modern industrial society. The invention and development of silicon steel was related in the previous chapter.

Silicon is added to steel in the form of ferrosilicon. The low grades of ferrosilicon contain from 10 to 17 per cent silicon and are usually produced in the blast furnaces. Higher grades of ferrosilicon are made in the electric furnace and range from 25 to 95 per cent silicon. The 50 per cent silicon grade is by far the most widely used. Silicon is also employed by the steel industry as a deoxidizer. After oxygen, silicon is the most abundant element in the earth. It is found widely in rocks and sands.

Titanium

Symbol	Atomic Number	Atomic Weight	Melt. Pt. (°F)
Ti	22	47.90	3,300 ± 180

No metal has had such a spectacular development in so short a time as titanium. It was regarded as a metallurgical curiosity until World War II. In 1940, the United States Bureau of Mines began research into methods for extraction and fabrication of titanium, and in 1946 put two pilot plants into operation. Two years later, the first private commercial plant was completed by E. I. du Pont de Nemours & Company, and in 1959 a second company, Titanium Metals Corporation, was formed to enter into the commercial production of titanium. In 1948, titanium sponge metal production in the United States was estimated at 10 tons and in 1957 reached 17,000 tons. Production has since fallen off and in 1960 amounted to 5,300 tons.

The intense interest in titanium arose from its unusual properties which place it approximately midway between steel and aluminum. Titanium is 40 per cent lighter than steel and only 60 per cent heavier than aluminum, yet its alloys approach the tensile strength of most alloy steels. High-speed aircraft, both military and civilian, missiles, and space vehicles are the major users of titanium metal.

USES IN STEEL

The chief function of titanium in steel is to act as a carbide stabilizing element in some stainless and heat-resisting steels. It is also used as a de-oxidizer and degasifier. For these purposes the American steel industry consumes a little more than 1,000 tons of metallic titanium a year. Titanium likewise contributes to the strength of super-alloys for severe high temperature service.

Titanium is added to steel in the form of ferrotitanium of low, medium or high carbon content, or sometimes in the form of alloys containing aluminum, silicon, or other elements.

OCCURRENCES

Titanium is the ninth most abundant element and the fourth most plentiful structural metal in the earth's crust. It does not exist in a pure state in nature because of its strong reactivity with other elements. Although it is widespread in the United States and throughout the world, only a few ores are commercially usable under present technology. There are two chief kinds of titanium-bearing minerals: ilmenite and rutile. Ilmenite, an oxide of titanium and iron, is used almost entirely for conversion into titanium dioxide pigment. Until World War II, almost all of America's needs of ilmenite were supplied by India. The disruption of seaborne trade compelled the United States to look for domestic sources with the result that extensive deposits were located. Ilmenite reserves in North America are described as more than adequate to take care of needs for both the metal and pigment up to 1975. The largest known occurrence of ilmenite in the world is in the province of Quebec, Canada. Ilmenite and titaniferous ores also occur in India, Norway, Japan, Egypt, Africa, Ceylon, Malaya, Sweden, Brazil, Mexico, and the USSR.

Rutile is the chief source of titanium sponge from which the metal is derived. Rutile is not available in the United States in large enough quantities to support an expanding titanium metal industry. Almost all American imports of rutile in 1960 came from Australia, which in that year produced 87 per cent of the world output. Other commercial production of rutile is on a minor scale and is carried on chiefly in the Union of South Africa.

Tungsten

Symbol	*Atomic Number*	*Atomic Weight*	*Melt. Pt. (°F)*
W	74	183.92	6,170 ± 35

Tungsten has the highest melting point of any metal and is extremely hard. When blended into steel as an alloy, tungsten is unsurpassed for adding hardness which is retained at elevated temperatures. These properties have made tungsten steel almost synonymous with tool steel, although most modern tool steels also contain chromium and some of them are also alloyed with molybdenum and vanadium. Due to the recurring scarcity of tungsten in periods of national emergency, molybdenum high-speed tool steels have been developed, in which chromium and vanadium are also present, and, generally, some tungsten.

Tungsten is added to steel in the form of ferrotungsten containing from 70 to 80 per cent tungsten. The metal is also added in the form of oxides such as scheelite and calcium tungstate.

Up to and during World War II, the major use of tungsten was in high-speed and other tool steels. A year before the end of the war, in 1944, the American steel industry absorbed 74 per cent of total tungsten concentrates domestically consumed. Since the war, tungsten carbide which is an extremely hard substance and is used to advantage in certain cutting tools where there is no shock or impact, has been gaining at the expense of tungsten steel. Between 1944 and 1960, the proportion of total tungsten consumption absorbed by the American steel industry fell from 74 to 26 per cent, and that of carbides rose to 41 per cent.

FORMER DEPENDENCE ON CHINA

Although the United States produces some tungsten, it has traditionally depended on China for the major part of its tungsten supplies, and when Japanese conquests in 1941 and 1942 cut off imports from China, it precipitated a crisis in the production of armor-piercing shells for which tungsten was an essential element. Fortunately, the development of National Emergency Steels, described in the previous chapter, made it possible to surmount this crisis as well as others related to alloy steels. But once the war was over, the United States lapsed again into more or less complacent dependence on China and in 1949 relied on it for roughly 4.5 million pounds of the 6.27 million pounds imported that year. In 1950 —the year of the Communist aggression in Korea—the United States was still dependent on China and obtained 7.4 million pounds of the 16 million pounds of tungsten metal imported. After the Communists consolidated their domination of China, tungsten imports from China into the United States trickled to a halt in 1951.

UNITED STATES EXPANSION PROGRAM

The United States in 1951 embarked on a vigorous program to stimulate the production of tungsten through loans up to 75 per cent of exploration costs and also sought to build up stockpiles of tungsten by paying premium prices to domestic producers. Tungsten concentrates were also purchased abroad by the government for resale to industry. The purchase program was to continue until 3 million-ton units of tungsten trioxide were acquired. Domestic production increased rapidly and in 1953 for the first time exceeded consumption. The stockpile goal was attained in December 1956, when the government suspended purchases of concentrate from domestic producers.

PRODUCTION, CONSUMPTION, IMPORTS

The Paley Report foresaw the demand for tungsten growing 150 per cent between 1950 and 1975. This would mean a rise from 6.5 million to 15 million pounds annually. The authors of the Paley Report were on the conservative side, for in 1955 domestic mine shipments of contained tungsten were nearly 16 million pounds, an all-time high. Thereafter available tungsten supplies greatly exceeded demand and mine shipments declined, reaching 6.7 million pounds of contained tungsten in 1960.

Consumption of tungsten in the United States since the end of the World War II has risen and fallen sharply with changes in demand. From approximately 6.5 million pounds in 1950, consumption was nearly doubled in 1951 as a result of the Korean War and rose to 11.5 million pounds. Then in 1954, a year of low steel production, tungsten consumption shrank to 4 million pounds, picked up in 1956 to 9 million pounds, fell off to 5.32 million pounds in 1958, and rose to 11.6 million pounds in 1960.

With the termination of tungsten imports from China the pattern of foreign suppliers to the United States underwent a change. About 83 per cent of total imports in 1960 came from Brazil, Australia, Portugal, and Bolivia, in order of importance. The remainder came from ten other countries.

WORLD RESERVES AND PRODUCTION

Workable tungsten deposits have been found in many areas of the world. A noteworthy concentration of better grade deposits occurs in a belt bordering the Pacific Ocean. Exceptions are a very productive mine in North Carolina, a large producing district on the Iberian Peninsula of Europe, and scattered deposits in Africa, Europe, and Asia. The commercial tungsten ores are scheelite and wolframite. The latter includes a number of tungsten-bearing minerals.

By far the largest and richest known tungsten deposits in the world are in China, which accounted for more than one-fourth of world production from 1905 to 1948, and in 1937, its peak year, produced almost one-half of total world output. In China, production costs are so low and the tungsten ore is of such a high grade that the possible re-entry of China into international markets is a powerful deterrent to large investments elsewhere in the world. The second largest tungsten reserves are in the United States, followed by those in South Korea, which are said to be one of the world's greatest accumulations of tungsten.

TABLE 11

ESTIMATED WORLD TUNGSTEN RESERVES
(measured, indicated, inferred)
(in millions)

Country	Units of Contained WO^3
China	130
United States	10
Korea	7
Burma	5
Brazil	2.5
Bolivia	2.5
Australia	1.6
Malaya	1.4
Portugal	1.2
Spain	.65
Peru	.55
Argentina	.5
Canada	.5
Thailand	.5
Mexico	.06

SOURCE: *Mineral Facts and Problems,* U. S. Bureau of Mines, Washington, D. C., 1956.

Known reserves of tungsten in the Free World are not considered ample to support production at the rate of the early 1950s for an extended period. "Without aggressive exploration and development" says a 1954 report of the Bureau of Mines, "it seems probable that in less than 10 and 20 years, respectively, domestic and foreign mines will be depleted to the extent that 1953-54 production rates could not be duplicated."

Vanadium

Symbol	Atomic Number	Atomic Weight	Melt. Pt. (°F)
V	23	50.95	3,150 ± 90

Vanadium, together with molybdenum, is one of the major alloying elements in which the United States is self-sufficient. It is not only self-sufficient, it is the world's largest producer and consumer of the metal.

USES AND CONSUMPTION

Vanadium steel was introduced in 1907 to the automotive industry by Henry Ford, who, by the size of his order, lifted alloy steel production from a small-order business to a tonnage basis. Vanadium continues to be used in steels for automobiles and has widened out into other applications, such as low-alloy structural steels and high-speed tool steels. The chief effect of vanadium is to improve the heat-treating characteristics and mechanical properties of steel and a little goes a long way. In high-speed tool steels, the vanadium content ranges from about 0.50 to 2.50 per cent, although occasionally it may be higher. Alloy tool steels, other than high-speed steels, contain 0.20 to 1.00 per cent vanadium. The quantity of vanadium added to engineering steels is only 0.01 to 0.25 per cent. Most steels containing over 0.50 per cent vanadium are for special purposes. Vanadium may be alloyed singly with carbon steel, but it is generally combined with chromium, nickel, manganese, boron and tungsten. Vanadium is added to molten steel in the form of ferrovanadium containing from 35 to 55 per cent vanadium. Domestic vanadium consumption in 1960 was 2,000 tons, of which more than 75 per cent was used in high-speed and other alloy steels.

RESERVES

Vanadium is widely distributed in minute quantities throughout the crust of the earth but deposits in which it is concentrated highly enough to justify extraction are few in number. The chief ores are patronite, carnotite, roscoelite (vanadium mica), and vanadinite. The principal world sources of vanadium are the sulphide deposits in Peru, the vanadium-bearing sandstone in the United States and the vanadate deposits in Northern Rhodesia and South-west Africa.

For many years vanadium production in the United States yielded uranium as a by-product, but with the advent of atomic energy, the enormous demand for uranium reversed the situation and vanadium is now a by-product of uranium. Since the Atomic Energy Commission entered the region of carnotite vanadium ores in the Colorado Plateau to procure uranium, the supply of domestic vanadium, plus imports from Peru, have exceeded consumption and the surplus has been stored in the National Strategic Stockpile. The surfeit of vanadium in the United States has had repercussions elsewhere. In 1956, for the first time in many years, Peru was not an exporter.

The principal deterrent to a wider use of vanadium is the present high cost of production. There are many steels in which vanadium could take the place of chromium, nickel, or molybdenum, but its higher cost limits its use.

Colorado is the leading vanadium-ore producer in the United States and normally accounts for about 70 per cent of domestic production, followed

TABLE 12

WORLD PRODUCTION OF TUNGSTEN ORE AND CONCENTRATE
(60 PER CENT WO[3] BASIS), BY COUNTRIES,
1950–1954 (AVERAGE) AND 1960, IN NET TONS

Country	(Average) 1950-1954	1960
North America:		
Canada	1,066	—
Mexico	454	198
United States (shipments)	8,398	7,325
Total	9,918	7,523
South America:		
Argentina	528	840
Bolivia (exports)	3,788	2,370
Brazil (exports)	1,606	2,205
Peru	715	573
Total	6,637	5,988
Europe:		
Austria	—	243
Finland	49	—
France	1,004	825
Italy	17	9
Portugal	4,982	3,203
Spain	2,437	830
Sweden	437	391
USSR[2]	8,300	10,500
United Kingdom	75	—
Yugoslavia	120[1]	110[2]
Total[2]	17,420	16,100
Asia:		
Burma	1,758	1,755
China[1]	18,300	22,000
Hong Kong	85	39
India	10	3
Japan	481	1,091

by Utah and Arizona. Production in the United States of contained vanadium was 4,971 tons in 1960, compared to the 1950-1954 average of 2,476 tons.

FUTURE OUTLOOK

Although little is known or published concerning potential vanadium reserves, because of the metal's close association with uranium and the consequent security restriction on such information, the Parley Report sanguinely expected the supply of vanadium to be ample for the Free World needs in 1975. If the situation should ever arise where the deposits

TABLE 12 (Continued)

WORLD PRODUCTION OF TUNGSTEN ORE AND CONCENTRATE
(60 PER CENT WO[3] BASIS), BY COUNTRIES,
1950–1954 (AVERAGE) AND 1960, IN NET TONS

Country	1950-1954 (Average)	1960
Korea:		
North[2]	1,410	5,500
Republic of	4,090	5,870
Malaya, Federation of	93	46
Thailand	1,565	486
Total[2]	27,800	36,800
Africa:		
Algeria	28	—
Congo, Republic of the, and Ruanda Urundi	1,073	1,138
Morocco: Southern zone	20	—
Nigeria	15	—
Rhodesia and Nyasaland, Federation of:		
Southern Rhodesia	298	11
South-West Africa	141	154
Tanganyika (exports)	13	—
Uganda (exports)	195	84
Union of South Africa	341	37
United Arab Republic (Egypt Region)	10	—
Total	2,134	1,424
Oceania:		
Australia	2,210	1,760[2]
New Zealand	42	11
Total	2,252	1,770[2]
World Total (estimate)	66,160	69,600

SOURCE: *Minerals Yearbook*, U. S. Department of the Interior, Washington, D. C., I, 1956, 1960.
[1] This table incorporates some revisions. Data do not add exactly to totals shown because of rounding where estimated figures are included in the detail.
[2] Estimate.

in the Colorado Plateau and Peru were insufficient to meet demands for full military mobilization, other large potential domestic reserves could be brought into use.

WORLD PRODUCTION

Since data on the quantity of vanadium recovered as a by-product from iron ore and other raw materials are lacking, it is impossible to determine the world production of vanadium from all sources. Table 13 excludes production by Republic of the Congo, Mexico, Morocco, Norway, Spain, and USSR. Peru, the world's leading producer for many years, shut down its mines in 1956, as mentioned earlier.

TABLE 13

WORLD PRODUCTION OF VANADIUM IN ORES AND
CONCENTRATE, 1950–1954 (AVERAGE) AND 1960, IN NET TONS

Country	1950-1954 (Average)	1960
North America:		
United States (recoverable vanadium)	2,476[1]	4,971
South America:		
Peru (content of concentrate)	403	—
Europe:		
Finland	—	550[1]
Africa:		
Rhodesia and Nyasaland, Federation of:		
Northern Rhodesia (recovered vanadium)	29	—
South-West Africa (recoverable vanadium)	565	839
Union of South Africa (Transvaal)	—	620[1]
World Total (estimate)	3,473	6,980

SOURCE: *Minerals Yearbook,* U. S. Department of the Interior, Washington, D. C., I, 1956, 1960.
[1] Estimate.

Zirconium

Symbol	Atomic Number	Atomic Weight	Melt. Pt. (°F)
Zr	40	91.22	3,200 ± 1,300

Zirconium is the best material found so far for nuclear reactors. It is another metal whose use by the steel industry is of relatively minor importance. Zirconium, added up to a maximum of 0.60 per cent to some stainless steels, improves machinability.

Zirconium is added to steel in the form of one or more of its alloys. One alloy contains 12 to 15 per cent zirconium and 39 to 43 per cent silicon and another 35 to 40 per cent zirconium and 37 to 52 per cent silicon. The alloys are generally added to the steel after it has been tapped from a furnace into a ladle.

Zirconium is closely associated with hafnium in nature and both are extracted from the same ores. Separation of the two metals is extremely difficult, but it must be done for nuclear purposes because even a slight trace of hafnium vitiates the low-neutron absorption property of zirconium. World reserves of zirconium are immense. United States reserves are greater than the foreseeable demand within the next one hundred years. The chief problem in the way to wider use of zirconium is to develop a continuous low-cost process for the extraction of pure metal from the ore.

The Fabulous Coal Chemicals

A few years ago, United States Steel Corporation published a booklet on the cover of which was the reproduction of a hand holding a lump of coal and above were the words, "What's that you've got in your hand?" The text began, "It's very likely that within the past five minutes you have picked up, touched or looked at some article made from coal." If the time element were stretched to include a normal day in the life of the average American, it may be said that in the course of it he could not escape picking up, touching, or looking at—and actually using—many of the thousands of useful products derived from bituminous coal. Some of these products might be dyes in fabrics or the coloring matter in plastics. Other products might be the fabrics themselves, such as women's and men's hose, other garments for both sexes, drapes, upholstery, and carpets. Or again, these products might be synthetic rubber in furniture cushions, pillows, or automobile tires; or if the day is rainy, in waterproof clothing. What would be encountered most frequently would be plastics, beginning with a toothbrush in the morning and perhaps a comb and hairbrush. Plastics would also be met in radio and television cabinets, telephone instruments, the handles of kitchen utensils, dishes and bowls, stain-resistant work surfaces on counters and tables. Chemicals from coal would find their way into detergents, used to wash the family dishes and laundry. Some products would be volatile. Women's perfumes and toilet waters and the fragrances of lipstick and soap contain synthetic ingredients that originally came from lumps of coal. These are but a few of the many thousands of products based to greater or less degree on chemicals

197

derived from coal which the average man or woman might encounter in a normal day.

Bituminous coal is a complex substance. It was formed millions of years ago when deep beds of organic material that originated in living plants were covered by thick layers of sediments. Over long periods of time, heat and pressure transformed the sediments into rocks and the organic material into coal. When bituminous coal is decomposed by dry distillation at high temperature in the ovens of a coke plant, the chemical elements making up the coal either are driven off as elemental gases; react with each other in a variety of ways to form complex chemical compounds that are the bases of coal chemicals; or remain in the ovens as a hard, cellular residue known as coke. The coal chemicals, as such, are not in the coal originally, but are formed either during the coking process or in the recovery processes. Over 350 chemical compounds have been identified in the products of the coking process and more compounds probably could be isolated. Most of the known compounds have no practical use, or are found in such small quantities that they are not recovered at present. The coal chemicals that are recovered have considerable commercial and industrial importance. These chemicals come from the volatile substances that issue from the breakdown of coal in coke ovens. The volatile substances fall into three main groups: gas, light oil, and tar. Further processing of the gas yields ammonia, and a fuel gas consisting of hydrogen, methane, and ethylene. Light oil products include benzene, toluene, xylene, and solvent naphtha. Tar is distilled to produce napthalene, creosote, pitch, tar acids, and tar bases. From these products, by synthesis and chemical reaction, many thousands of useful products are derived. The manufacture of coal chemicals has become Big Business in the full sense of the term. In 1960, coal chemicals used or sold in the United States were valued at $306,745,388.[1] Many products which trace their origin to coal have displaced traditional materials such as wood, glass, and natural fibers in hundreds of applications and offer rugged competition to steel, copper, brass, and aluminum. About one-fifth of all the coal mined in the United States is processed in coke ovens or gas retorts, and about 88 per cent of the coke made from coal is produced by the steel industry.

ORIGIN AND GROWTH OF BY-PRODUCT COKE OVENS

The origin of the coking process and the introduction of coke as a blast furnace fuel in the first decade of the eighteenth century was described in Chapter 5, and the rise and development of the coking industry in the United States was narrated in Chapter 10. In Chapter 5, we learned that coal was first coked in turf-covered mounds in the open air, similar to the method used in making charcoal from wood, and that the next step was to construct dome-shaped enclosures of brick called beehive ovens. The same kind of oven was described by the German alchemist, Glauber, in

1657 for making wood tar. One of the first patents, if not the first, dealing with the recovery of products from coal, was issued in England in 1681 to Johann Becher and Henry Serle for "a new way of makeing pitch, and tarre out of pit cole, never before found out or used by any other." But since wood tar was more fluid than coal tar, no use was made of the patent until the time of the American Revolution, when England was cut off from her supply of wood tar from the colonies; then she turned to coal tar to paint and seal the bottoms of English ships.[2]

It was nearly a century later before an attempt was made to recover by-products from the coking process on a commercial scale. In 1766 Johann Kaspar Staudt built at Sulzbach, near Saarbrucken, Germany, what may have been the first chemical recovery installation ever constructed. The battery of nine ovens was externally heated and the coal charge was totally enclosed except for a small outlet through which passed the vaporized products of the coking process. The light oil products were collected and used for miner's lamps, and the heavier tar products were recovered and sold as a grease for cart wheels. Lampblack and sal ammoniac were also collected. Goethe visited the plant in 1771, and in spite of Staudt's optimistic reports about the success of his operations, the poet reported that "all failed together on account of the many ends in view."[3]

In 1781, a patent was granted to Sir Archibald Cochrane, Earl of Dundonald, for a method of "extracting or making tar, pitch, essential oils, volatile alkali, minerals acids, salts, and cinders from pit-coal." The patents of Staudt and Sir Archibald did not attract much attention, possibly because they were not too successful commercially, and chemicals were not recovered from coal on any considerable scale until the advent of the coal gas industry at the turn of the century. The tar and liquor which were produced during the manufacture of illuminating gas were at first a source of trouble and embarrassment to the gas companies. The products were of no commercial value, a nuisance to store and could not be indiscriminately dumped.[4] It was the chemists who supplied the key to commercial uses of coal tar. In the first half of the nineteenth century, naphthalene and benzene were isolated from coal tar, and in 1856 the first aniline dyes were discovered, founding the very profitable coal-tar-dye industry. The coal chemical industry was born. It grew slowly for some years, its growth attendant on both the discoveries of scientists and the development of coke ovens capable of supplying coal chemicals in diversity and volume.

The growing markets for by-products of the city gas works were at first viewed with indifference by the manufacturers of metallurgical coke for the iron industry. There was some basis for this attitude because good quality blast furnace coke could not be made in the new, closed, retort type of ovens then being developed on the Continent.

The earliest records of a rectangular retort-type of oven are found in Germany dating from 1830. Vertical flues within the walls were used for the transmission of heat. The "slot-type" oven, with a common heating wall between each oven, built in a series called "batteries," like slices in a loaf of bread, underwent further development in Belgium. At the end of each oven were removable doors. When the coking process was completed, a ram was driven through the oven, forcing out the coke. Based on this principle, several varieties of chemical recovery ovens appeared in Belgium and France during the second half of the nineteenth century.[5] In 1882 Dr. Thomas von Bauer of Germany recommended the use of the Siemens regenerative principle for coke ovens, and in 1883 Gustave Hoffmann patented the idea. The German patent was bought by Dr. C. Otto and Company and applied to the Otto-Coppée oven. The first Otto-Hoffmann coke plant was built near Wanne in 1883. Improved ovens of this type produced good metallurgical coke and quickly gained popularity in Germany. By 1897, more than 10,000 Otto-Hoffmann ovens had been constructed in Germany alone. Many of them did not recover chemicals, but the plants of Dr. C. Otto and Company produced some 7 million gallons of tar, 400,000 gallons of benzene and 14,000 tons of ammonia products in that year. The chemical recovery coking industry of Europe was firmly established.[6]

Chemical Recovery Coke Ovens in the United States

The first chemical recovery coke plant in the United States was erected at Syracuse, New York, in 1892 to provide ammonia for the production of soda ash and caustic soda. The Semet-Solvay coke ovens were the type installed. They proved to be very successful, and in 1895 fifty Semet-Solvay coke ovens were constructed for the American Manganese Manufacturing Company at Dunbar, Pennsylvania, followed in 1898 by thirty similar ovens at Ensley, Alabama, for the Tennessee Coal, Iron and Railroad Company, which later became a subsidiary of U.S. Steel and is now a division. In 1898-1899 ninety Semet-Solvay ovens were erected near Wheeling, West Virginia, for the National Tube Company, which also later became a U.S. Steel subsidiary, now a division.[7]

Observing the advancements being made by the Semet-Solvay process in the United States, Dr. C. Otto and Company began to eye the American market and formed the Otto Coke and Chemical Company which was soon enlarged into the United Coke and Gas Company. The new company began construction in 1894 of sixty Otto-Hoffmann coke ovens with a full chemical recovery system for the Cambria Steel Company at Johnstown, Pennsylvania. This was the first chemical recovery plant built in the United States specifically to supply blast furnace coke. The United Coke and Chemical Company next moved into Pittsburgh with the intention of supplying the blast furnaces of the area with coke made from Pittsburgh seam coal. In 1897, 120 ovens with associated chemical recovery plants were built near McKeesport for operation by the Pittsburgh Coke and Gas

Company. The largest installation toward the end of the century was a coke plant of 400 Otto-Hoffmann ovens at Everett, near Boston, Massachusetts, for the New England Gas and Coke Company. Production began in 1899. In 1902, ten years after the work was commenced on the Semet-Solvay ovens at Syracuse, the chemical recovery coking industry had expanded from twelve ovens, producing 12,850 tons of coke annually to 1,669 ovens producing 1,403,588 tons of coke, with 1,346 ovens under construction.[8] In 1935 there were ninety chemical recovery coke plants which carbonized 97 per cent of the coking coal used in the United States.[9]

Early in the present century, U.S. Steel became interested in the production of better quality coke. The corporation's interest in the recovery of chemicals was secondary. Few people at that time could envisage the future growth of the coal chemical industry. In 1906, a group of U.S. Steel engineers visited Europe to study the coking processes being used there. After the engineers returned and made their report, U.S. Steel invited Heinrich Koppers, a German engineer and inventor of the Koppers coke ovens, to come to the United States for consultation. As a result of the talks, U.S. Steel asked Koppers to design and supervise construction of 280 ovens at the Joliet (Illinois) works of the Illinois Steel Company, a subsidiary. The first coke was pushed on September 15, 1908. The Joliet installation proved to be very successful, and in 1911 U.S. Steel installed 490 Koppers ovens at its large new steel plant, the Gary (Indiana) Works.[10]

In 1914 a group of Pittsburgh men bought a controlling interest in the H. Koppers Company and moved the headquarters of the company from Chicago to their own city. During World War I, the remaining German interests of the company were taken over by the Alien Property Custodian and eventually passed into American hands. The name of the company was subsequently changed to the Koppers Company, Inc. It grew into the largest designer and builder of chemical recovery coke ovens in the United States.

The chemical recovery coke industry developed at a fairly even pace in the twentieth century until World War I, during which production was more than doubled, rising from 11,219,943 tons in 1914 to 25,997,580 tons in 1918. There was another spurt of activity during World War II, when coke production reached a wartime peak of 67,064,795 tons in 1944. An all-time record production of 73,860,692 tons was set in 1957. These figures refer to coke produced in chemical recovery ovens.

On December 31, 1960, there were 15,323 slot-type chemical recovery coke ovens in seventy-four coke plants with a total annual capacity of 78,876,900 tons of coke. Of the 15,323 coke ovens, 13,298 located at fifty-four furnace plants, were owned by or financially affiliated with the iron and steel industry. The remaining 2,025 ovens at nineteen plants, are classified as "merchant plants."[11] Merchant plants, as defined by the Bureau of Mines, "include those that manufacture metallurgical, industrial and residential heating grades of coke for sale on the open market; coke plants associated with chemical companies or gas utilities; and those affiliated with local iron works, where only a small part (less than 50 per cent of their output) is used in affiliated blast furnaces."

PRODUCTION AND VALUE OF COAL CHEMICALS

Coal chemicals are of great importance to the organic-chemical industry. According to the Manufacturing Chemists' Association, Inc., the production of industrial chemicals since 1939 "has grown at an average rate of about 10 per cent." For many years, coal carbonization was the principal source of raw materials for the organic-chemical industry, but in a recent period, particularly since World War II, requirements of chemical raw materials increased at a faster pace than could be supplied by coke plants and new sources of supply became necessary. The processing of petroleum and natural gas increased tremendously the flow of chemical raw materials to the chemical industry. Whereas coal chemical recovery plants furnished most of the raw materials for manufacturing synthetic organic chemicals before World War II, it was estimated in 1959 that coke plants supplied less than one-third of the total used.[12]

Nevertheless, the coke industry remains an important source of coal chemicals. It will be seen in Table 14 that coal chemicals sold in 1960 were valued at $274,291,638. (Coal chemicals *used* and sold were worth $306,745,388.[13]

Modern Coal Chemical Recovery Ovens

The modern American coal chemical recovery oven is 30 to 43 feet in length, 10 to 14 feet in height, and 15 to 20 inches in mean width. A battery may consist of ten to one hundred ovens. In front, in back, and on top of the ovens are tracks. Those on top are for cars which carry the coal to be charged through openings in each oven. Each car contains the exact amount of coal, which may be as much as 22 tons, to be charged into the oven chamber. The chambers are heated by combustion gases which pass through flues or passageways within the silica brick walls which separate the individual ovens. It takes one hour per inch of oven width to convert coal into coke, or from fifteen to twenty hours. When the coke is ready to be removed, a machine moves along the tracks at one side of the ovens. It stops, successively, in front of each oven, from which the doors at both ends have been removed. A long plunger pushes the coke out of the opposite side of the oven where it falls in a fiery cascade into a "hot car." The car is drawn by a locomotive to a quenching station where the coke is cooled under a water spray. The coke, after passing over a screen, is transported to the blast furnace storage bins.

Air is excluded from the ovens in the coking process, during which the temperature reaches 1,900° to 2,000° F. As the heat progresses from the side walls to the center of the coal charge, the coal melts into a thick, bubbling, gummy substance, emitting gas and vapor which pass into a large collector main leading to the maze of pipes which constitute the coal chemical recovery plant. After all of the gases and vapor have been driven out of the coal, a hard cellular substance, called coke, remains in the oven. About 20 to 30 per cent by weight of the oven's charge of coal is in the form of vapor. After the coal chemicals are recovered from the vapor, the remaining gas is used as a fuel to heat the ovens and in other steel operations. If the gas is not so used, it is sold to outside customers.

About 75 per cent by weight of the coal charged into ovens is recovered as coke, about 17 per cent as gas, and 8 per cent as tar, ammonia, and crude light oil. A ton of coal yields 1,400 pounds of metallurgical coke, 100 pounds of screenings, 10,000 cubic feet of gas, 8 gallons of coal tar, 3 gallons of light oil, and 20 pounds of ammonium sulfate.

During passage of the vapors through the collector main, most of the tar condenses in it. Further cooling removes the rest of the tar as well as ammonia liquor. Both tar and ammonia liquor then go through to settling tanks for separation. Tar from the settling tanks is further refined. Several important coal chemicals are obtained by fractional distillation of the tar.

The ammonia liquor is treated with steam and lime to remove the ammonia, which is then mixed with the ammonia-laden gas leaving the tar extractor. Going through a vessel called a saturator, the ammonia is treated with sulfuric acid to form ammonium sulfate which is recovered in crystalline form.

After the tar and ammonia have been removed from the coke oven gas, it is cooled and treated with absorbing oil to extract the light oil, which is subjected to fractional distillation. The principal products of this distillation are benzene, toluene, xylene, and solvent naphthas.

NEW USES OF COKE OVEN GAS

Great as is the diversity and quantity of presently recovered coal chemicals, they tap only a small percentage of the total volume of coke oven gas. The gas averages 57 per cent hydrogen, 29 per cent methane, 2.5 per cent ethylene, 6 per cent carbon monoxide, and lesser amounts of other gases. Recovery of the hydrogen would more than double the amount of recoverable materials. The atmosphere abounds in nitrogen. A commercial process for extracting nitrogen from the air and combining it with hydrogen was developed in Germany in 1914. Nitrogen, separated from the air, can be combined with hydrogen to form anhydrous ammonia, which, in turn, can be combined with other materials, or chemically converted, to form ammonium nitrate, ammonium phosphate, and nitric acid.

The first synthetic ammonia plant in the United States designed to use coke oven gas as its source of hydrogen was placed in operation in 1956 by the Ketona Chemical Company at Ketona, Alabama. It has an annual

TABLE 14

COAL-CHEMICAL MATERIALS, EXCLUSIVE OF BREEZE, PRODUCED AT COKE-OVEN INSTALLATIONS IN THE UNITED STATES IN 1960[1]

Product		Produced	Sold Quantity	Value Total	Average
Tar, crude	gallons	687,559,703	333,253,840	$ 42,640,937	$ 0.128
Tar derivatives:					
Sodium phenolate		2,945,432	2,803,810	447,018	.159
Crude chemical oil		27,578,681	27,325,877	5,763,027	.211
Pitch-of-Tar:					
Soft	net tons	748,921	53,608	1,263,976	23.578
Medium		57,944	46,933	1,266,376	26.948
Hard		233,667	76,981	2,628,865	34.150
Other tar derivatives[2]		—	—	13,778,687	—
Ammonia:					
Sulfate	net tons	631,643	594,108	17,231,502	29.004
Liquor (NH$_3$ content)		14,884	9,397	635,833	67.663
Di-and mono-ammonium phosphate	net tons	46,067	36,523	3,977,336	108.899
Total		—	—	21,844,671	—
Sulfate equivalent of all forms	net tons	735,441	596,624	—	—
NH$_3$ equivalent of all forms		189,598	171,974	—	—

Gas:				
Used under boilers, etc. M cubic feet	835,292,413[3]	66,368,699	13,107,186	.197
Used in steel or allied plants		394,535,298	94,850,750	.240
Distributed through city mains		29,777,016	11,964,585	.402
Sold for industrial use		30,095,237	5,812,894	.193
Total	835,292,413	520,776,250	125,735,415	.241
Crude light oil gallons	234,500,663[4]	21,280,379	3,845,657	.181
Light oil derivatives:				
Benzene:				
Specification grades (excluding gallons	135,326,446	137,784,200	44,166,604	.321
Motor grade	769,949	774,291	141,858	.183
Motor grade	30,398,543	31,566,744	6,638,373	.210
Toulene (all grades)	8,075,608	7,853,506	2,061,013	.262
Xylene (all grades)				
Solvent naptha (crude and refined) gallons	4,586,363	4,578,240	1,209,360	.264
Other light oil derivatives	3,686,255	1,634,153	224,455	.135
Total	182,843,164	184,191,134	54,441,663	.296
Intermediate light oil	3,590,177	3,713,616	635,346	.171
Value of all coal-chemical materials sold	—	—	274,291,638	—

SOURCE: Coke and Coal Chemicals in 1960, Bureau of Mines, Washington, D. C.

[1] Includes products of tar distillation conducted by coke-oven operators under same corporate name.

[2] Creosote oil, cresols, cresylic acid, napthalene, phenol, phridine, refined tar, and tar paint.

[3] Includes gas used for heating ovens and gas wasted.

[4] 218,242,334 gallons refined by coke-oven operators to make derived products shown.

capacity of 45,000 tons of anhydrous ammonia. In 1957, Columbia-Geneva Steel Division of U.S. Steel put an anhydrous ammonia plant in operation at Geneva, Utah. It has an annual capacity of 70,000 tons of anhydrous ammonia and is the first such plant in the United States attached to an integrated steel works. In addition to anhydrous ammonia, the U.S. Steel plant produces ammonium nitrate and nitric acid. At Hamilton, Ontario, in 1958, the North American Cyanamid Company completed construction of a plant with an annual capacity of 52,500 tons of anhydrous ammonia and 66,000 tons of urea.

Anhydrous ammonia, which contains 82 per cent nitrogen by weight, is an excellent fertilizer. It is handled as a liquid, under pressure, and may be applied directly to the soil by special rigs or may be injected into irrigation water. As a quick source of nitrogen, its popularity is growing rapidly in farming regions. Ammonia is used industrially for the control of algae in the purification of water, as a refrigerant, and in several chemical processing procedures. Anhydrous ammonia is also used in the manufacture of ammonium nitrate, another valuable fertilizer. In the extraction of nitrogen from the atmosphere, considerable quantities of oxygen are also recovered. The oxygen thus obtained at U.S. Steel's anhydrous ammonia plant in Utah is uitlized by the steelmaking departments.

DISCOVERY AND APPLICATIONS OF COAL CHEMICALS

Dyes Established New Industry

Prince Albert, consort to Queen Victoria, may be called the first patron of the coal chemical industry. He took an active part in encouraging the development of English science, and after the Royal College of Chemistry was founded, he looked about for an eminent chemist to take charge of the laboratory. In 1845, he wrote to a German Professor of Chemistry, Baron Justus von Liebig, asking him to recommend someone for the post. Von Liebig suggested one of his most promising recent graduates, August Wilhelm Hofmann, who was offered and accepted the chair. Some years earlier, he was one of the few chemists who were experimenting with coal tar. He was the first to isolate benzene and from it made nitrobenzol, from which, in turn, he derived aniline. Benzene was used as a rubber solvent and was the basis of the first Mackintosh waterproof cloth. Benzene was also sold as a cleansing fluid.[14]

Hofmann had a precocious eighteen-year-old chemistry student named William Henry Perkin, who began investigating coal tars. He succeeded in making synthetic aniline purple, the first coal chemical dye. He patented his process in 1856 and a year later built a small dyestuff plant to produce the purple dye for the English textile trade. This was the first business created by the coal chemical industry. Perkin's dye was found to be superior to the purple dye then being used and he was rewarded with a ready market for his product. His French patent had flaws in its specification which made it invalid. It was pirated by French dyers who developed a purple shade which they named *mauve*. The new color became the rage and the era of its popularity is known as the Mauve Decade.

At this period, there were only three reasonably fast dyes: black, red, and blue. Fired by Perkin's success, chemists in England and on the Continent worked busily in their laboratories, and within five years half a dozen new colors were found and put on the market. The prospering dye industry literally created a market for coal tar, which was then produced exclusively at gas works.

An intense race developed among chemists to synthetize alizarin, the red coloring substance in madder root, the source of red dye since ancient times. The dyers of Thebes used madder to dye the mummy clothes of Tutankhamen, and the same coloring matter has been found in Egyptian tombs dating seven centuries earlier. Three German chemists won the race and patented their process for making synthetic alizarin in England on June 25, 1869. Perkin obtained a patent one day later. His process proved to be the more successful of the two. Within ten years, about 350,000 acres devoted to growing madder plants, chiefly in France, Holland, Spain, and Turkey, were withdrawn from production.

There was even more intense competition to synthetize indigo, the source of blue color. The German chemist, Adolf Baeyer, identified indigotin as the organic coloring ingredient of indigo in 1870. The prize to be won in synthetizing indigotin was greater than that for alizarin, since the value of indigo sold every year was double that of madder. It was twenty-seven years before a commercially feasible process was worked out for the manufacture of synthetic indigotin from coal tar, and the feat was accomplished in Germany. Within seven years, nearly one and a half million acres, chiefly in India, passed from growing indigo to raising millet and rice.

Such were the beginnings of man's utilization of coal tar to duplicate organic compounds of nature, and his efforts were first confined to dyestuffs. Later, chemists were to create new products never known before, such as plastics, synthetic rubber, nylon, certain medicines, and many others, but those days were still far off. From a brilliant start in England, the making of dyes from coal tar moved over to Germany long before the close of the twentieth century. England was content to sell the raw materials from her coke plants to Germany and buy back the extracted chemicals. By 1900, England was importing from Germany about 90 per cent of her dyes and almost all of her coal tar medicinals. Fourteen years later she was to pay dearly for this dependence.

Germany embarked on the coal chemical industry with zeal and typical Germanic thoroughness. The heads of chemical firms, themselves technically trained men, encouraged fundamental and applied research into the mysteries of bituminous coal and particularly synthetic dyes. The government, aware of the value of the new industry in peace and in war, lent a helping hand. In 1904, a number of leading chemical companies pooled their patents and divided up customers and markets in the German Dye Cartel which dominated world markets until 1914.

Struggles of American Dye Industry

A few attempts to manufacture dyes in the United States were made in the 1860s, and by 1870 Brooklyn and Albany were the sites of modestly successful small dye plants. The tariff law of 1871 provided protection behind which a coal chemical industry might have been built. Several firms boldly entered upon the distillation of coal tar obtained from gas works. The supply of coal tar was far from plentiful. It was not recovered from beehive ovens then in existence. It was to be another thirty to forty years before coal chemical recovery ovens produced chemicals in any appreciable quantity. By importing coal chemicals from Germany, it was hoped to obtain the necessary raw materials for synthetizing certain products, one of them being aniline for dyes. But the tariff law of 1883, which reduced import duties on dyes, dashed these bright hopes. Later the tariff was raised, but it was too late for the prostrate dye industry to recover.

Up until World War I, the German Dye Cartel sold at a lower price in America than in Europe all dyes manufactured by American firms until they were forced out of business. The Germans offered basic coal chemicals, such as benzene and naphthalene, at such low prices that it did not pay the American distillers to separate them from coal tar. When World War I shut off imports from Germany, the stocks of German imports were quickly consumed and there developed a famine in all coal chemicals. Less than one-quarter of the coke produced in America came from chemical recovery ovens. The first critical shortage was in phenol, the basis of explosives. The Allies were short of explosives and their supplies of phenol were woefully inadequate. Britain and France turned in desperation to the United States. Benzol must first be produced for conversion into phenol. The steel industry began rapidly to replace beehive ovens with coal chemical recovery ovens. From the end of 1915 to the end of 1918, monthly production of benzol increased from 1.75 million to 5 million gallons and of toluol from 525,000 to 1.4 million gallons.

The clamorous demand for dyes and medicinals also had to be met in order to replace the vanished German stocks. Dyes and medicinals required the same raw materials as explosives. The shortage of dyes threatened to throw 400,000 textile operators out of work. England put dyestuffs on her contraband list. Before the United States entered the war, Germany let it be known that she would be glad to exchange dyes and medicines for American cotton, but cotton, plus nitric acid, makes smokeless gun powder. England and France strongly opposed the shipment of cotton to Germany. Finally an arrangement was worked out by which England allowed 600,000 pounds of dyes to pass through her blockade. Later, the German submarine, "Deutschland," dove under the British blockade and bobbed up in Baltimore and New London with cargoes of dyes and medicines.

With more than forty coal tar intermediates coming from the expanding coke industry, scores of American companies launched into the manufacture of dyes. By the end of 1916, the dye industry had grown from seven to forty-two plants and was making nearly one hundred dyes and medicines never produced before in the United States. The courage of the dye makers exceeded their knowledge. They had to learn the business practically from the ground up. They did not have access to descriptions of German dye-making methods contained in German patents reposing in the Patent Office. After the United States declared war on Germany on April 6, 1917, the government seized the properties of alien Germans, including 4,500 chemicals patents. In order to prevent a few large companies from acquiring an undue share of the patents, President Wilson created the Chemical Foundation, a public non-profit corporation, which bought up all the German patents for $250,000. The foundation licensed the patents to any *bona fide* American chemical manufacturer. In this way, the patents of the German Dye Cartel fell into American hands as a prize of war. Profiting from the patents and aided by large research organizations, the American chemical industry has since become completely independent of any foreign country and has itself created many wonders in this age of chemical wonders.

Nature's Aromas Duplicated

Perfumes, incense, and salt were among the first articles of international commerce. Cleopatra and the ladies of her court were lavish in the use of cosmetics, painting their eyelids with kohl, a mixture of black lead with the oxides of copper and iron. Myrrh, frankincense, cloves, cinnamon, sweet oils, and precious ointments, gathered from the far corners of the known world, were the chief forms of aromatics so prized in antiquity.

From Egypt, the fashion of perfumes and cosmetics spread to Rome, where, during the latter days of the Empire, it went to fantastic extremes. After the fall of Rome, the perfumer retired with his art to Arabia. He came out of his seclusion during the Italian Renaissance. From Italy, the art of perfumery moved to France, where the Golden Age of Cosmetics flourished during the seventeenth and eighteenth centuries. Louis XIV commanded that his royal apartments be sprayed with a different perfume every day.

Still later, practitioners in the new-found world of synthetic chemistry did not allow costly perfume oils and rare spices to escape their curiosity. There were plenty of incentives to tempt chemists to duplicate nature's aromas synthetically. Fortunes were to be made in artificial frankincense, myrrh, or roses. The first person who deliberately tried to synthetize a perfume was Perkin, who succeeded in producing coumarin, the aromatic principle of the tonka bean, the nut of a South American tree which was ground up and macerated with alcohol to yield an odor used largely to flavor snuff and to simulate the fragrance of new-mown hay. The first artificial perfume had been prepared in a laboratory. Subsequently, chemists were able to synthetize the fragrance of the violet, rose, geranium, sweet pea, lilac, sandalwood, and many others.

Synthetic aromatic chemicals, based on derivatives from coal, have an important place in the cosmetic industry. Through the wizardry of chemists, nature's lovely fragrances are reproduced singly, or in blends, for lotions, creams, toilet waters, perfumes, soaps, dentifrice, and home deodorizers.

The First Wonder Drug

A young chemist in Vienna, Paul Gelmo, working for a doctor's degree, synthetized a coal chemical which he described in his thesis, published in 1908. He named the compound sulfonamide, which has since been renamed sulfanilamide. Other members of the sulfanilamide group, then used as dyes, were isolated. In 1913, it was discovered that one of the dyes of this family destroyed certain bacteria *in vitro*. The next important event in the history of sulfanilamide occurred on Christmas day, 1932. On that date, Drs. Fritz Meitzsch and Joseph Klarer, employees of the German Dye Cartel, filed an application for a patent on a new dye, a derivative of sulfanilamide. The following May, it was reported that the dye had cured a child of blood poisoning. The Dye Cartel named the dye Streptozon, which was changed the following year to Prontosil. In 1933 and 1934 a number of German physicians reported that they had administered Prontosil successfully against streptococci infections. The news created no stir in medical or chemical circles, but outside of Germany a few alert biochemists began to pick up their ears. Also in 1933, within the Dye Cartel laboratory a thousand mice were given heavy injections of streptococcus bacteria, followed with large doses of Prontosil. Every mouse remained as lively as a healthy mouse can be. A similar experiment with rabbits was made with identical results. These sensational tests were reported briefly in a German medical journal in 1935. The article attracted little attention at the time, but it caught the eye of a few alert medical men.

In December 1936, Franklin Roosevelt, Jr., son of the President of the United States, was gravely ill in a Boston hospital with a double infection of the deadly killers—streptococci germs. Several of the doctors in attendance had read the article in the German medical journal, and upon consultation it was decided to administer the chemical which had been used so successfully on mice and rabbits, but never, so far as was known, on a human being. Young Roosevelt was injected with doses of Prontosil and he was also given tablets of Prontylin, a German trade name for sulfanilamide. His soaring temperature dropped and within three days he was out of danger. "Sulfa," the first miracle drug, derivative of a coal chemical, had saved the life of the President's son. Later, other sulfa drugs were produced: sulfapyridine, a chemical scourge of of pneumonia, and sulfathiazole, conqueror of germs that infect the lower digestive tract, causing dysentery, cholera, typhus, and typhoid.

Chemical derivatives of bituminous coal have been made to yield other drugs and medicines which are helping man in his conquest of disease, the preservation of health, and the alleviation of malaise. Among these are a few of the wonder-working antibiotics; arsenical compounds which are killers of syphilis; isoniazid, for the treatment of tuberculosis; atabrine, a substitute for quinine, used as a protection against malaria; the anesthetic, procaine; the well-known heart medicine, adrenalin; the barbituate, phenobarbital; vitamins, such as B comblex, nicotinic acid, and vitamin K, a blood coagulant; numerous antiseptics, including phenol and mercurochrome; and the sedatives, aspirin and phenacetin.

Not Rubber, but Rubberlike

Until World War II, the United States was entirely dependent on foreign sources for its rubber and consumed two-thirds of the rubber produced in the world. Most natural rubber came from the end of a 10,000-mile lifeline. Nazi Germany was equally dependent on imported rubber, and one of Hitler's top research imperatives was to find a substitute for natural rubber in preparation for his war of conquest. In 1936, he was able to announce that Germany was "Positively and forever . . . free from foreign domination of our necessary supplies of rubber."

In the United States, Dr. Elmer K. Bolton, in charge of organic research for the du Pont Company was speculating in 1925 on the possibility of making butadiene rubber from acetylene. At a meeting of the American Chemical Society that year, the remarks made about acetylene by Father Julius Nieuwland, Professor of Organic Chemistry at Notre Dame University, intrigued him. From further information furnished by the priest-scientist, Dr. Bolton set up a research program at du Pont which resulted in the laboratory production of neoprene, the first truly successful synthetic rubber. Du Pont built a factory for its commercial production, and by 1934 more than one hundred manufacturers were buying every pound of the output.

Meanwhile, German research teams intensified their investigation of other types of synthetic rubber. These were the Buna rubbers, Buna S, a mixed polymer of butadiene and styrene, and Buna N, a combination of butadiene and acrylonitrile. These two excellent rubber substitutes were being commercially produced in Germany in 1936. In Buna S, Hitler had the rubber he needed for his motorized blitzkrieg.

In 1940, the Standard Oil Company (New Jersey) announced that it had discovered a synthetic rubber, which it named "Butyl rubber," made from petroleum by a process, which, it claimed, was simpler and more direct than that required to produce Buna rubber. Butyl rubber never became a general purpose rubber because of processing difficulties, but its air-holding properties won it immediate recognition as a rubber for making inner tubes. In 1960, some of the former processing difficulties having been removed, Butyl rubber made its bow as a premium quality tire tread rubber.

With the fall of France in 1940, the possibility of a rubber shortage in the United States became more apparent. The government, with the advice and cooperation of the rubber companies, created a synthetic rubber industry in less than two years. It was decided to concentrate on a general purpose synthetic rubber similar to the German Buna S rubber. It was manufactured from butadiene and styrene. The coal chemical benzene is frequently used as a raw material in the manufacture of styrene.

S-type rubber, as the general purpose rubber came to be called, has retained the dominant position it acquired in the war. Passenger car tires of S-type rubber outwear those of natural rubber and are far cheaper. All types of synthetic rubber combined now fill 70 per cent of the rubber needs of the United States, and the S-type accounts for 80 per cent of all synthetic rubbers.

Plastics

When the white man brought firearms to the jungles of Africa, he set off a chain reaction which led to the creation of the first synthetic plastic. White and native hunters slaughtered herds of elephants for ivory tusks. The annihilation of the herds was carried so far that the supply of ivory dropped dangerously low and the price mounted. The largest American maker of billiard balls, Phelan and Collander of New York City, became alarmed over the prospective loss of their essential raw material. They offered a prize of $10,000 in gold for the best ivory substitute. Among the contestants was a printer from Albany, New York, John W. Hyatt. He did not win the award, but he continued his experiments and in 1868 produced a new material made from cellulose, which he called "Celluloid." In doing so, he introduced mankind to the Age of Plastics.

A New York industrialist, Colonel Marshall Lefferts, saw great possibilities in celluloid and was instrumental in forming the Celluloid Corporation which was enormously successful. Plastics were something new under the sun. The material could be made into sheets, rods, and tubes of various dimensions. It could be colorless or given any shade or color in the dye maker's kit. It could be made to simulate tortoise shell, coral, ivory, agate, or amber. It softened when heated and could be molded into shapes which it retained in cooling.

Celluloid had one serious drawback; it was flammable. But the unique advantages of celluloid opened up a great new world of possibilities, scarcely explored. The outstanding pioneer in the exploration was Dr. Leo Hendrick Baekeland, a chemist of Ghent, Belgium. Dr. Baekeland undertook to make a synthetic shellac. Shellac was then the product of a minute insect, *Coccus lacca*, native to India, which sucks the sap from a certain type of fig tree and in so doing coats itself with a red resin, shellac.

Dr. Baekeland hoped to find the answer in the reaction of phenol and formaldehyde, but in trial after trial he failed to come up with a shellac-like substance. One day he switched his line of approach. He applied heat with pressure to the tarry mass with which he was experimenting and obtained a clear liquid which promptly solidified. He emptied his little retort and from it popped a clear hemisphere, resembling amber. Here was an ideal molding material. With it, he made billiard balls, phonograph records, cups and bowls and other products. He named his new product Bakelite and introduced it to the Chemists' Club of New York in 1909. Bakelite first reached store counters as imitation amber in pipe-stems and cigar holders.

Other forms of plastics appeared on the market and new varieties, with special applications, are still forthcoming. Plastics, in their various forms, infiltrated the American economy. They did so because they were an answer to a need in the age of mass production for a material that could be manufactured expeditiously and inexpensively in identical form from a master mold. Plastics are a man-made substance which does not need to be machined, cut, sawed or planed, and can be made in any color desired. They do not require paint to protect them from the weather.

Today plastics constitute the most important market for coal chemicals. One of the early commercial plastics was polystyrene, dating from the 1930s. This material is still breaking production records year after year, despite competition from a host of rival plastics. The original drawback of polystyrene—brittleness—has been eliminated by modification with rubber and combination with other plastics. Polystyrene is seen in re-frigerator door liners, toys, housewares, radio cabinets, phonograph records, packaging, wall tile, insulating foam, and many other products. A large quantity of polystyrene continues to be made today from benzene, extracted from coke oven gas by the steel industry.

Phenolic resins, pioneered by Dr. Baekeland, are still important. Their chief use is in electrical insulation articles. They are also found in bottle caps, household appliance handles, washing machine agitators, and caster wheels. A large and steadily growing use of phenolic resins is for adhesives for a wide range of products, such as formica, plywood, rockwool insulation, grinding wheels, and automobile brakes. Minor, but still vital uses, are in spar varnishes and interior coatings for tin plate cans. Benzene plays a role in the production of phenolic resin through its incorporation in synthetic phenol. The coal chemical phenol, a tar product, is also used in substantial quantities in the preparation of phenolic resins.

Many other plastics can be made from coal chemicals. The synthetic fiber, nylon, is an example. Nylon hose are too well known to need only passing mention. Zipper slide fasteners of nylon can withstand the heat of an iron. Because of nylon's great strength and lightness, most parachutes are made of this material. The strength of nylon makes it popular with anglers as a fishing line. Nylon is also used for racquet strings and window screening and for the bristles of tooth and hair brushes. Automobile tires are strong and long-lasting when reinforced with nylon. This remarkable substance can also be used in the form of a plastic in such products as combs and the bodies of hair brushes. Its high resistance to abrasion qualifies it for use in frictionless gears, electric mixer blades, and parts of electric shavers and sewing machines.

Epoxy resins, polycarbonates, and polyurethanes, three relatively new plastics, have bright futures in adhesives, molded products and foams, respectively. Each of these plastics uses coal chemical raw materials.

Vinyl plastics, serving a multitude of purposes, such as raincoats, shower curtains, and packaging, is plasticized (made flexible) by the addition of phthalic anhydride, another coal chemical derivative. Were it not for phthalic anhydride, shower curtains would crack and vinyl plastic waterproof garments would be stiff and unusable. Vinyl-coated steel sheets, now so widely used, are described in Chapter 19. Phthalic anhydride is also used to improve the qualities of celluose plastic, which is still with us, although it has been largely supplanted by more versatile plastics.

The growing use of polyester plastics, which utilize the steel industry's coal chemicals in several ways, bears an ironic note because these are the plastics which have made the greatest strides in competition with steel. Polyester plastics, reinforced with materials such as fiber glass, paper, or cotton, will not dent, corrode, rot or transmit heat or electricity. Because of these several properties, polyester-reinforced plastics are extending their uses. There has been talk of a reinforced plastic automobile body; the material has already rendered service as the body of a popular sport model. The fastest use of reinforced plastic is as a flat or corrugated paneling for skylights and the side lighting of industrial buildings and for private use in covers for car ports and outdoor patios. Small boats of reinforced plastic are gaining a large share of the market for pleasure craft.

Food for the Soil

After the early American farmers began to deplete the soil of its natural plant food, they added fish, wood ashes, and animal manure as fertilizers. In the early 1800s, it was found that nitrogen makes plants greener and in combination with other ingredients increases crop yields. For its supply of nitrogen fertilizer materials, the United States was dependent on Chile for nitrate of soda and Peru for guano. The Peruvian guano deposits gave out after 1875, and Chilean nitrate of soda remained the only important source of nitrogen fertilizer until the coal chemical recovery ovens began to produce ammonium sulfate around the turn of the century.

The nitrogen in coke oven ammonia orginated from the protein in the bodies of plants and animals during the formation of coal millions of years ago. In coking, part of the nitrogen in the coal is combined with hydrogen and is driven off as ammonia gas, which, as described earlier, is combined with sulphuric acid to form ammonium sulfate. Although several other nitrogen fertilizers are now produced primarily from the fixation of atmospheric nitrogen, also mentioned earlier, coke oven ammonium sulfate remains an important fertilizer material to enrich the soil for growing food in many parts of the world.

Creosote and Pitch

Tar, the first coal product to be investigated by chemists, is now distilled to yield five principal products—creosote, pitch, naphthalene, tar acids, and tar bases. The last three constitute less than 25 per cent of the tar. Creosote and pitch are the major volume derivatives of tar, the first representing 25 to 30 per cent and the second 50 per cent.

Creosote is one of the most effective wood preservatives known, and almost all of the creosote produced in the United States is used for that purpose. The creosote is introduced into the wood under pressure. Railroads were the first users of creosoted wood in the United States and are still the largest consumers of creosote for impregnating ties, poles, bridge timbers, and freight car floorings. Public utility companies are, however, a very close second as important users of creosote in their poles which are known to give thirty-five to forty years of reliable service. Creosoted wood is effective in marine piling, as well as in many branches of the construction industry where preservation against weathering and boring insects are important factors.

The longer life of creosoted wood over untreated wood has been recognized by farmers who use it advantageously in fence posts, in horizontal, box silos, and various other structures.

Pitch, which was originally used principally as a fuel, is of growing importance in electrodes, pipe coating, and fiber pipe. Electrodes, which carry powerful electric currents in the production of steel, aluminum, and ferroalloys, are made from pitch and petroleum coke.

Fiber pipe, a mixture of pitch and cellulose, is widely used for electrical conduit and low pressure water service. Pipeline enamel, made from pitch, coats 80 per cent of the cross-country oil and gas transmission lines in the United States.

Some Coal Chemical Applications

NAPTHALENE

dyestuffs
moth balls
plastics and plasticizers

rubber chemicals
wetting and tanning agents

PHENOL

adhesives
detergents
disinfectants
explosives
flavorings
insecticides

medicinals
perfumes
plant hormones
plastics
synthetic fibers
varnishes

CRESOLS AND CRESYLIC ACID

adhesives
disinfectants
gasoline additives

plasticizers
varnishes

PYRIDINE AND PICOLINE

analgesics
antihistamines
antiseptics
isoniazid

nicotinic acid (Niacin)
sulfa drugs
water repellants

AMMONIUM SULFATE

fertilizer
fireproofing agent

textiles
water purification

ANNHYDROUS AMMONIA

explosives
nitric acid
nitrogen fertilizers

refrigerant
rocket fuel (hydrazine)
uranium and rare metal
    processing

BENZENE

detergents
dyestuffs
medicines
nylon
perfumes
photographic chemicals

plastics
solvents
styrene
synthetic phenol
synthetic rubber

TOLUENE

aspirin
detergents
dyes
insecticides
paints and lacquers

perfumes
plastics
rotogravure ink
saccharine
TNT explosives

XYLENE

chemical intermediates
dye intermediates
insecticide carriers

miscellaneous solvents
printing ink solvents
protective coating solvents

17

Wire and Wire Products

Steel wire has a greater diversity of uses than any other product of the steel industry and is said to have 160,000 applications. We depend on steel wire in one form or another every day of our lives. One wire product, the steel spring, may serve as an example. Because a spring is generally unseen we may not be aware when we put it into action. We sleep more restfully, ride in cars more comfortably, sit with greater ease in chairs, thanks to hidden steel springs. When we open a door, a steel spring returns the knob to its original position. Every time we pick up the telephone, we rely on three steel springs to get the correct number. One spring returns the dial to its starting position, and the two others regulate the speed of the dial's return so that the correct number is transmitted to a central control panel.

MODERN WIRE DRAWING

The rod is the stock from which wire is drawn. Since the continuous rod mill was introduced in the third quarter of the last century, its production has been greatly improved, largely through better mechanical equipment, faster rolling speeds, additional lines, and the production of longer rods. The entire operation has been streamlined, permitting continuous operation from heating the billets for rolling to the delivery of the rod coils to the wire mill. A modern continuous rod mill in the United States produces rod coils weighing up to 1,000 pounds, the rod racing like a long white snake from the last stand at a speed up to approximately 6,000 feet a minute. Depending on the diameter of the rod, the length of the coils ranges from a few hundred feet to approximately 7,800 feet. The total output of a mill in eight hours will average as high as 500 tons.

After the rods have been automatically coiled on reels, the bundles of rods are allowed to cool on a system of hook conveyors, which take them to the wire mill or to freight cars for shipment to customers.

The basic principle of wire drawing has not changed over the centuries. A rod is drawn through a hole, or die, smaller in diameter than the rod. The die is tapered so that the smaller, or exit end, is the exact size and shape of the wire to be drawn. The interior of the die must be extremely hard to withstand the wear and pull of the wire. Tungsten carbide is the most widely used material. Diamond is frequently employed to draw very fine wire.

The die is fastened in a steel holder, which is mounted on a bench. Nearby is a coil of rod on a reel. One end of the rod is tapered to extend through the hole in the die. The protruding end is seized by a clamp, and the rod is pulled continuously through the hole by a power-driven block which winds the wire about itself. Wire is generally drawn through a number of dies, each one of smaller diameter, until the wire is of the exact size for its intended use.

Up until about 1900, all wire was made by what was called single draft wire drawing. That is, the wire was transferred from one draw plate to another of smaller diameter. Around the turn of the century the practice was begun of drawing the wire continuously through a series of dies, each one of smaller diameter.

Each time wire passes through a die it becomes harder. After passing through a series of dies the wire becomes so hard and brittle that further drawing may break it. To remove the brittleness and permit further drawing, the wire is heated in an annealing furnace. Certain wires, which require stiffness and resilience, such as spring wire, are not annealed.

Wire Coatings

Probably more than 20 per cent of all wire made is given a metallic coating either for decorative or protective purposes. Zinc is most commonly used; the process of applying it is called galvanizing. Molten zinc is contained in a pan wide enough for as many as forty strands of wire to pass through it at a time.

A small amount of wire is tinned, mostly for decorative purposes. The tinning process is similar in principle to galvanizing, and the wire is drawn through a bath of molten tin.

In recent years, aluminum has been applied to wire for uses where resistance to corrosion is a major consideration. Because of its demonstrated protective advantages, the variety of applications of aluminum-coated wire is growing rapidly. The product is often chosen for marine installations and industrial equipment where corrosive conditions exist, as guy strands for poles, smokestacks, and other structures. It is also manufactured into barbed wire, field fence, and chain link fence. Miscellaneous uses include market baskets, brooms, paper clips, tie wire, animal cages, and spiral binding. Aluminum is applied to wire by the hot-dip process, in which cold-drawn wires are immersed in a molten aluminum bath.

Improvement in the quality of wire, its manufacture in many grades of steel, including stainless steel, and the various coatings which are applied to wire, have greatly extended its applications. To meet all the requirements made on wire manufacturers, this product is produced in more than 10,000 specifications, involving combinations of different grades of steel, coatings, sizes and shapes. Wire may be round, square, hexagonal, oval, half-oval, triangular, or in thousands of special shapes. It can be given a tensile strength of 600,00 pounds per square inch, or more. Its diameter varies from four-thousandths of an inch to nearly one inch.

WIRE PRODUCTS

Wire Rope

Savages made rope by twisting rawhide or vegetable fibers and used them for such purposes as fastening tent poles together or binding light coverings on primitive thatched huts. People of ancient civilized nations were very accomplished rope makers. The painting on a drinking cup in the British Museum shows an Attic sailing ship of the sixth century B.C. equipped with rope. For many centuries, rope was made of hemp or flax, but generally of hemp, and was "laid" by hand on what was called a "rope walk." A man with the fiber wrapped around his waist walked backward feeding a large hand-operated wheel which twisted the rope. So great was the demand for rope that every community of any size had a rope walk, which often was 900 feet or more in length. It was the need for a better all-around material than hemp which gave rise to the wire rope industry. The first wire rope was braided by hand on rope walks exactly as hemp rope was made. It was produced in short lengths, but it apparently proved its worth because men began to design and build machines for its manufacture. It is known that wire rope was being made in England and Germany between 1830 and 1840. It is believed that the first wire-rope machine in England was built about 1840. Wire rope quickly proved its superiority over hemp rope and found ready application in mine hoists, ship rigging, mooring lines, and cargo hoists.

SUSPENSION BRIDGES

The modern suspension bridge originated in the United States and found its greatest glory on the North American continent. As early as 1796, James Finlay obtained a patent for a form of suspension bridge which was hung by means of hand-forged iron chains. At least fifty such bridges were erected in the United States between 1796 and 1810, the longest with a span of 306 feet over the Schuylkill River at Philadelphia.

The Philadelphia bridge may have suggested construction of a lighter span, suspended by wire. In 1816, Erskine Hazard and Josiah White built over the Schuylkill Falls, near Philadelphia, the first wire suspension bridge in the United States. It was a foot bridge, intended to support no more than six to eight persons at a time. In succeeding years, a number of suspension bridges were erected in Europe and the United States. In 1826, Thomas Telford built the famous Menai Strait Bridge in Wales, suspended by iron chains. It set a record with a span of 580 feet. In 1829, Louis Joseph Vicat built a wire suspension bridge over the Rhone, in which he initiated the modern air-stringing method of constructing cables in place. An American pioneer in the field of suspension bridges was Charles Ellet, who, in 1849, built a wire cable bridge over the Ohio River at Wheeling, West Virginia, with a record-breaking span of 1,010 feet. But it was an imaginative, inventive, and daring German immigrant, John A. Roebling, who was the greatest suspension-bridge builder in the last century.

While working on his farm at Saxonburg, Pennsylvania, in the 1830s, he often had occasion to observe canal boats being towed over mountains by means of hemp rope. The rope was bulky, expensive, and short-lived. It occurred to Roebling that rope of iron wire would be stronger and longer lasting rope than hemp. He had never seen wire rope, but he recalled that he had heard of it being made in his native Germany. He constructed a rope walk, bought some soft wire, and made his first rope by hand.

A canal sometimes had to cross a river, in which case the canal flowed through an overhead aqueduct. Roebling conceived the idea of suspending the aqueduct from wire cables, thus sparing the river traffic the encumbrance of piers and posts. His first aqueduct crossed the Allegheny River at Pittsburgh in 1844. It was hailed as a great success, and orders for other aqueducts followed.

It was logical for Roebling to go from aqueducts to suspension bridges. In 1854, he accomplished the seemingly impossible task of throwing a combination railroad and highway suspension bridge over the rapids of the Niagara Falls. In 1867, the longest suspension bridge up to that time, with a span of 1,057 feet, was erected by Roebling over the Ohio River at Cincinnati. His crowing glory was the Brooklyn Bridge which he did not live to see completed. It was opened to traffic in 1883. The Brooklyn Bridge was precedent-making in several respects. It set a record for length, with a 1,595-foot main span and cables 3,578 feet long. It was the first bridge in America to use steel wire cables.

The twentieth century is the era of suspension bridges. Beginning in 1903, one after another of these graceful structures was built, breaking previous records. In 1903 the Williamsburg Bridge over the East River in New York exceeded the Brooklyn Bridge by about five feet. In 1924, the Bear Mountain Bridge over the Hudson River near Peekskill, New York, set a new record of 1,632 feet, surpassed in 1926 by the Philadelphia-

Camden Bridge with a span of 1,750 feet. Next, the Ambassador Bridge at Detroit established a new record of 1,850 feet in 1929. This was outdistanced two years later by the George Washington Bridge across the Hudson River at New York with a span of 3,500 feet. It was built by the Bethlehem Steel Company. In 1937, the same company completed the longest suspension span in the world—4,200 feet long—known as the Golden Gate Bridge. It crosses the Golden Gate in San Francisco. A year earlier, the Transbay Bridge was completed, connecting San Francisco with Oakland. The entire bridge, including approaches, is 8¼ miles long. It is of suspension and cantilever construction. The suspension section consists of twin suspensions, put end to end, each 2,310 feet long. The Transbay Bridge was built by the American Bridge Division of United States Steel.

The upper and lower peninsulas of Michigan are two large land masses of a state separated by a wide breach of water, the Straits of Mackinac, where Lake Huron and Lake Michigan come together. Considerable travel existed between the two land bodies, which were linked by a ferry. When it was proposed to build a bridge across the straits, authoritative voices declared that it couldn't be done. But it was done, and the Mackinac Bridge, opened to traffic on November 1, 1957, is the greatest bridge constructed anywhere in the world up to that time. Its designer, D. B. Steinman, said that it is the "first long-span bridge ever designed and built to have perfect assured aerodynamic stability for all kind of velocities up to infinity."[1] It was erected by the American Bridge Division of United States Steel.

WIRE ROPE IN TRANSPORTATION

The cargo moved by ships every year throughout the world is tremendous. The bulk of it is loaded and unloaded by means of wire rope. Power-driven winches control drums on which the rope is reeled, feeding out to the ends of sturdy steel booms.

Steel wire cables are essential in the efficient and safe operation of an automobile. In a popular 1960 model, there were approximately 600 inches of cable in the emergency brakes, the heating and ventilating systems and other parts of the vehicle.

Steel wire cable is vitally important in the take-off, flight, and landing of aircraft. The pilot relies on steel cables to operate the aileron, rudder, and numerous other parts. Very large aircraft may have a total of 10,000 feet or more of cables, performing various functions.

Temperatures around a plane may change swiftly, expanding or slackening the steel cable. A plane on a runway in the hot summer sun may be heated to 100° F. or more. It may quickly climb to 30,000 feet altitude, where the temperature may be 60° below zero. The rapid tightening of the control cables under such conditions could interfere with operation of the craft. Or a reverse situation, a sudden change from extreme cold to summer terrestial warmth could have the same results. American Steel &

Wire Division of U. S. Steel overcame this problem by developing a wire cable, sold under the trade mark HYCO-SPAN, which expands and contracts at the same ratio as the body of the plane.

Aerial passenger tramways, operated by means of overhead suspended steel cables, have long been used in Europe, particularly in the Alps, to transport sightseers to scenic locations on the shoulders or tops of mountains. The universal popularity of skiing provided the incentive to adapt aerial conveyances as ski lifts. Many of these are kept in service, outside of the skiing season, to enable tourists to enjoy scenic splendors. Users of aerial tramways and ski lifts are probably unaware that the greatest use of overhead steel cables is industrial. In mining, lumbering, and other industries, the topography of the land is often such that the only means of transporting large quantities of materials is by this method. In some instances, topography is not a factor and aerial tramways are used for economy of operations.

WIRE ROPE IN MINING, PETROLEUM, CONSTRUCTION, AND MANUFACTURING INDUSTRIES

Mammoth quantities of the earth's crust are moved every year throughout the world in the surface mining of coal, copper, silver, iron, bauxite, and other metals, in the quarrying of limestone, sand and gravel, in building dams, in leveling ground for the construction of highways, and in preparing sites for buildings of various kinds. All of this work is unthinkable without mechanized earth-moving equipment, symbolized by the power shovel, some of which can gouge out 75 yards of overburden in one huge bite. A system of strong steel ropes raises and lowers the bucket, attached to a steel boom.

Second in importance to the power shovel in the handling of heavy materials is the crane, or derrick, which is used to lift or lower objects from one level to another by means of wire rope fed from the end of a steel boom. Some of these cranes are gigantic, such as those found in shipyards which are a maze of tall steel arms and their accompanying cables. Tall cranes may also be seen hoisting steel girders or other material to the upper floors of buildings under contruction. Another form, the electric overhead traveling crane, lifts and transfers heavy materials from place to place in manufacturing plants.

From the time raw materials enter a manufacturing plant until the finished product is loaded for shipment, the prompt, smooth handling of materials is important in the over-all efficiency and cost of operation. All manufacturing processes, however much they may vary in character, have one thing in common—handling of materials.

Wire in the form of rope or conveyor belting figures prominently in various handling functions. One kind of conveyor system consists of a traveling overhead rope to which hooks are attached at intervals. This conveyor is used for various purposes—moving meat carcasses in meat processing plants, and freshly-painted products of various kinds to a drying room. In the steel industry it conveys hot metal products, such as wire rods, from one department to another, as they cool off. Another conveyor system utilizes two parallel traveling ropes to carry products. The conveyor system which lends itself to more uses than any other consists of wire belting, which is a form of woven wire. In the food processing industry, wire belting is generally made of stainless steel for sanitary purposes; it serves to move products rapidly from one stage to another in sorting, washing, cooking, and packaging. In large bakeries, the freshly baked bread drops from the ovens onto a steel wire belt conveyor, which takes it through a cooling tunnel onto the wrapping line and delivers the loaves to waiting trucks—all in a continuous operation. In other manufacturing plants, wire belting quickly dispatches innumerable articles on their way from one process to the next, as they are manufactured, inspected, and packed for shipment—shoes, porcelain, small electrical products, soap, and hundreds of others.

The steel industry itself is one of the largest users of wire rope. Wire rope does its job in power shovels used in open pit mining and in limestone quarrying. At ore-loading docks wire rope raises and lowers chutes down which the ore flows into ore vessels. The bucket which unloads the ore from the ship at an unloading dock is manipulated by steel wire rope. The traveling electric ore bridge, which moves the unloaded ore to reserve stockpiles, lifts and lowers its clam-shaped bucket at the end of wire rope. Throughout steel mills, wire rope performs many functions, activating the ram which pushes coke from coke ovens, helping to charge blast furnaces and steelmaking furnaces, lifting the large ladle of molten steel as it is poured into ingot molds, moving semi-finished and finished steel products from point to point, and finally loading them into freight cars or trucks.

Large quantities of wire rope are used in drilling oil wells by the cable tool method. A heavy chisel-shaped steel bit is raised and let fall by means of a steel cable which loops over a tall steel derrick and extends to a "walking beam" on the ground level. By sheer force of weight, the falling bit forces its way into the earth, pulverizing rocks in its path. As it descends into the well, more rope is payed out.

WIRE ROPE IN AGRICULTURE

Mechanization has made wire rope indispensable in modern farming. It has been claimed that 95 per cent of agricultural implements employ wire rope in one way or another from plowing the earth to reaping the harvest. Innumerable pulling and towing operations call for the dependable strength of wire rope—removing an old stump, moving a building to a new site, and in tractor-towing of implements, such as gang plows, cultivators, and many others.

Wire rope is used for various hoisting purposes, such as stacking hay in the field, lifting baled and loose hay into the barn, raising milk cans from cooling tanks, and activating portable elevators and wagon hoists.

Many useful services are performed by wire rope in energizing parts of mechanized equipment, mostly for control purposes, such as brakes, steering mechanisms, and other functions in grain combines, side delivery rakes, corn shellers, and threshing machines.

Woven Wire

Iron wire was first woven into a fabric form early in the eighteenth century. It appears to have been made by an ingenious Connecticut Yankee who used it as a substitute for horsehair in sieves for sifting flour. In the beginning, all wire cloth was manufactured on hand looms, but after 1875 the machinery was driven by steam power. Shortly afterwards, Americans were happy to discover that woven wire with mesh fine enough to prevent the passage of flies and mosquitoes made an excellent insect screen for summer months, and the sale of wire screens experienced a great boom.

A Michigan farmer, J. Wallace Page, was the first to conceive of a fence made of woven wire. He wove such a fence on a handmade loom in 1884 and entered into partnership with another farmer to manufacture the new fencing material. In 1888, they installed a power loom. They had difficulty at first in selling their fence because the general public refused to believe that smooth wire could restrain cattle, but after successful demonstrations the battle was won and the Page Woven Wire Fence Company became large and prosperous. Woven fence has since found more uses than barbed wire and is manufactured in different styles for lawns, playgrounds and the protection of industrial and municipal properties. Another widely used wire fence is a flexible diamond mesh called chain link fence. It is the strongest of all fences for protective purposes.

Woven wire cloth took a different course in England, where it was made in a coarse hexagonal mesh for trellises and light fencing material. When it was found to be an ideal material for keeping chickens in their place, it became known throughout the world as poultry netting.

What is termed woven wire cloth, as distinguished from poultry netting, generally has square mesh and is manufactured in different mesh sizes and wire gauges for a variety of uses, from heavy screens for mining and quarrying to mesh diameter of 0.009 inch. The principal use of the smallest mesh wire is as a filter for dust catchers, water purification, air conditioning, and as reinforcement in brake linings and clear plastics, such as substitutes for window glass.

What is actually a heavier form of insect screen is called hardware cloth. It is used chiefly on the farm as strong screening on bins to protect grains, apples, and other products against rats. It is also used in small animal coops and to enclose baby chicks which can escape poultry netting.

Springs, Springs, Everywhere

A mechanical jack-of-all-trades, the steel spring is an indispensable go-between where energy cannot be transmitted, practically or economically, in any other way. A steel spring can be made to serve as a source of stored energy. When a spring is compressed, stretched or twisted, energy is stored in it which is released when the spring is let go. As was stated at the beginning of this chapter, most springs are concealed so that we are scarcely aware of our dependence on them. Every letter in every word in this book, originally written on a typewriter, brought into action one or more of about 180 springs that are present in a standard office typewriter in forty-two different designs.

There are four principal types of springs: (1) Compression springs, which have space between the coils because these springs are compressed to store their energy and go into action when released. An example of a compression spring is the one used in a pop-up toaster. (2) Extension springs are close wound because they are pulled out in order to store their energy which is released when the spring returns to a normal position. The spring in an overhead garage door is an extension spring. The springs in mattresses and chair seats are special forms of extension springs called "helical" springs. (3) Torsion springs are so named because they are twisted or wound in order to store their energy, which they release on returning to a normal position. An example of a torsion spring is the kind concealed in the hinges of some doors which causes them to spring shut when released. (4) Flat springs are made of strip steel or flat wire, wound spirally. They are known as clock and motor springs because they are used to energize clocks and various small motors, including children's toys.

In addition to these four standard types of springs, there are specially formed springs of almost endless variety in shape and size, each one generally designed for a specific purpose.

Springs vary not only in shape and function but in size. They range from giant springs weighing 600 pounds, down to springs which take 67,000 to weigh one pound. The smallest springs are used for tiny machines in classified military defense work. The principal use of the largest springs is for rolling doors. Another application is for duct work.

So far as the records disclose, the manufacture of extension and compression springs in the United States was begun in 1879 by Charles H. Morgan of Worcester, Massachusetts, who had been granted a patent on the oil tempering and coiling of springs. In 1881, the Morgan Spring Company was formed in Worcester and a spring plant was opened there. Before this time, very few coiled springs were in use. Morgan's process of oil tempering steel wire opened up a new field for springs and their uses were greatly multiplied. All springs were made by hand on wooden mandrels until about 1894, when automatic coiling machines were introduced.

The automobile offers a good example of our dependence on steel springs in this mechanical age. A 1960 popular passenger model contained 450 springs in 200 applications.

Aircraft cannot fly without steel springs. From the time a plane takes off until it lands, it depends on the faithful performance of hundreds of springs in the fuselage, motors, and control apparatus.

Springs are indispensable in every form of mechanized farm equipment. They are used to operate brakes and other controls. A large spring under the seat of a harvester makes riding more comfortable for the driver. Harrows obtain flexibility to withstand the shock of passing over large stones or stumps by means of springs. When the farmer plants seeds with an automatic seeder, he brings springs into play.

Business machines—cash registers, typewriters, duplicating machines, and various kinds of computing machines—represent another important area of service for springs. To assure swift and accurate functioning of these mechanisms, steel springs faithfully and instantaneously go into action when called on. A standard electric typewriter contains 250 steel springs and a medium-sized electronic computer has within it 400 coiled springs and 900 flat springs.

Steel springs stand by for many services in the home. They are in door handles and in the hinges of self-closing doors, or are attached outside on the door jamb. A steel spring does our bidding every time we raise or lower a window shade. Hundreds of springs are in innerspring mattresses and lesser numbers in sofas and chairs. The door handle of a refrigerator, when it is opened and closed, brings a spring into action. In the freezing unit, a small spring performs the job of seeing that the temperature does not vary more than one to three degrees. There are numerous unseen steel springs in the washing machine, the vacuum cleaner, clocks and watches, toys, and flashlights.

MISCELLANEOUS USES OF WIRE

When you ride over a modern concrete highway, you ride over steel as well as concrete. Concrete has great compressive strength but is relatively weak in bending and tensile strength. Steel excels in tensile and bending strength. Concrete and an inner grid of steel, each performing the work best suited to it, make an ideal combination—reinforced concrete—for roads, dams, buildings, and other structures. Both wire and bars of steel are used to form reinforcing grids in buildings and other structures. Electrically welded reinforcing fabric is generally used in concrete, roads, airport runways, and other pavements. It is also used in buildings and in bridge decking.

Passenger automobile and truck tires contain strands of fine steel wire in the bead, or that part of the tire that is fastened to the rim of the wheel. The purpose of the wire is to strengthen the bead so that it will remain securely attached to the rim. There is also beading wire in the tires of bicycles which make further use of wire in wheel spokes and in the springs for the seat. The inner fabric, or ply, of the conventional automobile tire is made of cotton, rayon, or nylon. Extremely fine wires, slightly thicker than a human hair, are made into cords for heavy-duty trucks in substitution of textile plies. Tires with an inner sheath of steel wire are said to stand the heat generated by heavy loads and high speeds better than tires with textile cords. Such tires are also practically puncture-proof and have a 50 per cent longer life than conventional tires.

Steel wire provides strength in a number of different "fasteners" that help to hold our modern world together: bolts, screws, rivets, nails, bale ties, stitching, and strapping wire. Thousands of articles, large and small, fragile and durable, require containers of many kinds for shipment. Containers range from fiber cartons and wooden boxes of various sizes up to huge crates for industrial materials. The products shipped are almost infinite: fresh fruits, canned goods, baby chicks, flowers, refrigerators, washing machines, automobile engines, and bicycles, to name but a few. Experience has shown that the best reinforcement material to keep various containers intact is steel, called strapping steel.

It is not always practical, for one reason or another, to ship articles in containers. It is better simply to bind them together with steel strapping. Newspapers, for instance, as they issue from the press, are automatically stacked and bound with wire for delivery to local newsstands or for shipment to other cities. Large bulky industrial products, such as culvert pipes, heavy machinery, and steel rails are fastened securely in freight cars by steel strapping.

Portable automatic machines are used to bind and tie steel strapping, which is either round wire or flat bands, the latter cut from strip steel.

Stitching with steel wire? It is practiced widely today and is an outgrowth of the ordinary desk stapler. Wire is fed into a machine which forms a staple, drives it into the material and fastens it. The machine sews rapidly, at the rate of eighty to one hundred stitches a minute. In the field of transportation it has been found especially suitable for fastening large cartons for the shipment of such products as bicycles, radios, and furniture. Manufacturers began asking for stitching wire capable of penetrating wood and leather and even metals. They also wanted to make "sandwiches" of metal and rubber, or metal and plastics. This required very strong, hard wire with enough pliability so that it would not break when clinched to form a staple. Metallurgists of U.S. Steel's American Steel & Wire Division developed a wire that met the requirements. Stitching wire finds extensive application in fastening materials into sandwiches in the fabrication of aircraft sub-assemblies.

Stainless Steel Wire

Stainless steel's high resistance to corrosion and heat and its great strength recommended it for many special applications. It is manufactured into bolts, screws and springs for use in corrosive atmospheres. Stainless steel wire is without peer for sanitary purposes such as surgical and dental instruments, fine and large mesh for filters and conveyor belting in food processing industries. It constitutes strong rust-resistant material for fishing tackle. Its resistance to heat accounts for its presence as mesh in parts of jet engines. In and around the home, stainless steel wire is found in needles, pins, zippers, sieves, refrigerator racks, and barbecue equipment.

18

Plates, Pipes and Tubes, Rails and Bars

The steel industry manufactures steel into a number of basic products which may be likened to the shapes, sizes, and varieties of wood in a well-stocked lumber yard. A builder selects the kind of wood he wants, in the shapes and dimensions required for a particular structure. A modern industrial economy is a complex structure for which steel is ordered in a wide variety of grades, furnished in certain basic shapes and sizes. Structural steel, strip, sheets, and wire have already been discussed. A number of other basic steel products will now be considered: plates, pipes and tubes, rails and bars. Extrusions, specialty products, will also be discussed.

PLATES

The rolling of thin flat iron began in the closing years of the seventeenth century. Some iron sheets were made into pots, kettles, and saucepans, but most of it went into tin plate. Tin plate, more than any other product, was responsible for the early development of the rolling mill. There was little need for heavier sheet iron until the first practical steam engine appeared in the first quarter of the eighteenth century and created a demand for boiler plate. The iron-plate industry may be said to have had its birth in the Industrial Revolution. As the stationary steam engine was improved, especially as higher steam pressures were evolved, demands were heard for wider and heavier plates. When steam power was adapted to propel trains and ships, the market for boiler plate was greatly enlarged. For a good part of the nineteenth century, the bulk of rolled iron went into boiler plate and rails.

230

Steel was first substituted for wrought iron in boiler plate around 1859. A few years later, plates were fabricated into the hulls and decks of ships and thus began one of the most important applications of plates. In 1863, a small paddle steamer, the "Banshee," was the first steel vessel to cross the Atlantic. In 1864, the "Clytemnestra," a clipper ship built of steel plates ⅜ inch thick, was launched in England. The English shipbuilding industry strongly influenced the development and output of plate mills. Until World War II, more than half of the world tonnage of ships was British-owned. Although steel ships were built in increasing numbers in the second half of the nineteenth century, the change from wrought iron to steel was not completed until about 1890.[1]

The next major influence on the plate industry came from the builders of armor-clad warships. The famous battle of the "Monitor" and "Merrimac" in Hampton Roads, Virginia, in 1862 signaled the end of wooden warships. Facilities were lacking at that time for rolling flat iron heavier than boiler plate. With one accord, the United States, Great Britain, and France sought means for making heavier, stronger plate and the naval armament race was on. Heavy armor plate was both rolled and forged. With the diminishing role of surface warships, the making of armor plate has dwindled in importance.

Between the thickest sheet and the thinnest plate there is only a marginal difference. By definition of the steel trade, steel plates are hot-rolled steel products which are:

0.180 inch or thicker, over 48 inches wide.
0.230 inch or thicker, over 8 inches wide.

Within these specifications, plates can be made in a great variety of dimensions. For practical purposes, plates are over 8 inches wide and ¼ inch thick. They may be as thick as 25 inches and nearly 200 inches wide.

In general, steel plates render structural and mechanical services beyond the limitations of sheets. Plates are found in bridges, dams, heavy machinery, pressure vessels, railroad cars, large-sized welded pipes, storage tanks, machine-tool frames, atomic reactors, and the hulls and decks of ships. A special type of plate with safety tread is rolled for the floors of factories, the steps and vestibules of railroad trains, subway stairs, and the steps of trucks and fire engines. Indentations on the last set of rolls in a plate mill cause the raised tread to be formed on the plate.

Evolution of the Plate Mill

The width and thickness of boiler plates were originally limited by the force that drove the mill, which was water power. Although John Wilkinson operated a rolling mill with a Watt steam engine as early as 1786,[2] he was ahead of his time and it was some years before steam power replaced water power in English plate mills. When boiler plate was first rolled in the United States by Isaak Pennock at the Brandywine Iron Works at Coatesville, Pennsylvania in 1810, the mill was driven by an overshot waterwheel.

The Brandywine mill was similar to contemporary plate mills in England and consisted of a single stand of two rolls. As in hand-sheet mills, the plate was lifted manually over the top of the rolls between each pass. This practice limited the size of plate that could be rolled, even after steam engines in the first half of the nineteenth century supplied greater power to drive the rolls.

To obviate the need of lifting the heavy plates in the "pull-over" mill, the reversing steam engine was developed and attached to a two-high mill. This innovation took place in England in 1854 for rolling plates. The same principle was given its first application in the United States in 1877.[3] The two-high reversing mill soon reached its practical working limit, particularly for rolling wide, lighter gauge plates. The entire sequence of rolling, from the slab to the finished plate, was done on the same pair of rolls and this increased the wear on the rolls which imposed a restriction on the gauge that could be satisfactorily finished. The problem was fortuitously solved by the introduction of Bernard Lauth's three-high mill in 1864. Such a mill consisted of two large outer rolls with a middle roll about two-thirds the diameter of the outer pair. A steam-operated "tilting table" raised the slab for each return pass and dispensed with the need for a reversing engine. When the slab passed between the bottom and the middle roll, the top roll served as a back-up roll. In the same way, the bottom roll served as a back-up roll when the slab passed between the top and middle rolls.

The advantages of the three-high mill were carried a step further with the introduction of the four-high mill which came into existence to roll armor plate for Andrew Carnegie at his Homestead Works in 1891.[4] It was invented by John A. Potter. The four-high mill was confined to the rolling of heavy plate until the originators of the continuous hot strip mill borrowed it to install in their finishing stands. In 1918, the Lukens Steel Company installed what was then and remained for many years the world's largest plate mill, with rolls 206 inches long. It is capable of rolling plate up to 192 inches wide and 25 inches thick. In 1962, United States Steel Corporation began operation of a still larger plate mill, with rolls 210 inches long, capable of rolling plates approximately 200 inches wide.

Two main types of plate mills have evolved over the years: the sheared plate mill and the universal plate mill. In the sheared plate mill, the plates are reduced by conventional horizontal rolls working on the surfaces of the slabs. Afterwards, the plates are sheared to prescribed dimensions. The universal mill has both horizontal and vertical rolls. While the former work on the top and bottom surface of the slab, the latter work on the edges. Universal mills are single-stand units, and, although some have rolled plates up to 60 inches in width, most of them produce plates 48 inches wide and under. Universal mills have diminished in importance in the United States in the last several decades because in rolling wide plates it is difficult to control the edges. Universal mills in 1960 produced 604,437 tons against 6,298,325 tons by sheared plate mills.

Most sheared plate mills in the United States are single-stand, three-high reversing mills. The steel industry also has semi-continuous and continuous plate mills. In the former, the preliminary rolling, or "roughing" work, is done on reversing mills, and the finishing stands are single-pass four-high mills. In the latter, as in the continuous hot strip mill, the hot slab moves continuously through the mill which contains six massive four-high finishing stands. The plate leaves the last stand like a wide red carpet of steel, 80 feet or more in length.

PIPES AND TUBES

Without the conveyance of fluids and gases through steel pipes and tubes, ranging from hypodermic needles to welded pipe 150 inches or more in diameter modern civilization could not go on. Steel pipe, as much as any other single agency, has made possible the growth of large cities with subterranean systems of pipelines to carry water for human consumption and fire-fighting, many miles of gas and sewer mains and conduits containing electrical cables.

Robert Daley, in *The World Beneath the City*, described the vast and complex system needed to supply the needs of New York City's population of 8 million people:

There are 7,000 miles of gas mains, 5,000 miles of sewers, 2,200 miles of TV cables and 15,000,000 miles of telephone wire—enough to circle this planet six hundred times. Subway trains, 8,700 of them a day, thunder along 726 miles of track. There are 87 miles of high pressure steam lines for tasks as varied as pressing trousers and heating skyscrapers. . . . Some 19,000 miles of electric cable bristle with current boosted to 69,000 volts. . . . Ordinary water courses through 5,528 miles of mains under such intense pressure that a single leak could cause the loss of 3,000,000 gallons a day.[5]

One fluid alone—petroleum—may be called the lifeblood of a machine economy. Hundreds of thousands of miles of steel pipes are needed to raise this lifeblood from deep in the earth and transport it to refinery centers.

Water, however, is the universal fluid on which human life everywhere depends, from primitive societies to the great metropolises of the world, and it was to convey this precious fluid that pipes were first used. They were probably made of bamboo. The next step was to fashion pipes of clay and bake them. Relics of pottery pipes have been found in the ruins of Egyptian and Aztec civilizations. It is known that lead pipes were used extensively by the Greeks and the Romans.

In medieval Europe, troughs were built of wood to channel the flow of water in mining, metal working, and other industries. Pipes were also made of hollowed logs. Water was delivered to towns and cities in open ditches which were susceptible to all kind of pollution. The Germans and French imitated the Romans and built some pipes of cast lead, but the high cost of such lines prevented their general adoption. New York City's first regular water works, planned in 1774, called for 60,000 feet of hollow logs, with an inside diameter of 9 inches. The project was abandoned after the outbreak of the Revolutionary War.

It was not until the introduction of gun powder and firearms in the fourteenth century that conditions were favorable for the manufacture of iron pipe. The earliest cannon were cast in bronze but it was soon found that cast iron was cheaper and more satisfactory. Musket barrels were hand forged. For a period, iron in cylindrical form, was restricted to military use. Some ingenious person thought of fastening discarded cannon barrels end to end to make a water line. The next step was to cast iron pipe expressly for that purpose.

The first cast iron water pipeline on record was installed in Dillenberg Castle, Germany, in 1455.[6] Louis XIV of France ordered cast iron pipe laid at Versailles and five miles of this line are still in use today. The use of cast-iron pipe water systems spread by degrees over Europe and England, and in the latter country the demand for cast-iron pipe in the early 1800s was said to be "amazing."[7] America's first major cast-iron water pipeline was installed in Philadelphia in 1817. New York City followed in 1832.

In 1801, an historic event occurred in Paris when Philippe Lebon used gas distilled from wood to illuminate a garden.[8] Over in England, a Scotsman, William Murdock, demonstrated that illuminating gas could be obtained from coal and in 1792 succeeded in lighting his house and grounds with it. Murdock was the first person to make a commercial success of gas illumination, but he must share some of the honor with a fellow Scotsman, Samuel Clegg, and a German, Friedrich A. Winzer, who changed his name to Windsor when he came to London to sell the citizens on the wonders of gas illumination. Clegg was the first person to purify gas by passing it over lime;[9] he also designed and patented a meter, which was indispensable for the extension of commercial gas systems. Windsor was indirectly responsible for the formation of the Gas Light and Coke Company, chartered in 1812. By 1832, gas lighted 200 miles of London streets and 60,000 homes. The first American city to adopt gas lighting on a large scale was Baltimore, where nightly illumination began in 1817. Gas was introduced in New York City in 1825, but it was not until 1841 that Philadelphia permitted use of the new method of illumination.

The distribution of gas required pipe. Cast iron pipe was not satisfactory because the joints could not be fastened securely enough to prevent leakage. Murdock and others took old wrought-iron musket barrels and screwed their ends together to make the first English gas mains. Demand soon exceeded supply. The man who rose to the occasion was Cornelius Whitehouse, who, in 1825, devised a method for making pipe in which he welded edges of sheet iron together instead of forging them, by what became known as the butt-weld process. He found that by drawing a red-hot section of sheet iron, called skelp, through a funnel-shaped die, or "welding bell," the edges would curl into the shape of a pipe and be welded into a tight joint. In the United States the first shop for the production of butt-welded pipe was established in Philadelphia about 1832 by Morris, Tasker and Morris. In 1887 pipe was first made of Bessemer steel at the Riverside Iron Works, Riverside, West Virginia. Butt-welded iron and steel pipe are still used widely today.

Seamless Tubes

The next major development in pipe manufacture was the successful production of seamless pipe, generally referred to as seamless tube. Its manufacture was first atempted in 1845 and actually was a deep-drawing process in which a flat steel plate was forced through a circular die, thereby elongating the steel into the shape of a tube with one end closed. This method is still used for certain tubular products. Another method was to pierce a hole through the length of a hot billet. It was found to be difficult to pierce a hole that was concentric with the billet throughout its entire length. To overcome this difficulty, a small hole was drilled through the billet and then the hole was enlarged by a piercer. A new principle of making seamless tubes was announced by Max and Reinhard Mannesmann in Germany in 1885. Instead of attempting to force a piercer through a stationary billet, the billet was forced over a stationary piercer. The hot billet was held between two rapidly rotating rolls whose spinning action moved the billet forward against the piercer. The rotating action tended to draw the steel away from the center of the billet, producing a cavity which the piercer enlarged and made of uniform size. A rough tube without a seam was thus produced. The tube was afterwards passed through other rolls which adjusted the diameter and wall thickness to prescribed dimensions. The Mannesmann process was first operated commercially by the Landore Siemens Steel Company of Swansea, England, in 1887.[10]

Introduction of the seamless process was propitious for the manufacture of tubings for bicycles whose popularity was sweeping Europe and the United States in the last decade of the nineteenth century. Bicycle manufacturers preferred seamless tubes because they could be made lighter in weight than welded pipes. Methods in use prior to the Mannesmann process were too crude and slow to supply the market. Orders for several million feet of seamless tubes had accumulated beyond productive capacity. The new process solved the dilemma and the bicycle tube business became large and lucrative. The first seamless tube plant in the United States was built in 1895 at Ellwood City, Pennsylvania, by the Elwood Weldless Tube Company, which was later acquired by the National Tube Company.

After the turn of the century, the automobile industry exerted a strong influence on the course of the seamless tube business. In 1906, automobile manufacturers put in large orders for seamless tubes in place of welded tubes. Seamless tubes went into the drive shaft, axles, axle housing, steering column, and exhaust lines. As the popularity of the automobile increased, the vogue of the bicycle faded and with it a large market for seamless tubes. But the automobile more than made up for the loss of market for bicycle tubing. At the same time, the expanding automobile industry created a demand for motor fuels and lubricants which generated a boom in the oil industry, opening up a vast new market for seamless products. Seamless tube producers next captured the large boiler tube market, which until then had been supplied by welded tubes of wrought iron or steel.

In the 1920s, the discovery in remote districts of the United States of immense natural gas reservoirs, from which gas could be conveyed to consuming centers only in steel pipelines, some over 1,000 miles long, resulted in another large market for seamless tubes. Altogether, the petroleum and natural gas industries of the world are the largest consumers of tubular steel products, which are needed in drilling wells, the removal of oil and gas and their transportation to distribution centers.

Cold-Drawn Tubes

Hot-rolled tubes are satisfactory for most purposes, but for certain uses, such as mechanical tubing found in airplanes, automobiles, agricultural machinery, household equipment, etc., for ball- and roller-bearing races, oil-well pumps, bicycle frames, and metal furniture, tubes must have thinner walls, smaller diameters, better surface finish and greater tensile strength than can be produced by hot-working methods. Tubes with these special characteristics are cold drawn. A hot-rolled tube is drawn through a die, similar in principle to wire drawing, except for one difference. As the tube is drawn through the die of smaller diameter than the tube, a blunt-nosed bar, or mandrel, is positioned inside the tube to support the wall and to assure a uniform diameter of the interior. Some tubes are drawn through a succession of dies, each one of smaller diameter. A hypodermic needle, cold drawn from seamless tubing in specialty plants, offers an example of the extent to which tubing may be reduced by cold drawing.

In addition to being made round, cold-drawn seamless tubes are manufactured in many shapes—square, rectangular, oval, octagonal, hexagonal, and still others.

Electric-Welded Pipe

There are many needs for steel pipe larger than can be formed by rolling. Some important uses of the larger pipe are in water lines, gas mains, oil pipelines, and penstocks. Large diameter pipe is made of steel plates, formed into a cylinder and welded together electrically. Pipe up to 42 inches in diameter can be manufactured by the electric-weld process, but larger sizes require special plate fabricating techniques.

Most electric-welded pipe is produced by the electric-weld process. The maximum diameter of pipe which can be produced by this process is limited by the width of available rolled plate. Three steps are required to shape the plate for welding. First, the plate is "crimped." Its edges are bent so that they will fit snugly together after the succeeding operations are performed. In the second step, a "U-ing" machine is brought into action. This consists of U-shaped dies, as long as the longest length of pipe, operated by a 2,000-ton press. The male die is moved down on the plate, slowly deforming it into a U-shape. The U-shaped plate now enters the "O-ing" machine, which consists of semi-circular dies. This machine, as its name implies, completes the shaping of the plate into a rounded form. Next, the edges are electrically welded.

Pipe over 42 inches in diameter is fabricated from two or more curved plates welded together along thin edges to attain the desired size. Although pipe of any diameter can be fabricated by this process, its size is generally limited by shipping conditions. Lack of headroom under bridges and in tunnels prevents the shipment of pipe over 150 inches on most railroads. Pipe exceeding 150 inches in diameter is usually shipped in sections and assembled and welded at the site. Plates in large cylindrical form, called tunnel liners, are used to brace the inside of tunnels. The plates are electrically welded.

Other Uses of Pipes and Tubes

In addition to automobiles, various forms of transportation make extensive use of steel pipes and tubes. In railroad trains, a system of pipes and tubes carry air for the brakes and steam and water for the convenience and comfort of the riding public in passenger coaches and Pullman cars. In ships, the boiler room contains many tubes, and from it a great circulatory system of pipes and tubes distributes steam and water.

The mechanism by which an airplane climbs or descends—the elevators, ailerons, and rudder—operate on hinges of steel tubes called torque tubes. The strong pressures exerted on these parts requires the supporting strength of alloy steel. The main use of aircraft tubing is in the fuselage and engine mounts. The latter hold the engine in place and support its weight. The motor itself contains alloy seamless tubing in various parts.

When a great jet airliner, weighing approximately 200,000 pounds, comes into an airport for a landing, the fate of its passengers and crew depends to a great extent on the strength of the steel in its landing gear. An assembly of landing gear struts, as they are called, connects the fuselage with the wheels and cushions the force of the landing. Because of the shock at the moment the wheels touch the runway, the landing gear is made of heat-treated alloy steel tubes. To withstand the heat generated in aircraft exhaust systems and in superchargers which supply oxygen within pressurized cabins at high altitudes, stainless steel seamless tubes are used.

In agriculture and food processing, steel pipes and tubes find use in tractors, farm machinery, milking installations, pasteurizers, condensers, milk bottling equipment, and other food processing plants.

Refrigeration in the home, commercial plants and ice skating rinks depends on steel tubes to circulate the refrigerant. We find steel tubes of various shapes in furniture for the home and office, in hospital beds and operating tables. Steel pipes and tubes are seen in ship masts and booms, flag poles, and in the poles for telegraph and telephone lines.

Modern existence in private homes and public buildings of all kinds is dependent on the distribution of hot and cold water and in many cases, steam as well, through pipelines. Sprinkler systems for use in case of fire consist of steel pipes. Radiant heating makes use of pipe coils placed within the floors, walls, or ceilings of rooms. Radiant heating is widely used for the prevention and removal of snow and ice from airport runways, driveways, and sidewalks.

In greenhouses, water is fed to plants by an overhead sprinkler system of steel pipes. Children's playgrounds make effective use of steel tubing. There was a time when all metal railings were made of wrought iron. Now most new railings are made of seamless steel tubes. Steel pipes are being used increasingly for structural purposes in scaffolding, crane booms, tower structures and buildings.

By closing both ends, steel tubing is converted into pressure cylinders to contain air, oxygen and various other gases and fluids.

RAILS

The history of rails in the United States offers a striking commentary on the sweeping economic and social changes which occurred in little more than a century. These changes may be summarized in a statistical statement: The proportion of rail production to total hot-rolled iron and steel production declined from a high of 41 per cent in 1887 to 0.64 per cent in 1961.

The history of American rails may be divided into three periods. In the first, extending from 1830 to 1900, a network of 258,784 miles of trackage was spread over the nation. After the great era of railroad building got under way in the 1860s, the steel industry for some twenty-five years existed chiefly to supply steel for the carriers, principally in the form of rails. In 1887, a peak year, rails absorbed 63 per cent of steel production.

The second period extended from 1900 to 1930. In these years, there was another surge of railroad construction. More than 170,000 miles of operated track were added, bringing the trackage to its maximum of 429,823 miles in 1930. Although rail production held up well, other expanding industries were claiming a greater share of steel production. In this period, rail output fell from 25 to 6 per cent of total hot-rolled production.

The third period in the history of rails—1930 to 1959—saw the position of the railroads as the chief means of transportation slowly deteriorate under competition from passenger automobiles, trucks, buses and aircraft. Whereas the railroads could boast in 1900 that they transported 84 per cent of travelers between the nation's cities, this proportion had dwindled to 4 per cent in 1958, with passenger cars accounting for 89 per cent and planes and buses dividing the remainder between them.[11] During this period, operated track declined to 385,264 miles. The falling off of railroad business was reflected in rail production. In 1958, only 586,000 tons of rails were produced, the smallest tonnage since 1867, except for the depression years of 1932 and 1933. In 1960, rail production was higher, but so was steel production. The proportion of rails to hot-rolled production reached its lowest point in 1960—0.64 per cent.

The development of the wrought-iron rail was described in Chapter 9 and the history of the Bessemer steel rail was related in Chapter 11. In 1902, open-hearth steel rails were introduced, and they made gradual inroads on Bessemer rails until about 1910, when open-hearth steel became the generally accepted material for rails. Rails increased in weight from 100 pounds in 1900 to 130 pounds in 1916 and 152 pounds in 1931. The heaviest rails now weigh from 135 to 175 pounds per yard. The standard rail length is 39 feet.

In a modern American rail mill, an ingot is rolled into rails in one continuous process in seven minutes. The ingot may weigh up to 5½ tons. It first goes through a blooming mill which reduces it to a cross-section of about 8 by 8 inches. After the ends are cropped, the bloom is cut into two lengths and the two sections are now ready to be shaped into rails. The bloom enters the roughing mill which rolls it into the rough shape of a rail. Then the steel goes in a continuous process through a series of five or six stands, each of which make it longer and more rail-shaped. The finished rail is approximately 120 feet long. It is sawed into rails lengths. Every rail goes through rigid inspection before shipment from the mill.

BARS

A steel bar is one of the most ubiquitous steel products. It is also the most difficult to define. A bar, according to *Webster's Dictionary*, is "a piece of wood or metal, long in proportion to its breadth and thickness, such as one used for a lever, support, barrier, or fastening." Yet a thin flat section of steel up to 12 inches in width is a bar. Such steel might conceivably be confused with strip. Their difference is due to the type of mill in which they are rolled, the one in a strip mill and the other in a bar mill. Flat bars may be as thick as 4 inches which is thicker than many plates. Also in the category of bars are structural forms of steel such as angles, Ts, Zs and many other odd shapes made for specific purposes, so long as their cross-sectional dimension is under 3 inches. What we commonly think of as a bar comes in round, quadrangular, hexagonal, and octagonal cross-sectional shapes. Bars are both hot-rolled and cold-finished.

Steel bars, manufactured in a wide diversity of shapes and sizes, have a multitude of uses in an industrialized economy. One has only to think of machinery, large and small, to realize the indispensability of such material in moving parts and in others where bars serve structural purposes. There are bars in the typewriter on which the manuscript of this book was written. By far the largest users of bars is the automotive industry which absorbs annually one-quarter of all bars produced in the United States. Another important use of bars is in reinforcing concrete for roads, buildings, bridges, and dams.

Although iron sheets were rolled at an earlier date than bars, modern rolling practice began in England with the bar mill of Henry Cort, who took out his first patent for grooved rolls in 1783. Grooves, indented on the face of the rolls, shaped the iron into the form of a bar. It was a two-high mill, run by water power. The first mill to roll bars from puddled iron in the United States was put into operation near Connellsville, Pennsylvania, in 1816.

In the early days of rolling bars, the mills kept a stock of various shapes and sizes on hand for the convenience of visiting merchants. The mills became known as merchant mills, a designation that persists to this day.

Almost all the early bar mills were two-high. In rare instances, there were three-high mills. In the two-high mill the bar was delivered manually over the top of the rolls for the next pass as was done in two-high hand-sheet mills. The physical limitations of the mill and the weight of the bar restricted their length to 16 to 20 feet. From here on, the evolution of the bar mill closely parallels that of the rod mill, described in Chapter 10.

STEEL EXTRUSIONS

Extrusions are specialty products formed by forcing a heated solid section of metal through a die. The extrusion process has long been used in the non-ferrous industries, and has been applied for some years in Europe to a limited extent in the production of carbon steel tubes and bars. A number of difficulties were encountered in extruding steel satisfactorily and economically. One of them was the required high temperature of the steel which destroyed all known materials used as lubricants and heat insulators between the hot steel and the extrusion die. In the late 1940s, the French inventor, Jacques Sejournet, successfully developed the use of glass as a lubricant. The glass becomes liquid at the extrusion temperature.

Extrusion makes it possible to produce steel shapes which are difficult or impossible to form by other processes; also to shape some steels which are difficult to roll or forge and other steels which otherwise could only be shaped by casting. One advantage of the process is that it can be used to produce steel sections in small lots which cannot be rolled economically. Extruded steel has a fine and uniform structure, adaptable for further processing by cold drawing or machining.

To the engineer, steel extrusion offers greater freedom of design than is possible for hot-rolled sections, since shapes that are more complicated can be extruded. Extruded steel can mean savings for both the engineer and manufacturer through reducing the number of machining, welding, and assembly operations.

Hot-rolled round billets up to twenty feet long are the stock for steel extrusions. These are cut into short billets of the weight required for the extrusions to be made. A steel stud is welded to the back end of each billet so that it may be suspended from an overhead conveyor which takes the billets through a pre-heat furnace into a molten salt bath and finally to the press. In the pre-heat furnace, the billets are heated to about 1,600° F., just below the point where scale forms. The surface of billets must be fairly smooth because any undue roughness will affect the finished product. The billets are brought to a uniform extruding temperature in the salt bath where no scale forms. From the bath the billet is rapidly conveyed to the press, which holds the die. The stud is removed and the billet drops on the inclined platform of a carriage. While the latter is being moved into position before the press, the billet rolls down the inclined platform into a trough where it wraps itself in a glass mat to serve as a lubricant. For additional lubrication and insulation, a pad of glass is placed between the billet and the die. The ram of the press which can develop 2,500 tons pressure, pushes against the billet to force the hot plastic steel through the die. The extrusion usually takes only two or three seconds. The extruded steel, depending on its grade, is immediately quenched in water or allowed to cool in the air. The glass coating is removed and the finishing operations, such as straightening, cutting, and testing, are performed.

Coatings for Steel

Ordinary steel will corrode when exposed to the atmosphere or other corrosive conditions. Various coatings are applied to protect steel and for decorative and utilitarian purposes. The principal ones are tin, zinc, aluminum, porcelain enamel, paint, lacquers and vinyl. Aluminum is applied mostly to wire, as described in Chapter 17.

Tin is the most widely used coating for steel. Tin plate has won first place as a food container because it combines a number of advantages. Steel provides strength to protect the can's contents in ordinary handling and in rougher treatment in shipping. Steel as thin as 0.006 inch thick furnishes adequate strength, permitting the can to be extremely light in weight. The coating of tin on each side is 0.000015 to 0.00008 inch thick, about one-fortieth the thickness of a human hair. A coating so thin provides protection against food contamination by acids. Tin is non-toxic. Furthermore, tin plate is attractive in appearance and may be decorated by lithographing or lacquering.

In World War II, Japanese armies cut off 75 per cent of the world's tin supply, precipitating a tin crisis in Western nations. Since the end of the war, production by Far Eastern nations has been resumed. The principal tin-producing nations in 1960 were Malaya, China (estimated smelter production), Indonesia, Bolivia, USSR (includes USSR in Asia), Thailand, Republic of the Congo and Ruanda Urundi, Federation of Rhodesia and Nyasaland, and Nigeria, in the order named. World mine production of tin in 1960 was 179,700 long tons, compared to a record high of 200,300 long tons in 1957.[1]

The United States is the leading consumer of tin and requires about half of the tin consumed in the world for tin-plating. The principal use of primary tin in the United States is for tin-plating and in the period 1952-1958, this use averaged about 60 per cent of total primary tin consumption. In 1960, the proportion was 65 per cent. Nearly 90 per cent of tin plate consumed is for the manufacture of cans, the remaining 10 per cent being used for such products as bottle caps, jar closures, kitchen utensils, hollowware, toys, and a great variety of other products. Of the tin plate used for making cans, about 60 per cent is for packing food, including beverages, and the balance for containers of oils, paints, greases, powders, toiletries and tobacco.[2]

ELECTROLYTIC TIN-PLATING

Tin-plating, which originated in the early thirteenth century, did not alter in principle until the late 1930s, when the electrolytic process was introduced. Originally, iron sheets were immersed in a bath of molten tin, coating both sides. This was called the hot-dip process. Considerable improvements were made, both in the rolling of sheets and in the hot-dip process, chiefly through mechanization, but the basic principle of tin-plating remained unchanged.

Invention in 1926 of the continuous hot-strip mill heralded important changes. The American Sheet and Tin Plate Company, a United States Steel subsidiary, quickly seized the opportunity and was the first to use hot-rolled strip to replace "break downs" hot-rolled from sheet bars on hand mills at its Gary (Indiana) Tin Mill. This was in 1927. The strip was cut into sheets of appropriate size, which were matched together and pack-rolled in a hand mill to reduce them to proper thinness, which the hot strip mill was unable to do. Elimination of the "breaking-down" operation materially reduced costs. The tin plate was of better quality.

Meanwhile, the company's laboratory had begun experiments in electrolytic tin-plating some years earlier. About this time an important event took place which led the way directly to the successful operation of the electrolytic process. This was the introduction, about 1929, of the cold reduction mill, which was capable of reducing hot-rolled strip to the thinness and widths required for tin-plating. Now the way was open for great savings in tin-plate production through continuous rolling in the hot strip and cold reduction mills.

Concurrently, experiments by the American Sheet and Tin Plate Company had advanced beyond the laboratory stage and a pilot plant for electrolytic tinning was built in June 1936. In 1937, the company installed an electrolytic tinning line at its Gary Works which began production the following year. This was the first commercially successful electrolytic tinning line in the world.

It had never been possible with the hot-dip method to apply a tin coating much less than 1.25 pounds of tin per base box. Uniform distribution of the tin was impossible. The electrolytic process consumed about 0.50 pounds of tin per base box, a saving of 0.75 pound per box. Later, the coating was reduced to 0.25 pound per base for certain products. Goaded by competition from aluminum cans, experiments began in 1959 with tin plate thinner than 0.008 inch in full widths. The figures proposed were 0.0071 to 0.005 inch or even less. The objective of rolling thinner steel is to obtain more tin plate from a ton of steel, which would mean to the can manufacturer more cans per ton of tin plate and lower material costs. There would also be a reduction in freight rates, an important part of tin plate costs to the container maker. It is anticipated that the thin tin plate will more closely approach the unit weight of aluminum cans and at the same time will be superior in strength; this will permit it to be handled more easily and economically than any substitute material.

The electrolytic process deposits tin more uniformly than the hot-dip process and makes a superior product for certain uses.

The electrolytic process was given its first major impetus by the demand from canners of dry products for a thinner tin coating than could be produced by the hot-dip process. By 1942 electrolytic tin plate represented 3.3 per cent of total tin plate production in the United States, which had meanwhile become a belligerent in World War II. Far Eastern tin supplies, which accounted for 92 per cent of American tin imports, were completely cut off. The limited stockpile of tin was not enough for both military and civilian needs. The shortage became so critical in 1942 that the government planned to send all goods in tin cans to its armed forces and to allied armies through lend-lease. There would have been practically no tin to spare for civilian needs. The availability of the electrolytic process for conserving tin was providential.

United States Steel suggested to the government that more electrolytic tinning lines be built as rapidly as possible and offered to share its knowledge of the new process with other tin-plate manufacturers. U.S. Steel added nine electrolytic tinning lines and other companies also installed them, making a total of twenty-seven units in the United States during the war. Enough tin was saved to permit the government to spare tin plate for civilians, though on a rationed basis. By the end of the war in 1945, electrolytic tin-plate production amounted to 33.6 per cent of total tin-plate output. The proportion continued to rise year after year and in 1960 reached 94 per cent. The remaining percentage was represented by the hot-dip process.

When an electrolytic tinning line is in operation it works continuously. One coil of cold reduced strip follows another through the line. The instant one coil has nearly gone through the line, it is welded to the front end of a new coil, thus providing a continuously moving strip of steel. The steel first passes through various cleaning solutions to prepare its surface for the plating operation. The strip then passes through the electrolytic tinning tank containing a tin salt in aqueous solution. The tin, existing in a soluble form in the plating bath, is deposited as a metallic film on the steel surface by the passage of an electric current. In the succeeding step, the strip is cleansed of any adhering electrolytic solution and then moves on to a tower, which is insulated for heat conservation. Here, the temperature of the strip is brought to the melting point of tin, causing a momentary fusion of the tin on the surface of the strip. The strip, thus covered with molten tin, is quickly quenched in a tank of cold water and emerges with a bright surface.

As the strip of tin plate moves on through the line, it is given a visual inspection and is also scanned by a pin-hole detector. The gauge is checked by a continuous micrometer. The hole detector and the micrometer are synchronized to reject automatically sheets with holes and those of improper gauge. After the flying shear has cut the strip into sheets, visual inspectors can reject individual sheets by pressing a reject button. The prime tin plate is generally stacked on wooden pallets in lots of 1,120, 1,344, or 1,680 sheets and then passed on for packaging. The strip of tin plate is not always cut into sheets, but is sometimes wound in a coil at the end of the line and shipped in coil form to customers.

GALVANIZING

Zinc is an excellent metal to protect steel exposed to the weather and other corrosive conditions. Coating steel with zinc is called galvanizing. Next to tin, zinc is used to protect a greater area of steel than any other metal.

The greatest use of galvanized sheet is on the farm where it is used as roofing and siding for grain bins and other farm buildings, poultry equipment, pails, manure spreaders, hay loaders, tractors, and wagons. Galvanized sheets are used as roofing and siding on other buildings, as well as for eave troughs. Uses elsewhere include air ducts, air-conditioning equipment, chimney flues, metal awnings, garbage, oil and ash cans, pails, deep-freeze units, automatic washers and dryers, storage tanks, culverts, and prefabricated walls for commercial and industrial buildings.

Galvanizing is done by immersing individual sheets in rapid succession in a pot of molten zinc, or by passing strip steel continuously through a bath of molten zinc. The former process is known as hot-dip sheet galvanizing and the latter as continuous hot-dip galvanizing. A more uniform coating of zinc is obtained in the continuous process, which is the modern production method.

VINYL-COATED STEEL

Plastics created a new world of materials, a world that was extended by combining the decorative and functional value of plastics with the strength of metals. The particular plastic is vinyl which has a hard, smooth surface, and is highly resistant to wear, abrasion, and chemical action.

Vinyl can be given any color and can be embossed with any texture that can be engraved on a printing roll. The most popular textures are leather and textiles. Vinyl is coated on steel, aluminum, magnesium, brass, and copper. Steel is most widely used. The vinyl coating is bonded onto a metal so firmly that the combination can be fabricated by conventional forming methods.

Vinyl-coated metals were introduced in 1954 by the Hood Rubber Company, a division of the B. F. Goodrich Company. A strip of solid vinyl was laid on a sheet of metal and the two were bonded by heat and pressure. Only one sheet was coated at a time. In the same year, the Naugatuck Chemical Division of the United States Rubber Company, using the same bonding technique, announced a high-speed continuous process.[3]

Vinyl-metal laminates found a welcome market. About 1 million square feet were consumed in 1955. Estimated consumption for 1960 was 18 to 22 million square feet.[4]

The steel industry watched the rapid growth of this new product and several companies decided to get into the business themselves. Vinyl-steel laminates offered a wider outlet for steel sheets which were suffering from an invasion by various plastics into long-accepted markets of sheets.

In 1959, United States Steel commercially introduced a process for bonding vinyl to steel. It differs from other processes in that liquid vinyl is applied to cold rolled or galvanized steel in sheets or in coils. The process is continuous. Embossing is done before the plastic cools.

The strength, tough wearing qualities, and handsome appearance in many textures and colors of vinyl-steel laminates account for their acceptance in a rapidly growing number of applications. They are used in the seat backs of passenger automobiles and buses, in the interior paneling of railroad coaches, and in the trim of airplanes. They have made spectacular gains in the curtain wall construction of buildings, where they may be readily hung on the interior steel framework for all surfaces. Vinyl-steel laminates are also used as wainscoting in office buildings, schools, restaurants, hospitals, homes, and theaters.

The plastic and steel combination makes an ideal material for various forms of furniture—bridge tables, folding chairs, outdoor and office furniture. Other uses include television, radio and record player cabinets, and supermarket checkout counters.

PORCELAIN ENAMEL

Porcelain enamel is to be distinguished from other enamel coatings which depend on hardening in the air. Porcelain enamel, as applied to steel, consists of a layer or layers of a glassy material intimately bonded to the metal. The enamel coating is formed by a fusion of a finely powdered mixture of several constituents, called frit, with the steel sheet surface, fired in an oven heated from 1,200° to 1,500° F.

Enamel was known 2,000 years ago. It was first applied as glass beads fused to copper, gold and silver jewelry, and decorative ware. The art of enameling flourished during the Byzantine Empire and from there it spread to Western Europe. Until the fifteenth century, enamel was applied by one of two methods: champlevé, in which a design was cut into the metal and the enamel was put into the hollows, or cloisonné, in which a design was formed by small metal bands soldered on a metallic background and filled in with enamel.[5]

Artisans in Limoges, France, toward the end of the fifteenth century, discovered that enamel would adhere to metal if the combination were fired. This was the beginning of porcelain enamel as we know it today. In Bohemia in 1830, cast-iron cooking utensils were porcelain-enameled for the first time. As the advantages of the hard, durable, easily cleaned surface of porcelain enamel were quickly appreciated, its uses spread to bathtubs, sinks, and ranges.[6] Progress was slow, however, in the last century because of the uneven surface of iron and later of steel. It was not until after World War I that porcelain enameling became a fairly large business. The sudden growth of the industry was due to steel sheets of improved quality, produced by the continuous hot and cold-rolled strip mills. Since World War II, there has been a tremendous demand for porcelain enameled-steel for ranges, refrigerators, freezers, dish washers, sinks, home laundry units, and display cases for frozen foods.[7]

Porcelain-enameled steel has a number of important industrial and architectural applications. The handling of corrosive, syrupy materials in the plastics and rubber industries is facilitated by the protective glass-smooth surface of porcelain enamel in many parts of the equipment. The non-absorbtive surface of porcelain enamel makes it ideal for hygienic purposes in the food processing and pharmaceutical industries.

Ceramic materials, including porcelain enamel fortified with special heat-resistant materials, are playing an increasingly important role in turboprop, turbo-jet, and ram-jet aircraft. Typical applications are the combustion chambers, turbine blades, and afterburners.

Since World War II, porcelain-enameled steel has made a dramatic entrance into the curtain wall construction of buildings. The beauty of color in unlimited shades is combined with a durable finish that will not stain or fade. Maintenance costs are at a minimum.

World Iron and Steelmaking Resources

> *But today they (people of underdeveloped nations) know and under-*
> *stand that hunger, disease, fruitless toil and early death are not inevita-*
> *ble, that it is possible to create conditions in which they and their children*
> *can have a better life. What has aptly been termed "the revolution of*
> *rising expectations" is under way.*
>
> —Halvard Lange, Foreign Minister of
> Norway in Address to the North
> Atlantic Treaty Organization.

Steel is in the warp and woof of modern industrial society, and, as such, is caught up in the movements and forces—sociological, scientific, technological, and others—which shape the way man lives. In the next quarter-century, the steel industry will probably undergo its greatest transformation in history, both in the location of steel centers and in manufacturing processes, with beneficient consequences spreading around the globe.

This transformation will be epochal because the world itself is experiencing epochal changes. What distinguishes the present state of change, or ferment, if it may so be called, is its global nature. Formerly, regional changes, such as the Industrial Revolution, rippled slowly out to the world; there are still vast areas it has not yet penetrated. From now on, the process will tend to be reversed and domestic changes will more and more reflect world currents.

A second feature of the present world ferment is the rapidity of its action. Unquestionably this is largely due to the contraction of time and space by modern means of communication and transportation. Another important factor which adds momentum to the forces at work—and also shrinks continents and seas—is the existence of world bodies, such as the United Nations, where delegates and specialists in many fields may discuss mutual problems and exchange information, as in a professional or

"Steel in Long Strips Like Paper"

The prediction of John Butler Tytus, father of the continuous hot strip mill, is realized in a modern 80-inch hot strip mill. Sheet steel races from the rolls of the last of six massive stands at a speed of nearly 2,000 feet a minute.

Electrolytic Tinplating

Tin plate for the canning industry is coated with tin electrolytically. Strip steel, moving from right to left, receives a dull, electrolytic coating of tin in tanks at the right. The coated strip then passes through a tower-like structure, where the tin coating is melted to give it a bright, metallic luster. After other treatments, the tin plate leaves the line where

This gasoline refinery, where corrosive conditions and high temperatures are encountered, illustrates one of the many uses of alloy steel. An example is also given of seamless steel tubing. Carbon steel pipe transports petroleum products from refinery centers to distribution points. (*Courtesy of Cities Service Company, Fritz Henle*)

Coke falls in a fiery cascade from a coke oven into a quencher car. Gases driven off from bituminous coal during the coking process are collected and processed in an adjoining coal chemical recovery plant.

Molten steel gushes forth from an electric furnace and pours into a ladle.

Fastest growing of the new steelmaking techniques is the use of a jet of pure oxygen to refine pig iron to make steel. This converter, in a French steel plant, is in full blow. (*Photograph by Lacheroy, France*)

A copper crucible is removed from a consumable-electrode vacuum-melting furnace, which can produce steel ingots up to 50 inches in diameter, weighing approximately 30 tons. Vacuum-melted steels and other metals serve in missiles, supersonic aircraft, atomic reactors, and other products requiring metals of exceptionally high purity. (*Courtesy of the Allegheny Ludlum Steel Corporation*)

R-N Process

The R-N process utilizes low-grade carbonaceous fuels to reduce iron ore in a rotary kiln. The product is iron briquettes, suitable for stock in steelmaking furnaces. The view of this semi-commercial plant in Birmingham, Alabama, is toward the feed end. (*Courtesy of the R-N Corporation, New York*)

trade convention. The history-making changes now occurring in the world are too numerous and complex for analysis here. We shall concern ourselves only with those which can be expected to impinge upon the steel industry. For simplification, we shall reduce them to three, all interrelated.

FACTORS AFFECTING THE STEEL INDUSTRY

1. A scientific and technological revolution which is proceeding faster than any previous similar revolution in history. "Research," said a 1956 report of the American Association for the Advancement of Science, "has placed in human hands the power to influence the life of every person, in every part of the earth." While science is lifting our eyes to the heavens in anticipation of landings on the moon, it is discovering a whole new universe within the atom. It may be from greater knowledge of the atom that new steels will be forthcoming of unheard of strength for structures and mechanisms of the Atomic-Space Age. It has been possible in a laboratory to produce a single crystal of pure iron in the form of a filament with a tensile strength approaching 2 million pounds per square inch, more than three times the strength of the strongest steel known today.

2. An unprecedented growth in population almost everywhere on the globe, especially among non-whites. Before World War II, population in Asia was growing at the rate of 1.2 per cent a year. Since the war, due to the wider health and hygiene measures, the mortality rate has fallen, but the fertility rate remains more or less constant, with the result that the population has been increasing at the rate of 1.7 per cent annually and in some countries about 3 per cent.[1] Although family planning has been officially adopted in the most populous countries, notably China, India, and Japan, the indications are, according to a 1959 report of the United Nations, that the total population of these nations will very likely double within the "next three decades and be equal to the present population of the whole world,"[2] which exceeded three billion in 1961. Commenting on the "exploding population" of the world, a report of the Stanford Research Institute of California, published in 1959, estimated that world population will double by the year 2,000. The report said that some means of controlling population growth "are inescapable."

3. The universal striving, particularly of people in underdeveloped nations, for higher living standards. As Halvard Lange was quoted as saying at the head of this chapter, "the revolution of rising expectations" is now under way. Accompanying this surge is a restless yearning of many ethnic groups to determine their own destinies. Science sometimes brings mixed blessings. Underdeveloped nations, indebted to science for a lower death rate, find that the resulting extra population may be a drag on their economic development. A rising share of their resources must be devoted to consumption merely to maintain the same living standards. There is an actual danger in some nations with a high population growth that efforts

to lift themselves up by their own bootstraps may be frustrated and there will be a decline in living standards. "Unimpeded fertility," said Marriner Eccles, former Chairman of the Board of the Federal Reserve System of the United States, "is giving the backward countries exactly what they do not need—more people—and hindering what they do need—more capital, more skills and greater productivity."[3] Many underdeveloped nations struggling to take their first steps toward industrialization, or to expand existing industries, appear to be afire with the belief that the basis for a machine economy is the manufacture of one's own iron and steel. In this respect, although they may possess adequate iron ore deposits and other raw materials to support a local steel industry, they may be putting the cart before the horse. Industrialization, even on a small scale, requires diversified steel products, such as plates, sheets, pipes and tubes, wire, bars, rods and girders, not only for a manufacturing plant and the products it makes, but also for other buildings, roads, bridges, pipes, and conduits for various purposes, and other auxiliary structures and equipment. But these products, in a nation of small industries, can be consumed only in small quantities, and it is not economical to produce them in small quantities. Their manufacture requires a sufficiently large domestic market, which does not exist in underdeveloped countries.

Other obstacles to the growth of an iron and steel industry in underdeveloped nations are:

1. The absence in many nations of coking coal, hence the interest in such nations of processes which do not require coke.
2. The lack of trained personnel on both the managerial and plant level.
3. The lack of capital and foreign exchange.

In spite of these disadvantages, many underdeveloped nations are progressing, though slowly, in setting up iron and steel works or in the expansion of existing industries. Their efforts have been aided through technical knowledge imparted by experts from Western steel-producing countries, and through various forms of educational and financial assistance. Since the end of World War II, a number of nations became steel producers or are planning to produce steel in the near future. Among these are: Argentina, Chile, Columbia, Peru, Cuba, Uruguay, Denmark, Ireland, Greece, Switzerland, Algeria, Egypt, Israel, Rhodesia, Morocco, Taiwan, Burma, Pakistan, South Korea, Philippines, and Bulgaria.

EXPLOSION IN STEEL PRODUCTION

Coincidental with the population explosion in some areas of the world is an explosion in steel production, and it is worldwide. Already it is having repercussions on the quantities of steel produced, imported and exported by all nations and on suppliers of steel to non-producers, and in so doing is changing the pattern of world steel markets. These repercussions and their effects are bound to be accentuated in the future, as world steel production is increased by present and new participants. "Everybody wants to get into the act," to borrow a phrase from the theatrical profession. Traditionally, steel-producing centers have been located for accessibility to raw materials within or near their borders. This was the case with Britain, Germany, France, and the United States. In recent years, other considerations, such as potential markets, and even national politics, have had a bearing on the location of new steel plants. Evidence of this may be seen in the number of small steel mills springing up in Latin America, in the growth of the Japanese steel industry, sustained to a large extent by imported raw materials, and in the geographical dispersion of steel mills within the United States and Europe to take advantage of local markets.

World steel trade is in a continuing process of readjustment. Some nations, traditionally importers of steel, are importing less; other nations are exporting steel for the first time or expect to do so in the near future. In a word, customary export markets for some nations are diminishing or disappearing and for other nations new export markets are opening up. The case of the United States is exceptional, rather than typical, for a number of reasons. For many years, the United States was a major steel exporter, its foreign shipments considerably exceeding imports, but in a recent period, the situation has been reversed. In 1961, the nation exported 1,989,179 tons of steel mill products and imported 3,164,256 tons. The import of some steel products into the United States amounts to more than domestic production. The tonnage of steel exports from the United States declined from 15 per cent of world steel trade in 1950 to only 7 per cent in 1960, while steel imports into the United States increased from 1.5 per cent of domestic supply in 1950 to almost 5 per cent in 1960. The unhappy position in which the American steel industry finds itself is due only in part to the loss of certain foreign markets through increased self-sufficiency. Wage costs in the United States, which have risen faster than productive efficiency, are far above those of any other steel-producing nation and, in consequence, most American steel products are higher priced.

As may be seen in Table 15, total hourly employment costs in the steel industry of the United States were considerably higher in 1952 and 1960 than similar costs for the same years in seven European nations and Japan. Total employment costs include wages and numerous "fringe" and employee benefits which constitute a sizeable proportion of total employment costs.

The competitive disadvantage of the United States is compounded by restrictive tax depreciation allowances of the federal government which put a brake on investments in new, modern facilities, whereas some nations, such as Belgium, France, Italy, and Japan have adopted realistic depreciation allowances to stimulate industrial strength through rapid modernization of plants.

TABLE 15

STEEL INDUSTRY EMPLOYMENT COSTS PER HOUR,
UNITED STATES AND EIGHT OTHER COUNTRIES,
1952–1960

Country	Employment Costs Per Hour		Increase 1960 over 1952 Cents		Foreign as % of U.S.	
	1952	1960	Per Hour	%	1952	1960
Luxembourg	$ .98	$1.40	$ .42	43%	42%	37%
Belgium	.82	1.22	.40	49	35	26
France	.72	.99	.27	38	31	26
West Germany	.69	1.21	.52	75	30	32
United Kingdom	.64	1.09	.45	70	28	29
Italy	.63	.98	.35	56	27	26
Netherlands	.53	1.08	.55	104	23	28
Japan	.32	.56	.24	75	14	15
United States	2.32	3.82	1.50	65	100	100

SOURCE: 1952—European Coal and Steel Community countries, from *Information Statistique,* published by the E.C.S.C.; United Kingdom from annual report of British Iron and Steel Federation; Japan from annual report of Japan Iron and Steel Federation; United States from Annual Statistical Report, American Iron and Steel Institute.
1960—E.C.S.C. countries, United Kingdom, and Japan from private sources; United States from Annual Statistical Report, American Iron and Steel Institute; 1960 data for the United Kingdom and Japan were partially estimated, based on reports of the B.I.S.F. and the J.I.S.F., respectively.

STEEL PRODUCTION AND CAPACITY

In view of the explosion in steel production and the "revolution of rising expectations" taking place in the world, it may be of interest to examine Table 16. It will be noted that world steel capacity planned for 1965 is given as 591,680 tons, an increase of approximately 50 per cent over production in 1961. Increases in steel capacity will not be uniform in all countries. In general, it may be expected that the rate of increase will be greater in countries which have imported all, or a large part of their own requirements. Only in the United States has capacity been established far in excess of domestic needs in order to meet peak loads, provide for national emergencies and have capacity available for export purposes. Capacity in the United States will increase only moderately by 1965, since the industry in producing 98,014,000 tons in 1961 utilized but two-thirds of its capacity. In countries where capacity and production are nearly the same, growth in capacity will be more pronounced. Compared to production in 1961, capacity planned for 1965 will increase 400 per cent in the Middle East, over 100 per cent in Latin America, 80 per cent in the Far East Red bloc, and 76 per cent in Africa.

WORLD IRON ORE RESERVES

To furnish iron ore for projected future steel capacities, it is estimated that world ore requirements, in terms of contained iron, will rise from approximately 209 million metric tons annually in 1960 to about 363 million metric tons annually in 1972-1975. There will be ample iron ore available to meet these needs. Iron is one of the more abundant and widely distributed elements in the earth's crust, constituting 4 per cent of the total. Its concentration in iron ore beds is virtually limitless in almost all regions of the world. Most of this iron is not in a form that can be utilized in current iron and steelmaking practices. Because of its position in the earth's crust, much of it is not readily accessible. It is estimated that world reserves of iron ore, as defined below, amount to 68 billion metric tons of iron-in-ore, enough to last more than two hundred years. Iron-in-ore is used as a measure, rather than tons of ore, because the iron content in ore varies widely. There will be no worldwide lack of iron ore, even without taking into account the immense deposits of iron-bearing materials such as laterites, itabirites, and fine-grained, non-magnetic taconite, whose existence is proven but for which no adequate metallurgical treatment has yet been developed.

Thus, the quantity of available iron ore presents no problem. Now let us consider its quality. For many years in the United States the availability of low-cost iron ores and low-cost coke and generally lower operating costs did not press blast furnace operators to get the utmost production of pig iron from their furnaces. When it became necessary to increase capacity, the tendency was to build new furnaces. Now the situation has completely changed. Under the pressure of higher costs of raw materials, facilities, and operation, American blast furnace owners are striving to obtain maximum productivity from existing furnaces.

One way to obtain more iron from a furnace is to improve the quality of the iron ore or the coke, or both. This consideration is chiefly responsible for the growing practice of upgrading or beneficiating ores, both chemically and physically. Beneficiation is economical when its added cost is recovered in greater blast furnace production. All large steel producing nations are today beneficiating ores and the worldwide trend is expected to continue toward 100 per cent beneficiated blast furnace feed. Some low grade ores, which, because of their chemical composition and texture, can be economically beneficiated into high quality blast furnace feed, may be preferred to less tractable but higher grade ores.

NEW METALLURGICAL PROCESSES

New metallurgical processes will affect the iron ore industry of the future as much as the preparation of blast furnace burden is affecting it

TABLE 16

WORLD PRODUCTION (1961*) AND PLANNED CAPACITY
OF CRUDE STEEL AND CASTINGS (1965)
(thousands of net tons)

Countries	Production 1961*	Planned Capacity 1965
North America	104,480	169,900
United States†	98,014	160,000
Canada	6,466	9,900
Latin America	6,093	13,810
Argentina	490	2,200
Brazil	2,970	4,400
Chile	431	770
Columbia	195	330
Cuba	20	150
Mexico	1,844	4,370
Peru	55	550
Venezuela	55	850
Others	33	190
Europe	221,293	310,510
Western Europe	119,067	167,570
ECSC	80,741	109,470
Belgium-Luxembourg	12,243	17,100
France	19,400	27,000
Saar		5,000 ⎫
West Germany	36,880	42,480 ⎬
Italy	10,050	14,550
Netherlands	2,168	3,340
Other Western Europe	38,326	58,100
Austria	3,418	4,070
Denmark	358	390
Ireland	45	90
Finland	320	660
Greece	72	160
Norway	535	880
Portugal	75	440
Spain	2,568	4,390
Sweden	3,921	4,620
Switzerland	313	440
Iceland	n. a.	n. a.
Turkey	310	1,100
United Kingdom	24,736	38,100
Yugoslavia	1,655	2,760
Eastern Europe (Red Bloc)	102,226	142,940
Bulgaria	331	990
Czechoslovakia	7,763	11,680
East Germany	3,748	5,950
Hungary	2,310	2,650

TABLE 16 (Continued)

WORLD PRODUCTION (1961*) AND PLANNED CAPACITY
OF CRUDE STEEL AND CASTINGS (1965)
(thousands of net tons)

Countries	Production 1961*	Planned Capacity 1965
Poland	7,826	9,920
Rumania	2,315	3,640
U.S.S.R.	77,933	108,110
Africa	2,833	4,900
Rhodesia and Nyasaland	90	220
Union of South Africa	2,723	3,960
Others	20	720
Middle East	250	1,280
Egypt	165	550
Iran	—	330
Iraq	—	70
Israel	85	330
Far East	35,922	53,550
India	4,517	10,300
Japan	31,165	41,890
Pakistan	15	380
South Korea	25	110
Taiwan	150	440
Others	50	430
Far East (Red Bloc)	17,406	31,380
China	16,535	30,000
North Korea	871	1,380
Oceania	4,370	6,350
Australia	4,295	5,500
Philippines	75	470
New Zealand	—	380
Total Free World	273,015	417,360
Total Red Bloc	119,632	174,320
Total World	392,647	591,680

SOURCE: American Iron and Steel Institute
n. a.—not available.
* Estimate.
† United Nations estimate.

today. Examples are the oxygen converter and the practice of injecting oxygen into the open hearth furnace. In both cases, the necessary oxygen for steelmaking is provided in a gaseous state rather than by release from iron ore, as is the case in the conventional open hearth furnace. In a word, oxygen substitutes for part of the iron ore. This trend in the use of oxygen, together with the increasing use of the electric furnace to make specialty steels, portends that the demand for open hearth quality lump ore for oxidizing purposes may never increase beyond present requirements. There may even be a decline in the demand for natural lump quality in ore for the open hearth furnace.

A third example of metallurgical development which may be expected to influence the iron ore industry of the future is the direct reduction of the ore. A number of direct reduction processes are in use and others are in development stages. These are described in Chapter 22. Their adoption may well cause a further dispersion of steelmaking facilities throughout the world, particularly in underdeveloped areas possessing local raw materials but with only a limited market for steel. Even though producing on a small scale from local ores, direct reduction processes will utilize some local ores that would not otherwise be mined, and thereby reduce the over-all demand for iron ore from other sources.

PRICE-QUALITY RATIO

As has already been indicated, iron ore reserves are large enough to last the steel industry far into the future. But what is iron ore? It contains iron, certainly, but the iron content of ore in current use varies so widely that what would be classed as ore by one blast furnace operator might not be acceptable to another. The principal ores now being used in France, containing less than 25 per cent iron, would not be considered iron ore in Brazil or India, or in many other countries. The Thomas process for steelmaking, widely used in Europe, is designed to utilize high phosphorus ores, which are unsuitable for American open-hearth furnace practice. Iron-bearing material, while in the earth, is of use to nobody. It only becomes a commercial product after it is removed from the earth and is in a usable form, ready for shipment. Then its classification as an ore depends upon its marketability, which, in turn, is determined by its delivered price to the consumer in relation to its quality. This is referred to as the price-quality ratio. It is the criterion by which an ore is judged competitively in a particular market. From a commercial standpoint, an iron ore may be defined as an iron-bearing material which could be economically used at a particular place under current cost and market price conditions. Under this definition, ferruginous quartzites would be classed as iron ore in Soviet Russia because they are being used there, but in India they would not be classed as ore. Coarse-grained, non-magnetic taconites now being worked near Marquette, Michigan, would be classed as ore in the United States but not in South Africa or Brazil, because in these countries such ores are not at the present time commercially usable. The same reservations apply to iron-bearing materials in many parts of the world. The above definition of iron ore was applied in estimating world reserves at 68 billion tons of iron-in-ore.

INTERNATIONAL IRON ORE TRADE

The distribution of world iron reserves is shown in Figure 1. It will be noted that not all large reserves of ore are close to major steel producing

PRINCIPAL IRON ORE RESOURCES
OF THE WORLD

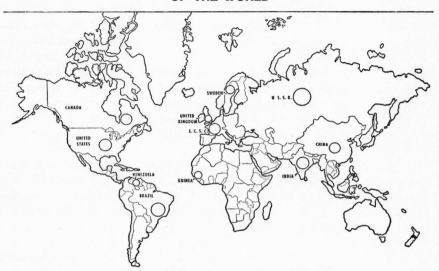

Fig. 1. Principal Iron Ore Resources of the World

centers. The problem confronting the iron ore industry is to make the most practical and economical use of world reserves to meet demands of the steel industry. In the past, nations with the largest steel industries have generally also been the foremost iron ore producers. The importation of increasingly large tonnages of iron ore into major steel production centers is fairly new in the long history of the steel industry. Although a relatively small proportion of the world production of iron ore—about 24 per cent—entered the export market in recent years, this amount of ore and the reserves behind it compete in many areas with domestic ores and influence iron ore prices throughout the world. Before World War II, no one would have foreseen that some day iron ore would move from Nevada to Japan or from India to Western Europe, or even from Chile via the St. Lawrence Seaway to ports on the Lower Great Lakes, such as Detroit, practically at the gateway to the Lake Superior ore region.

Most of the exported ore flows to four large markets: the United States, Britain, the European Coal and Steel Community, and Japan. The export pattern is by no means fixed. On the contrary, it is continually changing as consumption demands shift from one center to another, as ocean freight rates fluctuate, as new ore deposits are discovered and equipped for production, and as currency controls and exchange regulations affect purchases. Most of the ore in international trade is transported long distances over the ocean, averaging 2,000 miles or more. Ocean transportation is one of the most important factors in the international iron ore market. Total freight charges constitute a major, if not the major, cost in the delivered price of ore.

Reasons for the rapid increase in the consumption of imported ores since World War II, particularly since 1952, differ from country to country. In Britain and Japan, the cost of utilizing domestic ores to keep up with substantially increased steel production would have been excessive. In the United States, the rising cost of domestic ores and high inland transportation costs made it more economical for steel mills in coastal areas to import ore rather than draw on distant large domestic sources. For all importing nations an important factor was lower ocean freight charges realizable by the use of large, specially designed ore carriers and more efficient ore handling facilities. In every case, however, the determining cause of increased ore imports was a more favorable price-quality ratio for the imported ores than for the displaced domestic ores.

As a result of the appearance of large tonnages of iron ore in world export trade, international ore competition has become intensified. Some domestic ore producers, by improving the quality of their product or by adopting more efficient mining and beneficiation methods, have been able to defend a good part of their home market from imported natural ores, at least temporarily. Exporters of iron ore, on their part, are likewise striving to lower costs and improve ore quality, so that exported ores can be expected to play an increasingly important role in international ore trade, especially in relation to new steel producing facilities, as they come into existence.

OUTLOOK FOR THE FUTURE

Looking into the future, it may be assumed that the price-quality ratio of an ore at a consuming point will largely determine whether it will find a market there. The price part of the price-quality ratio is influenced principally by two factors: mining and transportation costs.

Mining costs are determined mainly by plant efficiency and labor and tax costs. In general, mining costs, in terms of cents per unit of contained iron, are lower in ore exporting than in importing countries, due chiefly to lower labor costs. Taxes, whether local or national, are also important items in over-all mining costs.

As we have seen, lower shipping rates have figured prominently in the rise of the iron ore export trade. Before World War II, an ore carrier of 10,000 dwt. tons was considered a large vessel. Now iron ore carriers of 20,000 to 25,000 tons are common and some are as large as 40,000 tons and even 60,000 tons. Still lower rates per ton of ore might be obtainable for certain routes with vessels exceeding 60,000 tons. However, these super-ore carriers, to be effective, require deep water and elaborate ore handling facilities at both ends of the run to load and discharge ore in minimum time. The capital investment involved in the larger carriers is considerable and can only be justified if depreciable through large annual tonnages. Therefore it can be expected that the iron ore export trade will tend to become concentrated in enterprises that can support large-scale, low-cost ocean transportation.

Following this general review of the world iron ore trade, it may be of interest to consider briefly how it may affect the principal ore consuming and producing nations.

North America

UNITED STATES

The United States, with iron ore deposits containing an estimated seven billion tons of iron-in-ore, possesses one of the world's largest iron ore reserves. It also contains roughly 45 per cent of the world's known coking coal. Both the ore and the coal are more than sufficient to take care of any foreseeable needs of the domestic steel industry. Until 1958, the United States was the world's largest producer of iron ore. In that year, its output was surpassed by the Soviet Union, which produced 97,884,240 tons, or 23 per cent of total world production, compared to 75,834,000 by the United States, or 18 per cent of total mined ore.

In spite of its huge iron ore reserves, the position of the United States, since the end of World War II, has changed from a net exporter of iron ore to a net importer. In 1961, imports of 28,943,959 tons amounted to 28 per cent of consumption, while exports of 5,546,826 tons were 6.9 per cent of production. The anomolous situation of the United States, possessor of one of the world's largest iron ore reserves, and at the same time the world's largest importer of iron ore, is the result of two postwar developments.

The first was the dispersal of steelmaking capacity in western and southern states and on the Atlantic seaboard—locations far removed from the major source of domestic ore, the Lake Superior area. This region, which contains 80 per cent of the nation's iron ore reserves, was, to a large degree, responsible for the concentration of steelmaking capacity in a great complex embracing such steel centers as Chicago, Pittsburgh, Detroit, Cleveland, and Youngstown. However, Lake Superior ores are now commercially inacccessible to the new steel plants on the eastern, western and gulf coasts or the western interior, where much of the postwar steelmaking expansion took place. These other areas, now accounting for about 50 per cent of the nation's capacity, must obtain their ore from rather inadequate local sources or by import. As already pointed out, the cost of transportation is an important factor and, in many cases the most important factor, in determining the source of iron ore for a particular steel plant. The use of large ocean-going ore vessels and complementary ore-handling docks and equipment have so reduced ocean freight that, under favorable conditions, the per-mile cost of transporting ore by sea may be only 5 to 10 per cent of the cost of rail transportation, with the result that imported ores can in many cases be delivered to seaboard plants at costs comparable to or lower than the price of available local ores, and considerably lower than Lake Superior ores.

The second reason for increased ore imports into the United States has been the rising costs of iron and steelmaking, due to labor costs outstripping improvements in output per man-hour and inadequate depreciation allowances. As a result, it has become more economical to increase production from existing blast furnaces by using higher quality raw materials, even at higher prices, than to construct new furnaces. Many foreign ores in their natural state are of better quality than natural domestic ores and for that reason are preferred by furnace operators. In consequence, foreign ores have to some extent replaced local ores in Alabama and Texas, and Lake Superior ores in Pittsburgh.

The demand for high quality iron ore has had important repercussions on the domestic ore industry itself. Since the Lake Superior ore fields were opened in the last century, the ores shipped from there have varied from 50 to 55 per cent iron, with 8 to 10 per cent silica. Originally, the Lake Superior ores were shipped in their natural state, but since 1910, as we shall learn in the next chapter, upgrading of the ores through beneficiation has been increasing from year to year. In 1960, 45 per cent of all natural ores shipped from the Lake Superior district received some form of beneficiation. While beneficiation has made it possible for Lake Superior ores to maintain an average shipping grade of 50 to 55 per cent iron, the methods in use do not yield the high-quality blast furnace feed which operators are now demanding. The steel industry has consequently been searching for beneficiation processes which will yield a more desirable product from available domestic ores, including low-grade ores, particularly those of the Lake Superior region.

The primary source of Lake Superior iron ores is an original iron formation in the form of a layer of siliceous rock carrying iron carbonates, silicates, and oxides, formed by sedimentary deposition in an inland sea hundreds of millions of years ago. The primary formation, subsequently buried under thick layers of rocks, was altered to some extent by the resulting pressures and high temperatures. The dominant iron minerals are often in the form of oxides, usually in one or two forms: magnetite, a strongly magnetic mineral, and hematite or goethite, an essentially non-magnetic mineral. Regardless of what the oxide may be, the iron content of the primary iron formation varies, as a rule, from 25 to 35 per cent. The iron beds which stretch through the Lake Superior country as long sinuous bands have been exposed by erosion in certain places, and subjected to weathering which leached out the silica to greater or less extent. The more intensive the weathering, the more silica was removed, and the higher the resulting concentration of iron. When the iron content reached 50 to 55 per cent in the natural state, the material in the past could be utilized without beneficiation and accordingly was termed "direct-shipping" ore to distinguish it from less weathered ores which needed some beneficiation by washing or gravity to make them usable.

While some of the primary iron formation in the Lake Superior area was leached enough to produce direct-shipping ore, "wash" ore, or "heavy media" ore (concentratable by complex means involving gravity), some of it was quite unleached, and some was only partly leached, but not enough to create a concentratable ore. In Minnesota and Wisconsin, the unleached iron formation has been popularly termed "taconite," either "magnetic" or "non-magnetic," depending on the form of the iron oxide, while the partly leached iron formation, not concentratable by existing commercial processes, has been termed "semi-taconite." In Michigan, the name "jasper" has been generally applied to hematitic iron formations, for the most part non-magnetic, now under development.

In an effort to produce a high-quality blast furnace feed, the iron ore industry has been turning its attention to various types of low-grade ores, because, in spite of their lower iron content, they can be more readily concentrated into high quality furnace feed than can the more or less oxidized ores that have been utilized in the past. After many years of research and experimentation, technologies have been developed for the concentration of these low-grade ores. All require fine grinding to permit the separation of the silica from the iron oxide. The iron oxide particles of magnetic taconite can be separated from the siliceous gangue material by magnetic attraction. Flotation has been found effective in separating specular hematite from silica in certain of the Michigan jaspers. The iron oxides found in semi-taconites and other non-magnetic iron formations can be rendered magnetic by roasting in a reducing atmosphere, with subsequent separation of the iron particles by electro-magnets. The concentrates of all these low grade ores contain from 62 to 67 per cent iron with 5 to 9.5 per cent silica. When agglomerated, they make a highly desirable blast furnace feed.

Three commercial plants are producing premium quality blast furnace feed from magnetic taconites of the eastern Mesabi Range; three plants are operating in Michigan on relatively coarse-grained jasper; and two pilot plants are conducting further experimentation with fine-grained, non-magnetic taconite and semi-taconite of the western Mesabi Range and with Michigan iron formation not amenable to flotation. It seems probable that in the not distant future, most of the Lake Superior shipments will consist of concentrates or agglomerates derived from taconites and jaspers of one kind or another.

What has been happening in the Lake Superior region has been going on to a lesser extent elsewhere in the United States. The need to make use of low-grade ores has, however, been less insistent in other parts of the country, since suitable foreign ores are available to most consuming centers. This is particularly true along the eastern seaboard where competition from foreign ores has caused a decline in New York mine production in recent years. In Alabama and Texas, difficulties in concentrating the local, rather low-grade ores has made it more attractive to utilize imported ores rather than upgrade local ores. The inter-mountain steel centers of Colorado and Utah, not commercially accessible to foreign ores, have had to follow much the same course as the Lake Superior area and make out with local ores. More and more their quality is being improved through beneficiation. There is even a taconite plant being constructed in Wyoming.

CANADA

Explorations carried out since World War II have boosted Canadian reserves to more than four billion tons of iron-in-ore, and this tonnage will increase rapidly in the years ahead as the Labrador Trough and its extensions are more thoroughly explored. The bulk of the Canadian reserves are low in iron content and require beneficiation. This, and the short ocean-shipping season in some of the far-northern regions will increase costs. However, the reserves are strategically located in relation to markets both in the United States and Europe. Canada's tax provisions and general mining policy encourage iron ore development. It may be regarded as certain that Canadian iron ore will compete vigorously in certain American markets with domestic and South American ores, and also in Western Europe with West African and South American ores.

Western Europe

E.C.S.C.

The European Coal and Steel Community at present obtains a large percentage of its ore requirements from domestic or nearby sources, chiefly Sweden. Iron ore reserves within the Community, although low in iron content, are large enough to meet rising demands. However, because of price-quality considerations, it may be expected that ores from newly developing deposits in West Africa will become competitive in some seaboard or near seaboard areas, particularly in Italy and along the English Channel and North Sea coasts. Iron ores from Canada, West Africa, and South America will also emerge as major competitors in these areas. Availability of low-cost ocean transport, accompanied by deep-water handling and transfer facilities, as well as future tariff policies, will have an important bearing on the extent to which foreign ores will ultimately penetrate this very important market.

UNITED KINGDOM

What has been said of the European Coal and Steel Community applies almost equally well to the United Kingdom. From its reserves of more than one billion tons of iron-in-ore, the United Kingdom could meet its needs for many years. But the iron content of the Cleveland ores is low, generally below 30 per cent, and the ores are not easily beneficiated. Therefore, it may be expected that the United Kingdom, with easy access to ores from Sweden, Eastern Canada, North and West Africa, and South America, will continue importing a large part of its ore requirements. The volume of these imports, as in the case of the Coal and Steel Community, will be strongly affected by future ocean freight and handling charges. When and if deep-water dock and handling facilities are ever built in United Kingdom ports they can be counted on to stimulate imports at the expense of domestic production.

SWEDEN

For several centuries, Sweden has been noted as an exporter of high-grade ores, supplied chiefly to Western Europe. Since World War II, ores from more distant areas have become increasingly competitive in Western European markets, strongly challenging Sweden's position. To meet the challenge, Sweden has expanded its mine production and is improving its shipping facilities. Because of the nation's proximity to Western European markets and the relatively high phosphorus content of its ores, which makes them suitable for the Thomas steelmaking process, Sweden should be able to maintain its competitive position in the European ore market in spite of increasing competition from other sources.

SPAIN

Spain has long been known for her iron ore, exported chiefly to the United Kingdom and Western Europe and consumed internally by the domestic steel industry. Reserves are estimated at a little over half a billion tons of iron-in-ore.

Production of iron ore in 1960 was 5,136,000 tons, considerably less than before World War II but sufficient to permit exports of some 3 million tons, while still meeting the needs of the local steel industry, supplied in part by imports from Morocco. Thus Spain continues to be a factor in international iron ore trade. However, with plans to double steel capacity by 1965, bringing it to 4.39 million tons, and with ores that are rather low grade by present standards, it is anticipated that future production will be consumed largely by local steel mills and that the nation will play a decreasingly important role in international iron ore trade.

Soviet Bloc

It is considered unlikely that the Soviet Union will exert a strong influence on world iron ore trade in the next several decades. Because its steel plants are located far inland in proximity to domestic iron ore reserves, it is improbable that foreign ores will ever find a significant market in the USSR. The remote location of the ore fields, which generally contain low-quality ores, makes it safe to assume that Russia will not figure significantly in world export markets, except possibly to Japan. In 1959, the USSR supplied Eastern European nations (Czechoslovakia, East Germany, Hungary, Poland, and Rumania) with some 13 million gross tons of ore to supplement their own production, augmented by 1 million gross tons imported from Western Europe, 760,000 tons from Brazil, 758,00 tons from India, and 170,00 tons from Africa. Since the ore has to be transported by rail a considerable distance, it appears probable that East Germany, Poland, and Czechoslovakia will eventually cease their dependence on Russia and once more import ore from sources outside of the Soviet bloc. Bulgaria, Rumania, and Hungary will very likely continue to meet their needs from local ores or from the USSR.

Asia

JAPAN

The resurgence of the Japanese steel industry from a production of 608,470 tons in 1946 to 31,165,000 (estimated) in 1961, based largely on imported ores, demonstrates how foreign ores can be utilized to a nation's economic advantage. The logical source for Japanese ore imports is Communist China and Southeast Asia. With supplies from the former cut off, at least temporarily, Japan must rely chiefly on Southeast Asia. In 1959, about 8.9 million gross tons of ore were imported from India, Portuguese India, Malaya, and the Philippines, with 1.16 million tons from the United States and Canada, and nearly 500,000 tons from South America. Super ore carriers may in the near future make ore from the west coast of South America and even from Brazil competitive in the Japanese market.

COMMUNIST CHINA

The steel industry of Communist China has been expanding very rapidly since World War II. So far, steel has been produced principally in numerous, widely scattered, small primitive furnaces, using local ores. But as the steel industry grows, it is becoming more centralized and will require large scale ore mining operations. Information concerning China's iron ore reserves is far from complete, but reserves are known to be widespead, varying in iron content which generally exceeds 50 per cent. With adequate domestic reserves and inadequate rail transportation, it is unlikely that China will become an importer of iron ore. It may, however, enter the world market as an exporter. As early as 1956, small tonnages were being shipped to Poland and Japan, and, should political obstacles be overcome, China may well become a major source of iron ore for Japan at the expense of Western Hemisphere sources and India.

INDIA

India has very large reserves of high-grade iron ore to support a domestic steel industry. The country consumes some 3 million gross tons of native ore and, in addition, is slowly entering export markets, shipping 2.5 million gross tons in 1959—most of it (1.6 million tons) to Japan and to Czechoslovakia (nearly 500,000 tons). India, together with China, appears destined to become the future source of iron ore for all of Southeast Asia. Some ore from the Goa and Bombay districts is reaching the Mediterranean area, and even going as far north as Poland. However, it is doubtful that India will be able to compete seriously in this market with ores from Canada, South America, and West Africa, which are not faced with the shipping restrictions of the Suez Canal.

South America

BRAZIL

Brazil has more than 10 billion tons of iron-in-ore, much of the ore containing over 60 per cent iron, and is at the present time second only to the USSR in the size of its iron ore reserves. In relation to these huge reserves, consumption of about 2 million tons and export of 4 million tons in 1959 were insignificant. The inland location of the reserves, the high cost of rail transport, inadequate shipping facilities, and the remoteness of the nation from the principal iron ore consuming centers explain why Brazil's exports have been limited almost entirely to premium-priced open-hearth ores. Plans to expand mine production are under way and improved shipping facilities were scheduled for completion at Vitoria in 1961-1962. Brazil intends to play an increasingly important role in the world market. The high quality of its ore will be a factor to be reckoned with it spite of the country's remoteness from major steel consuming centers.

VENEZUELA

Although Venezuela's iron ore reserves do not qualify it as one of the potentially large producers of iron ore, it is playing an important role in the export market. The current production of about 14 million gross tons of iron-in-ore is marketed partly in the United States, and partly in the United Kingdom and the European Common Market. Chemically, Venezuelan ore is acceptable, but physically it leaves much to be desired because of the large proportion of "fines" which must be agglomerated before they can be effectively used in the blast furnace. How successfully Venezuelan ore will be able to compete in Europe with higher grade ores to be produced in West Africa, and in the United States with other South American and Canadian ores, remains to be seen.

West Africa

West Africa will probably become an important factor in the world iron ore trade in the next ten years or so. The production of about 4.75 million gross tons of iron ore in 1959, all of which was exported, does not make the West African countries important exporters at present, but does reflect a continuing increase in outut during recent years. However, partially explored reserves of well over 1 billion tons of high-grade ores are strategically situated for sale in both Western Europe and the east coast of the United States. Active exploration or development plans are underway on recent impressive discoveries in Liberia, Guinea, Mauritania, and Gabon. Some of these reserves will certainly develop into producing mines within the next five to ten years, and additional important discoveries will be made as prospecting is pushed further inland. The high quality of the ores, the relatively low labor costs and accessibility to the ocean, should make West African ores increasingly competitive throughout Europe and to a lesser extent in the United States.

Conclusion

In conclusion, it may be said that the most important factors in the development of the world's iron ore trade in the next few years will be as follows:

1. Abundant iron-bearing material, distributed throughout the world, will amply provide enough iron ore to take care of any foreseeable requirements. It is conceivable that some shortages, of a temporary nature, may develop in certain localities for many reasons, but there will be no over-all shortage of iron ore.

2. Due to recent discoveries of direct-shipping ores and the improvement of techniques to beneficiate low-grade taconite type ores, the world's productive iron ore capacity has increased faster than the iron ore needs of steelmaking facilities. As a consequence, keen competition has developed for available iron ore markets.

3. Economic considerations—the price-quality ratio—will determine at any given time what markets an ore may capture. Lower quality ores must be priced relatively lower in a market if they are to compete as sources of supply.

4. Comparatively lower production costs, more economical ocean transport costs and better quality ore will enable some export ores to capture larger shares of some markets during the next few years at the expense of domestic ores.

The Blast Furnace, 1881–1960

That venerable Goliath, the blast furnace, smelter of iron ore for more than six hundred years, is today being challenged by not one but scores of Davids. In the swiftly changing technology of the iron and steel industry, the blast furnace is being reappraised and is being asked to justify itself as the most efficient producer of iron. The chief immediate reasons why the blast furnace is being challenged is the depletion of rich iron ores and coking coal in advanced industrial nations and the desire of underdeveloped countries with little or no coking coal to set up an iron and steel industry. There are said to be 180 alternate processes under "more or less active consideration," but only a dozen or so are in use or well along in development.[1] According to one American advocate of new iron smelting processes, the blast furnace "has apparently reached the stage of its existence where every possible commercial step will be taken to replace it. . . . Every hot metal and pig iron user in this country and Europe is patiently waiting for the time when iron can be directly reduced (in low cost equipment) to either liquid or solid iron."[2] Defenders of the blast furnace are confident that the "future of the blast furnace is not to be shrouded in a gloomy curtain of black; rather, it is a picture as rosy as the dawn."[3] The present chapter reviews the major developments which have taken place in the blast furnace since the closing decades of the last century and considers present and probable future trends.

DEVELOPMENT OF MODERN BLAST FURNACE

The ironmasters of Britain and Europe originated the blast furnace and nursed its early development, but it may not be too much to claim for their American confreres that the modern blast furnace grew to maturity in the United States. There was good reason for it: Americans were primarily interested in greater output per furnace. This goal necessitated modifications in the furnace and in auxiliary equipment.

Until the great Mesabi range was opened up in the Lake Superior region in 1892, the ores charged into blast furnaces were hard and coarse and of relatively low iron content. The rich hematite Mesabi ores were soft and fine. Their high reducibility permitted faster driving rates in the furnace, but the fine ores did not descend uniformly, causing jamming and hanging of the burden in the stack. When a movement occurred, it was often with explosive violence. Blast furnace operators struggled with this problem for twenty years. It was finally solved by United States Steel Corporation around 1918. A relatively minor change in the contour of the brickwork in the lower part of the furnace was found to make all the difference between success or failure in the utilization of Mesabi ores.

HANDLING AND CHARGING RAW MATERIALS

After the problem of smelting the Mesabi ores was solved, attention was given to the construction of larger blast furnaces. The larger units made themselves felt all the way back to the iron ore ranges. Mining was increasingly mechanized, larger and faster ore vessels were built to transport the ore down the Great Lakes, and unloading equipment at the terminal ore docks was also mechanized. Now it became necessary to expedite the handling of a growing volume of raw materials at the furnace site. The pressure of these needs brought about extensive mechanization of auxiliary equipment which made possible still higher production rates.

After the introduction of steam power to the iron industry, raw materials in wheelbarrows were raised to the top of the furnace on a vertical hoist, operated by a steam engine. The wheelbarrows were transferred to a loading platform where "loaders" manually dumped the contents into a large charging bell at the top of the furnace. A major step toward greater productivity came with the inclined skip hoist, first installed in 1883. Small skip cars travel up the inclined hoist from the furnace stock house to the charging bell where they automatically dump their loads. As a result of this innovation, the methods for stocking raw materials and feeding them to the furnace charging bins were inadequate to keep pace with furnace needs. The practice of transferring raw materials from their original point of discharge from ore vessels or railroad cars to reserve stockpiles by hand shoveling gave way to mechanization in 1895. This was achieved by the introduction of an entirely new system, made possible by the invention of the traveling ore bridge. This gigantic machine, running on rails, carries a huge clam-shaped bucket which scoops up iron ore or limestone from the discharged pile and dumps the contents in the storage yards where stockpiles are accumulated to last throughout the winter. The new system of transferring raw materials also included the construction of an improved stock house containing bins from which the raw materials descend by gravity to the charging area below or at ground level. Subsequent changes were made here, and now the raw materials flow from the bins into traveling scale cars which automatically weigh the materials as they are withdrawn from the bins and dump them into skip cars, ready to take their loads up the hoist to the top of the furnace.

Disposal of Pig Iron and Slag

Blast furnaces of larger capacity necessitated improved methods for handling greater volumes of molten pig iron and slag as they flowed from the furnace. Traditionally, the molten iron was run into a large sand mold from which channels led to smaller molds, where the iron solidified into "pigs." The pigs were later remelted for conversion into steel. The famous Captain Bill Jones, of the Carnegie Steel Company, did away with all that in 1889 by inventing the Jones Mixer, a vessel in which the molten iron from the furnace remained molten at the steelmaking department. This permitted the introduction of hot metal ladles, the first of which were the open-top type. A major improvement was made in 1915 by the Jones & Laughlin Steel Corporation with the introduction of the torpedo-shaped ladle, with a small opening on the top, mounted on railway trucks. Heavy linings of fireclay brick or natural silica firestone permit the iron to remain molten for thirty-six hours. These mixers range from 75 to 210 tons capacity. The mixer ladle is tilted to pour the iron into transfer ladles, which carry the iron to the hot metal mixer or to the steelmaking furnaces as required.

The handling of large slag accumulations also presented problems. Prior to 1883, the slag was allowed to flow into molds located on what was termed the "cinder wharf." The slag was later broken up and loaded manually into railroad cars for transfer to slag dumps. A number of improved handling methods resulted in the 1890s with the appearance of an open cast-iron ladle, called a cinder pot or slag thimble, into which the slag is allowed to run. The pot has a dump mechanism and is mounted on a railroad buggy. A long line of cinder pots, filled with slag, is hauled to a slag dump. Some of the slag is recovered, crushed, and screened into different sizes. The principal uses of slag are in roads, railroad ballast, concrete aggregate, cement, and fertilizer carriers.

Improved Blowing Engines

An enormous volume of air is required to blow a modern blast furnace. To smelt a ton of pig iron, an average furnace consumes a little less than 2 tons of iron ore, under 1 ton of coke and about half a ton of limestone and 3½ tons of air in the blast. A blast furnace capable of smelting 1,500 tons of iron a day will use 5,000 tons of heated air, generate 6,000 to 7,500 tons of gas and necessitate the circulation of 5 million gallons of water every 24 hours.

The pressure under which air is blown into the furnace determines the height of the charge which can be effectively penetrated by the blast. The replacement of water-driven bellows by steam-powered blowing machines at the end of the eighteenth century made possible a progressive increase in furnace size and output. The rapid development of reciprocating steam-driven blowing engines marked the beginning of high blast volume rates in the United States from about 1880 to 1905.

The next step was to use some of the waste gas from the furnace to fire gas-driven blowing engines. These gases contain about 25 per cent carbon monoxide, an excellent fuel, and it had long been a challenge to the steel industry to make more efficient use of this byproduct. The first gas-driven blowing engine, introduced in 1903, quickly won a place for itself because it could be run with excess furnace gas and also because its thermal efficiency was greater than that of the steam-driven engine. The next development in blowing engines was the steam turbine, or turboblower, which first appeared in 1910. Its small size and freedom from reciprocating parts earned it an unchallenged position for many years as a generator of air blast. In 1958, United States Steel Corporation reported that tests made with a gas-turbine blower indicated that it is more economical and efficient than the best steam-driven turbine blower.

Science Comes to the Blast Furnace

Before the turn of the last century, blast furnace operators devoted their thought and energies mostly to building larger units. Meanwhile, steel users were presenting more severe requirements to the operators of steel-making furnaces, who, in their dilemma, summoned metallurgists to their aid. Under the tutelage of the metallurgists, the steelmakers were made to realize that their efforts to improve the quality of steel were handicapped by the quality of iron they received. "In the mania for larger and larger units, and greater and still greater outputs," wrote a critic in 1905, "the chemistry of the blast-furnace has been sadly neglected, and the nature of the raw materials has not received proper attention."[4] Foundrymen joined their complaints to those of the steel melters. At that time, the only way that pig iron was graded was by the appearance of its fracture. In 1904, a subcommittee of the American Society for Testing Materials prepared standard specifications for pig iron based on chemical analysis.

Blast furnace operators were caught flat-footed by the demands thrust upon them. Their knowledge of chemistry was fragmentary; they knew almost nothing about the flow of gases or the temperature conditions within the furnace. The operators' greatest deficiency was a lack of uniformity in the composition of iron ores and coke. To remedy this situation, the various ores were graded and afterwards blended to yield standard grades of specified chemical composition. Still later, the washing of coal to reduce the ash and sulphur resulted in a coke of more uniform chemical composition. Once the metallurgist and the engineer moved in on the blast furnace, it became the object of as much investigation and research as any unit of the steel industry. Methods and devices for chemical and metallurgical control, following one another rapidly, have made the blast furnace into a highly efficient instrument. More than 90 per cent of the iron in the ore is recovered directly as pig iron. To that may be added the iron blown out of the furnace as dust, which is recovered and is usually returned to the furnace, bringing the net efficiency of the blast furnace to 95 per cent or more.

Growth in Size of the Blast Furnace

In the early years of the present century, American blast furnaces seldom smelted more than 600 tons of pig iron a day and most of them produced considerably less. The size of furnaces began to increase following the successful utilization of fine Mesabi ores. In 1929, a blast furnace of United States Steel Corporation was smelting slightly more iron in one day than the record of 1,000 tons a week established in 1881 in the famous battle between the Lucy and Isabella furnaces. Blast furnaces and their auxiliary equipment continued to grow in size, and in 1945 another U.S. Steel furnace was producing more than 1,600 tons of iron a day. This production rate was exceptional. Not many years ago, a 1,000-ton-a-day furnace was considered a giant of the industry, but that output is no longer remarkable and the new giants are producing more than 2,000 tons a day. It is known that blast furnaces in the Soviet Union have produced 2,910 tons in twenty-four hours, and units are reported under construction capable of smelting 4,400 to 5,500 tons a day.[5] United States Steel Corporation has built a 3,000-ton-per-day blast furnace and its attainment of full capacity rate is only a matter of properly beneficiating the raw materials and improving operating practices.

RECENT INNOVATIONS

Pressure Blowing

The air blast volume in the blast is one of the chief factors governing the productivity of the blast furnace. The air enters the furnace at a very high velocity, estimated to be about 350 miles an hour. The air, converted into gas, passes through the furnace in a matter of seconds, and the gas leaves the furnace through offtakes at the top at great speed. The disadvantage of high "wind" rates is the amount of fine iron ore, or flue dust, which is blown out with the gas. This obstacle has been overcome by what is known as pressure blowing. Special valves at the top of the furnace slacken the velocity of the gas and build up pressures within the furnace. Under this pressure, the gas more effectively penetrates the charge and reduces the iron ore. Republic Steel Corporation began experiments with top pressure blowing in the United States at one of its furnaces in 1944. Mechanical difficulties caused pressure operation to be suspended. Successful pressure blowing was achieved in 1946, and since that time has been continued at the furnace. Experience has shown that pressure blowing significantly increases pig iron production. In the Soviet Union, at the beginning of 1956, 69 per cent of all pig iron was being produced in blast furnaces with high top pressure. According to a United Nations study,[6] "By raising the top pressure to 0.7 atm (atmospheres), blast furnace productivity is increased by 5.5 to 8.5 per cent, specific coke consumption is reduced by 0.5 to 5 per cent and the amount of blast furnace dust given off is reduced by 20 to 50 per cent." The resulting pig iron was said to be more uniform in composition.

Oxygen-Enriched Blast

Durrer says that "the main defect of the traditional blast furnace, from which all of its disadvantages stem, is the utilization of ordinary air for the combustion of that part of the carbon which generates heat." Every volume of oxygen in the air blown into a furnace, he says, carries four equal volumes of "dead weight in the form of nitrogen," which is chemically inert. Its function is to carry heat up through the charge and help prepare it for reduction, but in absorbing heat the nitrogen tends to keep the internal furnace temperature relatively low. The rising gas column, says Durrer, "has the dual function of transferring as much as possible of the heat it carries to the burden which is traveling in the opposite direction, and also of reducing the iron oxides of this burden by the action of carbon monoxide (indirect reduction). In order to perform these functions, the blast furnace must have a considerable height: some 30 meters. This in turn results not only in high construction costs, but in the necessity of utilizing raw materials of very great mechanical strength, in view of the height and weight of the burden. The only reason why we are not struck by these drawbacks is that we are so accustomed to the thermally very efficient blast furnace that we cannot imagine smelting operations taking place on a large scale without it."[7]

Men theorized that if the blast could be enriched with a small amount of oxygen, less nitrogen would enter the furnace with the smaller volume of air that would be needed and that, in turn, would mean a shorter furnace, less expensive blowing engines, heating stoves and other accessory equipment. At the same time, higher temperatures could be attained in the furnace hearth.

Tests made by Jones & Laughlin Steel Corporation in the United States showed that with 1.5 per cent oxygen enrichment of the blast, under moisture control, there was a 9 per cent gain in furnace output. Other tests in the United States have demonstrated that if the oxygen content of the blast is increased to 30 per cent, compared to 20 per cent oxygen in normal air, and the volume of air correspondingly reduced, there is insufficient transfer of heat to the upper part of the furnace stack. Experiments in the Soviet Union in recent years, using a 25 to 26.5 per cent oxygen enriched blast, raised the output of iron 11.5 per cent, with no change in coke consumption.[8]

Another method under investigation is a steam-humidified blast of constant humidity. In the United States, air-conditioned blast is sometimes used. The Soviet Union in 1955 smelted more than 90 per cent of its pig iron in blast furnaces operating with a constant humidity blast. It is estimated that the changeover to a constant humidity blast, based on the average annual absolute humidity, raises the average pig iron output by 7 per cent and reduces the coke consumption by 2 per cent. The chief reasons for the increased productivity through the use of constant humidity wet blast is its enrichment with oxygen and the increased reducing power of the blast furnace gas.[9]

New Blast Furnace Fuels

Blast furnace operators, in their drive to increase efficiency and reduce costs, are turning to other fuels to replace a substantial portion of the coke. The injection of natural gas into the furnace is already in commercial practice. The gas furnishes carbon for reduction of the ore and in that respect serves the same function as coke. Blast furnaces using gas are said to consume about 25 per cent less coke and to increase iron output an equal amount.

Experiments have been made in the use of heavy heating oil partially to replace coke. The oil, like gas, yields carbon. The results, so far, indicate that atomized oil can be blown through the furnace tuyeres. Tests also show that oil can be used interchangeably with gas.

Trials being conducted also point to the feasibility of injecting powdered coal into the blast furnace. One method is to blow coal through the tuyeres with the hot blast and another is to inject a mixture of fine coal and oil. Here, again, the reduction in coke is said to be as much as 25 per cent.

Which new fuel or combination of fuels will be most economical will be determined by relative local prices.

PROBLEMS OF THE BLAST FURNACE

As the old monarch, the blast furnace, stands beseiged by a host of, as yet, tiny rivals, its greatest problem in defense is the available quantity and quality of ore and coking coal. The high production rates of a modern blast furnace have led generally to the exploitation of only the largest ore and coking coal deposits. A 1,500-ton-per-day furnace, for example, annually consumes the equivalent of almost 1 million tons of ore with 50 per cent iron content, requiring a deposit of at least 20 to 25 million tons, the minimum needed to amortize a modern blast furnace plant. Thus, major steel producing centers scarcely ever utilize small deposits. Correspondingly large coking coal reserves are also needed, since about 1¼ tons of coal, before transformation into coke, are usually required to smelt a ton of pig iron. Another formidable problem is the high capital cost of a modern blast furnace, estimated to be around $25 million in the United States, plus another $25 million for the supporting coke ovens. The high capital investment needed for such an installation, the greater availability of high-grade iron ore concentrates and, in many areas, the paucity or absence of good quality coking coals, is spurring on the development of alternate processes.

Blast furnace operators are looking with increasing interest toward automatic controls as a further means of raising efficiency and lowering costs. United States Steel has installed a static control system which charges the furnace in accordance with a preset program. Static control means that the regulating devices are completely static, without moving parts. Since there are no parts to wear out or get out of order, no adjustments need to be made in the system. The new system is controlled by pushbuttons, selector switches, and indicating lights on a control panel. A report on this blast furnace innovation, said: "It is believed that in the not-too-distant future new blast furnace plants will have stockyards that will be entirely conveyorized and have means for making automatic analyses of the ore and other materials, computing the proper mix of these materials, and automatically feeding them to the skip hoist. The result will be a complete charging operation that could be set up for any particular grade of iron by means of suitable punched cards."[10]

In addition to the new techniques—pressurized blowing, oxygen enrichment of the blast and controlled humidity—perhaps the greatest emphasis is now being placed on the beneficiation of ore and coal, now to be considered.

BENEFICIATION

Coal

Beneficiation of iron ore and bituminous coal represents the response of the iron and steel industry to diminution of the earth's raw materials that are being consumed at an ever faster rate. The availability of good coke, its rate of consumption, and its cost per ton of pig iron produced, are the most important factors in the economics of the blast furnace; they are chiefly responsible for the drive to develop substitute processes. Mention has been made that few steelmaking countries in Europe produce sufficient coking coal for their needs and that Austria, Italy, Luxembourg, and Sweden have none. The better grades of coking coal are becoming scarcer in the United States. To counteract this situation, greater attention is being paid to its beneficiation and to obtaining the ultimate B.T.U. (British thermal units) from the consumption of a ton of coke within the blast furnace in order to reap the fullest advantage from the steadily rising proportion of high-grade iron ore agglomerates now being charged into the furnace. It is held to be inevitable that iron and steel companies in Europe will have to find means to utilize lower-grade coal for the manufacture of metallurgical coke. The problem is being partially met by the successful development of processes for blending good and poor grades of coal to give a satisfactory coke.

The use of beneficiated coal and ores, combined with improved techniques in blast furnace operation, have resulted in a significant drop in the rate of coke consumption. In 1948, an average of 1,908 pounds of coke were consumed in American blast furnaces per ton of iron produced; in 1961, the rate was down to 1,416 pounds.

Iron Ore

Iron ore beneficiation, in one form or another, has been carried on since medieval times. Its purpose is to remove waste material and thereby raise the iron content. Iron ore beneficiation on a large scale in the United States was begun experimentally by United States Steel at Coleraine, Minnesota, in 1906. In 1910, the company erected a full-size commercial concentrator which decreased the silica content of the ore by means of washing and sedimentation. Many other methods have since been introduced for ore beneficiation and large establishments have been built for that purpose in the Lake Superior region and elsewhere in the nation. In 1961, there were 90 beneficiation plants in the United States, seventy of which were in the Lake Superior region. The processing of taconite, a low grade ore found abundantly on the Mesabi Range in Minnesota was described in the previous chapter. Today, iron ores are being beneficiated in all large steel-producing nations and the proportion of treated ores has been increasing rapidly in recent years. In 1960, 50 per cent of iron ores shipped from American mines were beneficiated, compared to 27 per cent a decade earlier.

In the Soviet Union, it has been reported that the better grades of iron ore in the Krivoi Rog basin, largest Soviet iron producer, are virtually exhausted and that plans are underway to beneficiate the lower grades. The Soviet's largest steel plant at Magnitogorsk in the Urals is also said to have used up most of its available rich ores and is in urgent need of finding ways to utilize the poorer grades.[11] Sweden has long been world famous as an exporter of the finest grades of iron ore, but in recent years it has installed what has been described as one of the largest and most technically advanced ore beneficiating plants.

As long as it was possible to increase blast furnace production rates and decrease fuel consumption with currently available ores by building larger units, it was logical that furnace development in Europe and the United States followed along these lines. But the rapid depletion of the better grade ores in the United States, and the swelling volume of imports from Latin America, Africa, and Canada, a large portion of which were of fine texture, were bound to alter blast furnace practice. All fine ores, as well as concentrated taconite, must be converted to a lump form by some process of agglomeration before they can be effectively used in the blast furnace. There are four major methods for accomplishing this end: sintering, nodulizing, pelletizing, and briquetting. In sintering, fine material is mixed with a pulverized fuel and placed on a grate where the mixture is burned to a clinker under a forced draft. Nodulizing is performed in a rotary kiln. As the fine material moves through the kiln at temperatures near the fusion point, it is agglomerated into nodules by the rolling motion of the kiln. In pelletizing, fine damp material is formed into balls in a revolving cylinder, or disc, without being heated, and the balls are subsequently hardened by heating them in a shaft furnace or on a moving grate. In briquetting, fine material, occasionally mixed with binders such as cement, is molded under pressure into briquettes.

Opinions differ over which of the four methods is preferable, but sintering is the most widely used. Of the 62,256,337 tons of agglomerated ores produced in the United States in 1961, sinter represented 72.5 per cent, pellets 26 per cent and briquettes, nodules and others 1.5 per cent. Until about 1947, sintering was done by the steel industry merely to convert blast furnace flue dust, an otherwise waste material, into an agglomerate that could be charged back into the furnace. Because it was regarded as a salvaging operation, blast furnace operators gave it little serious attention, and the quality of the sintered product left much to be desired. There was a divided opinion in blast furnace circles whether sinter was beneficial to furnace operation.

The general experience has been in the large iron-producing centers of the world that sinter raises the productivity of the blast furnace from 10 to 25 per cent and lowers the coke consumption by 7 to 20 per cent, depending on the quality of the burden. In recent years, there has been a marked tendency to use a fluxed sinter, produced by the addition of limestone and dolomite. Fluxed sinter has a higher reducibility than ordinary sinter because the lime and magnesia in the flux combine with silica of the ore to minimize the formation of iron silicate that is difficult to reduce. The Magnitogorsk combine in the Soviet Union changed over to fluxed sinter, resulting in a 12 per cent greater blast furnace output and a 3.4 per cent lowering of coke consumption. Late in 1959, it was reported that the Kokura Steel Works in Japan had been using 100 per cent fluxed sinter for well over a year with a marked saving in coke consumption. The cost of the pig iron was also reduced. Fluxed sinter is also applied in Western Germany, the United Kingdom, and Sweden; in the last-named country it is the only kind used.

The United States has been active in building sintering plants in recent years. In 1955, it produced approximately 26 million tons of sinter and in 1961, approximately 45 million tons. When present construction plans are completed, the nation's total sintering capacity will amount to 64 million tons annually—enough to allow America's blast furnaces to operate with 50 per cent sinter in their charge.

BLAST FURNACES, TODAY AND TOMORROW

American defenders of the blast furnace have enough confidence in the traditional iron smelter to foresee giants with a daily capacity of 4,000 tons, and there must be a similar confidence in the Soviet Union, where, as mentioned earlier, units capable of producing 4,400 to 5,500 tons in twenty-four hours are said to be under construction.

United States Steel has recently manifested its confidence in the blast furnace by making intensive studies of blast furnace operation in a small-scale furnace and by beginning construction of a large furnace of advanced design, scheduled for completion in 1962. Both are near Pittsburgh, the first at Universal and the second at Duquesne.

The experimental furnace, completed in 1961, is about one-seventh the size of a conventional furnace. It has a working height of 19½ feet and a hearth diameter of 4 feet. One feature of the furnace is the generation of 5,000 cubic feet of air blast per minute. The stoves will heat the air to a maximum temperature of 2,500° F., which is nearly twice the customary temperature. Although iron smelting in a blast furnace began more than 600 years ago, much of what happens in the process is still a mystery. U.S. Steel anticipates that studies facilitated by the small size and special features of the experimental furnace will afford a closer scrutiny into these mysteries and that the knowledge gained will result in still greater efficiency in commercial furnaces.

The furnace at Duquesne originally had a rated capacity of 850,000 tons of pig iron a year, but new features may raise actual capacity to 1,275,000 tons, making it the largest capacity blast furnace in the free world. It will have a number of other innovations never before incorporated in one blast furnace. It will be the first to have two tapping holes, which will permit the cast house crew to prepare runners between casts every two-and-a-half to three hours. It will also have automatic probing of the stock column, high top pressures up to 30 pounds per square inch, hot blast temperature of 2,000° F., an air-cooled hearth, controlled size of the burden, and advanced instrumentation.

The probes will record carbon monoxide, carbon dioxide, hydrogen, methane, and water content and remove samples of material at three levels above the mantel. It is expected that the probes will give more precise information on actions taking place at different stages of the smelting process.

The top pressure of 30 pounds, compared to 11 to 13 pounds in other top-pressure American furnaces, will accelerate reduction and keep the burden sliding smoothly down the furnace sides. In order to control the high pressure better, the furnace will have three charging bells, instead of two, as in all other blast furnaces in the United States.

The 2,000° F. hot blast temperature will reduce the amount of coke needed and thereby increase furnace capacity, since the space saved by reducing the amount of coke can be used for iron ore. At the stockhouse, raw materials will be automatically weighed and fed onto a conveyor for charging the furnace. (At another blast furnace, in Gary, Indiana, U.S. Steel installed in 1961 what it described as the "world's first automatically controlled blast furnace stockhouse." The computer-controlled system automatically withdraws various raw materials from a series of storage bins, assembles them in proper proportion and then charges them into the blast furnace.) Cooling the hearth by a flow of air at the rate of 1,500 cubic feet per minute under the hearth will reduce the amount of erosion and hence the size of the salamander—the liquid iron that accumulates in the eroded hearth of a blast furnace.

The blast furnace has not reached the apogee of its performance and further improvements in design and operating efficiency can be expected. At some future day the blast furnace may be completely automated. In such a furnace, any variation in the carbon content of the coke will be automatically adjusted to assure a constant supply at the desired rate. Ore beneficiation plants will produce agglomerates of uniform chemical content, containing the fluxing agent. Heating stoves will be self-adjusting to maintain a uniform high temperature in the furnace blast. The result will be pig iron of unfailing quality. The hot metal flowing from the furnace will be desulphurized, dephosphorized, and probably decarburized. Such an innovation is already in use in Germany, where the Rotor steelmaking process is successfully converting pig iron as it comes from the blast furnace directly into crude steel, which may or may not require further treatment in the open hearth furnace. These changes will not come overnight, but they represent goals to be attained in a step-by-step process. The metamorphized blast furnace may still have a future "as rosy as the dawn."

Goliath is Challenged

It is now time to consider the most forward of the many Davids who challenge that towering Goliath, the modern blast furnace. In order to gain a proper perspective of the relative sizes of Goliath and his threatening Davids, it may be well to recall that the largest modern blast furnaces can pour out more than 2,000 tons of pig iron daily, with the expectation of more than doubling this output in the fairly near future, whereas the production by any one of the alternate processes is measured in hundreds of tons in twenty-four hours. The alternate ironmaking methods account for less than 2 per cent of all the iron and steel made in the world today.[1] Reduction of iron ore in the United States by methods other than the blast furnace, according to one estimate, may be as high as 10 per cent of total iron production by 1969.[2]

The end products of alternate processes are iron in a molten state, in porous lumps called sponge iron, or in powder form. Because all three types of iron can serve as a substitute for blast furnace pig iron and steel scrap in steelmaking, interest in the alternate processes is not confined to large steel-producing centers, but is worldwide. These processes have a special appeal to underdeveloped nations which desire to furnish part or all of their iron and steel needs to further their industrialization. The $50 million required for capital investment in a modern blast furnace plant complete with the necessary coke ovens, is more than many small nations can afford. One alternative for such countries is to use scrap instead of blast furnace pig iron as a steelmaking stock, but under-industrialized areas generate little scrap and the imported product is very expensive. In regions possessing iron ore, but little or no coking coal, some of the alternate processes offer an opportunity to enter upon small-scale ironmaking with low capital investment.

In regions with large, established steel industries such as Europe and the United States, several reasons account for the current interest in substitutes for the blast furnace. Foremost, perhaps, is the vanishing supply of high-grade coking coal. In America as well as in Europe, the growing practice of sintering and pelletizing iron ores adds further to the over-all capital costs and operating expenses of a blast furnace plant.

Another factor, applicable to the United States and also to other areas— Mexico, for example—is the existence of vast reserves of cheap natural gas which can be used to provide a reducing gas mixture for some of the ore-reduction processes. A still further consideration is the uncertain supply and variable cost of scrap. The production of iron in appreciable quantities and suitable form, by one or another of the alternate processes, would provide steelmakers with a source of iron that would be less affected than scrap by fluctuations in supply and cost.

For these various reasons, proponents of direct-reduction processes are busily engaged in development and experimental work, with sanguine expectations for their creations, some of the advocates even looking upon the traditional blast furnace as an outmoded metallurgical instrument. From their joint labors have come forth no less than 180 direct reduction processes, but only a dozen or so, as was pointed out in the previous chapter, are in use or well along in development. The most important of these processes will now be described. In considering them, it is worth bearing in mind that blast furnace operators have not been idle meanwhile and have made impressive gains in the past five years. Cost studies show that there is no direct-reduction process now in operation that can compete economically with the traditional blast furnace, using the most advanced techniques. Rejuvenated Goliath is not only holding off his challengers, he is winning the battle. This is not meant to discredit other processes, some of which, under particular circumstances, can be advantageously applied. The point made here is that the blast furnace is still the most economical producer of iron.

ELECTRIC IRON SMELTING

The historical development of electric processes for iron and steel making is reserved for the succeeding chapter. Only enough will be said here to explain the basic principles of the process. Briefly, electrical energy is converted into heat either by induction or by passing a current down electrodes within the furnace. In the latter case, the current leaps from the ends of the electrodes to the charge creating intense heat. The electric process is adapted to produce both pig iron and steel.

Electric iron smelting recommends itself to regions possessing hydro-electric power or the potentialities for it, but having little or no coking coal. The Tysland-Hole electric smelting furnace, the type most widely used, generally utilizes a mixture of coke and coke breeze as a reducing agent, but it can also operate with anthracite coal, charcoal, or even lignite. With the carbonaceous material serving only as a reducing agent, the heat normally supplied by a portion of the coke in the blast furnace to melt the charge is replaced by electrical energy. Hence the quantity of carbonaceous reducing agent needed is much less than in a blast furnace per ton of pig iron produced. For this reason, electric iron smelting is being advantageously used in several nations which are producing iron and steel for the first time.

More pig iron is being produced by electric furnaces than by any other alternate process. Total world capacity of electric pig iron furnaces installed or under construction in 1960 represented between 1 and 2 per cent of total world production. In 1961, there were thirty-seven electric pig iron furnaces of the Tysland-Hole type in operation and fifteen under construction throughout the world. Operating furnaces were located in the following countries: Canada, Finland, India, Israel, Italy, Japan, Norway, Peru, Philippines, Portugal, Spain, Sweden, Swirtzerland, Venezuela, and Yugoslavia. When hydro-electric power projects reported to be underway in Indonesia and Burma are completed, these nations will be in a position to install electric smelting furnaces.

Electric smelting suggests a dependable economical way of escaping the vagaries of widely fluctuating scrap prices. It would enable a foundry to obtain a supply of pig iron without the high investment cost of a blast furnace. The electric smelting furnace, it is claimed, has the added advantage of flexibility. From 100 to 250 tons of molten iron can be produced a day from a single unit, depending on its size, or much larger tonnages from multiple units. All things considered, costs are the determining factor in the selection of an iron- or steelmaking process. The choice between electric smelting and the blast furnace in a given location will be decided in the long run by the relative costs of electric power and coke.

KRUPP-RENN PROCESS

The Krupp-Renn is the second largest producer of iron by methods other than the blast furnace. It is intended particularly for the use of poor quality ores so high in silica that they cannot be smelted economically in the blast furnace. In Germany, it has been utilized to smelt ore with as little as 23 to 32 per cent iron content, containing 23 to 34 per cent silica. In one respect, it may be looked upon as a pyro-metallurgical beneficiation process for siliceous and titaniferous ores that cannot be beneficiated in any other way. Since any kind of solid fuel may be used, the process is applicable in countries with little or no coking coal.

Crushed iron ore and coke breeze or bituminous coal fines are charged into a rotary kiln, which resembles that used in making cement. The Kupp-Renn kiln is preferably fired with pulverized coal. At a temperature of 2,190° to 2,300° F., the iron ore is partially reduced and individual particles of iron—free of slag—are welded together in nodules called *luppen*. The semi-molten material on discharge from the kiln has the consistency of a cake dough in which the *luppen* are distributed like raisins. After cooling, the material is crushed and the iron is removed by magnetic separation.[3]

A disadvantage of the Krupp-Renn process is its inability to remove sulfur or phosphorus from the *luppen*. Consequently, only ores low in sulfur and phosphorus are suitable for conversion into *luppen* intended to be charged directly into electric and open hearth furnaces. In Germany, *luppen* are used as a high-grade blast furnace feed, the resulting pig iron being refined into steel in basic Bessemer converters.[4]

A report in 1958 said that about 550,000 tons of iron were being produced annually by the Krupp-Renn process, and that Krupp-Renn installations were in Germany, Spain, Czechoslovakia, Greece, and in the Far East. Late in 1959, a large new Krupp-Renn plant went into operation at Essen-Borbeck, Germany, with an annual capacity of over 500,000 tons of *luppen*, to be used as blast furnace feed. Four large kilns have been installed at Salzgitter-Watenstedt, Germany, and two in Spain. A Japanese kiln, built before World War II, has been reactivated and has successfully treated low-grade titaniferous iron sands.

SPONGE IRON PROCESSES

The third class of alternate processes in order of importance has several variations, but all yield the same product—sponge iron. It can serve as a melting stock in place of scrap in the electric and open hearth furnaces for the production of steel.

Höganäs Process

The earliest sponge-iron producing process was invented in Sweden by Sieurin in 1910 and was developed under his supervision at the Höganäs Company, which began commercial production a year later. It has become largely identified with the name of Höganäs.[5]

Rich magnetite iron ore concentrates with an iron content of 70 to 71 per cent are used. The process consists of packing refractory molds known as saggers, or seggers, with the ore and an excess of coke breeze, mixed with some lime to absorb the sulphur from the coke. A great many saggers are charged into the furnace which is in the form of a tunnel kiln, resembling a brick kiln. As the saggers pass through the kiln, most of the carbon monoxide given off by the reduction of the ore by the carbon in the coke is burnt in the kiln to furnish a large part of the heat, which is kept between 2,100° and 2,190° F. The total time from the charging of the containers into the kiln and their removal is nine to twelve days. The sponge iron product is about 97 per cent iron.

The fuel consumption of the Höganäs process is low compared to that of the blast furnace. A low-grade fuel may be used which makes the process applicable in countries possessing poor quality coking coal. The original object of the Höganäs process was to produce a high-grade sponge iron for the manufacture of tool steel, but a large proportion of the output is converted to iron powder for powder metallurgy. The process is being applied in Sweden, the United States, Canada, and Mexico. Total world output in 1958 was over 100,000 tons.

Wiberg Process

This process was invented by Martin Wiberg in Sweden in 1918 and was first given industrial application in 1932 at Söderfors, Sweden.[6] It is, accordingly, sometimes referred to as the Wiberg-Söderfors process.

The Wiberg process is of historical interest in a number of respects. It is the first iron-reducing method in which the ore and the fuel do not come into contact with each other. Reduction is effected entirely by gases— carbon monoxide and a little hydrogen. This marks the introduction into ferrous metallurgy of hydrogen as a reducing agent on a large scale which, as we shall soon see, is assuming considerable importance.

Production of sponge iron by the Wiberg process is carried out in a shaft furnace, somewhat similar to a blast furnace. It is a continuous process, the sponge iron being removed from the bottom of the furnace periodically. Only high-grade ore is used, preferably above 56 per cent iron content. The ore should be low in phosphorus, since any of that element in the ore remains in the sponge iron.

Since there is no mixing of iron ore and fuel, a low-grade fuel may be used. The lack of contact between the ore and the fuel obviates the danger of sulphur from the coke getting into the iron. The Wiberg process has the lowest fuel consumption of all pyro-metallurgical iron-reducing processes. The consumption of electricity is also low compared to the electric smelting furnace. The process may be modified to utilize oil, natural gas, or coke oven gas as fuels.

There are five Wiberg plants in Sweden with an estimated yearly capacity of 150,000 tons of sponge iron. Stora Kopparbergs Bergslags, licensor of the Wiberg process, has announced that a plant with initial annual capacity of 10,000 tons, with provision for expansion, will be built in Japan. No Wiberg installation has been made or planned in North America.

Bassett Process

The Bassett process was invented by a Frenchman, Lucien P. Bassett, and patented by him in 1921. Bassett's original intention was to produce molten steel directly from the ore in a rotary kiln. His announcement created quite a sensation in metallurgical circles. However, his hopes were dashed because of insuperable difficulties he encountered and he abandoned his original plan, and, instead tried to produce pig iron. Pilot plants were built in France in the 1930s and later commercial units were constructed in Spain, Japan, and Portugal. None of these is now operating.

The Bassett process may be regarded as an inversion of the Krupp-Renn process. In the latter, the slag is melted to a viscous liquid and the iron remains solid and agglomerates into nodules. In the former, the iron is melted and the slag stays in a solid form and unites into nodules. The main feature of the Bassett rotary kiln method is that oil, natural gas, or powdered coal may be used instead of metallurgical coke and that ore fines, not too low in iron, or pyrite cinders, may be used without preliminary treatment. Molten pig iron is tapped about every ninety minutes through a small opening in the kiln.

After a United Nations commission in 1955 studied the applicability of iron manufacture without coking coals in Asia and the Far East, it reported that the high sulphur coals and low-silica rich iron ores of Pakistan, Thailand, and the Philippines may prove suitable for the Bassett process and recommended an investigation of it by those countries.[7]

HyL PROCESS

Mexico possesses coking coal, but the location of the beds and inadequate transportation are obstacles to its use in the iron and steel industry. Electric steel refining furnaces exist at the plant of *Hojalata y Lamina* in Monterey, the industrial heart of Mexico. The high cost of scrap, which drained dollar reserves, induced the company to look for ways to obtain a cheaper melting stock for steel production. The discovery of large reserves of natural gas suggested a solution to the problem. Plant engineers developed a technique for the utilization of iron ore and gas to produce sponge iron. It's name—HyL—is a contraction of *Hojalata y Lamina*. A pilot plant proved to be successful, and in 1958 a commercial plant capable of producing 200 tons of sponge iron a day went into operation.[8] Toward the end of 1959, the plant had produced 100,000 tons of sponge iron. A 500-ton-per-day plant went into production in late 1960.

HyL is a batch process in which rich ore is reduced in a retort by hot hydrogen and carbon monoxide, "reformed" from natural gas. No coke is required. By using high-grade ores or concentrates, the HyL process yields a sponge iron sufficiently low in gangue to be converted directly into finished steel in the electric furnace. The regular practice at the *Hojalata y Lamina* plant is to charge the electric furnace with 75 per cent sponge and 25 per cent scrap.

IRON REDUCTION PROCESSES UNDER DEVELOPMENT

Low-Shaft Furnaces

The low-shaft furnace, which is usually blown with oxygen instead of atmospheric air, is a modification of the traditional blast furnace, and is receiving, perhaps, as much attention as any of the alternate processes. To avoid confusing the two furnaces in this section, the term "blast furnace," will mean the traditional furnace, blown with atmospheric air. Durrer, one of the leading exponents of the low-shaft furnace, was quoted on page 272 in giving his explanation of the "main defect of the traditional blast furnace." The reader is referred to that explanation for a better understanding of Durrer's further remarks on the low-shaft funace, summarized below. "This characteristic drawback," of the high-shaft furnace, he went on to say, disappears whenever it is possible to perform smelting operations adequately while keeping the burden low.[9] A much greater liberty is allowed in the choice of raw materials, resulting in a reduction of cost, because the materials do not have to have the same mechanical strength as in a blast furnace where the weight of a tall burden has a crushing effect on the materials in the middle and lower parts of the furnace stack. In addition, he said, certain raw materials unsuitable for the blast furnace may be utilized in low-burden reduction, so that iron can be smelted in some regions where the nature of the raw materials makes smelting impossible by conventional methods.

The transition from a deep to a shallow burden is made possible by still retaining the principle of alternate layers of ore and carbonaceous fuel, but by reducing the specific volume of gas so that a deep burden is unnecessary.

Electric smelting in a low-shaft furnace is feasible because only a small quantity of reducing gas is produced—about one-seventh of that in a blast furnace. The shaft need be only a few feet high and can be adapted to local ores unfit for the blast furnace without expensive beneficiation.

Reduction in a low-shaft furnace is facilitated by blowing in oxygen, eliminating the need of nitrogen to carry and transfer heat to the upper part of a tall stack. The elimination of nitrogen, said Durrer, drastically reduces the volume of gas which rises in the furnace. Thus the oxygen-blown furnace need be only a few feet high.

A trend is developing that favors the low-shaft furnace, Durrer continued, motivated by the basic drawback of the tall blast furnace, namely the utilization of an atmospheric blast.

In conclusion, he said, "It may be considered as certain that the mass-production of iron from ore will shift from high-shaft to low-shaft furnaces with a concomitant changeover from air blast to oxygen blast." This will take place at the latest, he believes, when the raw material conditions impose the change upon iron smelters. In this regard, the Organization for European Economic Cooperation (OEEC), in order to seek a solution to the problem of reducing fine iron ores with coal unsuitable for coking, formed the International Low-Shaft Blast Furnace Research Committee, with headquarters in Paris. The participating countries are Austria, Belgium, France, Great Britain, Greece, the Netherlands, Italy, Luxembourg, and the United States. A pilot plant was constructed near Liège, Belgium.

The Committee believes that the chief advantages which might accrue from a low-shaft furnace blown with oxygen are: (1) utilization of cheaper and more abundant solid fuels than coke, (2) a higher percentage of fines could be used, (3) a richer outgoing gas. The chief drawbacks envisaged are: (1) the necessity for handling a large supply of oxygen, and (2) the need for physical, and possibly chemical, preparation of the burden.

The interest of the Committee centers chiefly on the production of pig iron that can be converted into steel by the basic Bessemer process (Thomas process) using fuel of low commercial value, such as coke fines, semi-cokes, and fines of low-quality coal, lignite, etc. Consideration is also given to the production of pig iron and ferroalloys from ores such as chrome ore from Greece or manganese ores of the Republic of the Congo which are difficult to utilize in the tall blast furnace.

Experimental work with the low-shaft furnace is also going forward in Germany, with promising results. In 1954, a pilot plant capable of producing 11 to 16 tons of pig iron daily was put into operation in Cologne. The plant performed so satisfactorily that it was decided to erect a commercial unit with a capacity of 100 to 120 tons of iron a day at nearby Troisdorf. Operations were scheduled to begin in late 1957. The furnace is approximately 7×14 feet in cross-section at the tuyere level and about 13 feet high to the charging line. There are ten tuyeres through which heated air is blown into the furnace.[10]

The objective of the German investigators was to design a new type furnace which can utilize some non-cooking grades of bituminous coal and fine iron ore, can be built with a low investment cost per ton of iron compared to the blast furnace, and operated inexpensively. In the German low-shaft furnace, briquettes composed of intimately bound particles of iron ore, flux and coal, are smelted at high temperatures. Such briquettes permit a rapid reduction of the ore.

Low-Temperature Reduction by Gases (below 2,170° F)

The Wiberg and HyL processes, two methods employing carbon monoxide and hydrogen as reducing agents, have been discussed. Other related processes, one of them in actual use, relying chiefly on hydrogen as the reducing agent, will be mentioned here.

The hydrogen reduction process became the object of lively attention in the United States following two important technological advances in the domestic petroleum industry during and after World War II:

1. Techniques were perfected for obtaining hydrogen from crude oil or natural gas. The gas is liberated either by the use of steam in the "reforming" process or by the use of oxygen for partial oxidation. Both methods make it possible to produce large quantities of hydrogen at comparatively low cost. Since the announcement of these two developments, a large-scale plant has been built to generate hydrogen from coal gasification.

2. Concurrently, practical application was made of the principle of fluidized solids, which has become known as the fluidized-bed technique. By close control of gas velocity, bulk quantities of solid particles can be suspended in a rising stream of gas in such a way that the material behaves much the same as a liquid. By varying conditions slightly, the solid matter can be made to flow through pipes or vessels. In the case of iron ore reduction, finely divided, high-purity ore is used.

The fluidized-bed technique dispenses with the need of high-grade coking coal. Although the process is under development chiefly in the United States, interest in it is being alerted in many countries which produce natural gas beyond their own needs.

In the United States, one variation of the process—the H-Iron process—is in commercial production and two others are under investigation at pilots plants. The H-Iron process was developed by Bethlehem Steel Company and Hydrocarbon Research, Inc. The process uses natural gas or oil to obtain hydrogen which is pre-heated before being passed into a pressurized fluidized-bed reducing vessel. The Alan Wood Steel Company began operating a H-Iron plant with 50 tons daily capacity at its Conshohocken (Pennsylvania) Works in 1959. The plant produces low carbon iron powder for sale to powder metallurgy markets. The Bethlehem Pacific Coast Steel Corporation installed an H-Iron plant at Los Angeles in 1960 and although its operation was described as successful, the plant was closed down in August 1961.

A second variant of the fluidized-bed technique is the Nu-Iron process, developed by U.S. Steel. Iron ore concentrates are pre-heated and a heated mixture of hydrogen and carbon monoxide, produced by reforming natural gas with steam, is passed upward through a fluidized bed. The product is an iron powder which can be pressed into briquettes.

A third variant is the Esso-Little process, which takes its name from Standard Oil Company and Arthur D. Little, Inc., joint investigators. It represents still a different method in the use of natural gas for the production of hydrogen and carbon monoxide and in the passage of the gases through a fluidized bed.

The R-N Process

The R-N process, like the Krupp-Renn process, reduces iron ore in a rotary kiln. It is under development in the United States by the Republic Steel Corporation and the National Lead Company, which joined forces in 1952 to build a pilot plant in Spaulding, Alabama. In 1957, the two companies formed the R-N Corporation to exploit the process commercially.[11]

The R-N process can utilize low-grade carbonaceous materials such as coke breeze, anthracite fines or bituminous coal char as reducing agents, and employs gas or oil to heat the kiln. It has an advantage over most other direct processes in that it can be applied to the lowest as well as the highest grades of iron ore to produce melting stock in the form of briquettes for the electric furnace or other steelmaking units. This was demonstrated in trial runs at the Alabama pilot plant, where low-grade local ores of 34 to 35 per cent iron content and high-grade magnetite concentrates containing 68 to 69 per cent iron were smelted. The former ores were converted into two grades of briquettes, one containing 80 per cent iron and the other 90 per cent. The product of the magnetite ores contained 95 to 96 per cent iron.

ELECTRIC SMELTING AGAIN

There are two electric smelting processes, one under development, and the other still in experimental stages.

Dwight-Lloyd-McWane Process

This process, under development, might be described as an accelerated, low-cost variation of electric smelting. Concentrated iron ore fines, mixed with about 33 per cent non-coking coal and limestone are formed into pellets, held together with a small proportion of binder. The pellets are fed into a Dwight-Lloyd sintering machine where they are dried and heated under controlled temperature so that the carbon in the coal effects a 55 to 60 per cent reduction of the ore. The pellets are then charged into a conventional submerged arc smelting furnace. Coke and flux are added to complete reduction of the ore and to convert the iron into molten pig iron. It is said that, because the pellets are partially reduced, the electrical consumption is only 1,000 to 1,100 kilowatt hours per ton of pig iron, which is 40 to 45 per cent of the rate in Europe for direct electric smelting.[12]

Lubatti Process

The Lubatti furnace is under experimentation in Italy. It is an open, shallow furnace and differs in principle from other electric smelting furnaces in that the heat is not produced by an electric arc. Instead, the electrodes are submerged in a thick layer of slag, on which floats a mixture of fine-grained ore and coal. The necessary heat is evolved within the slag. The purpose of the Lubatti furnace is to make it possible to smelt iron ore concentrates and pyrite cinders without previous sintering.[13]

CONCLUSION

In this chapter, we have discussed the most advanced and promising alternate iron reducing processes. All of them are capable of utilizing non-coking coals, or other fuels, such as oil or natural gas. Some are adapted to take advantage of the increasing supply of high-grade iron ore concentrates and quite a number can smelt low-grade ores. It is worth recalling that all of these processes in actual use account for less than 2 per cent of all the iron made in the world annually.

Alternate processes offer a ray of hope to a group of nations: (1) Those already producing steel, but handicapped in expansion plans because their coal is of a non-coking quality. (2) Nations with an established steel industry, large or small. They may lack coking coal or their best reserves may be diminishing, but they have large petroleum and natural gas resources within their borders. (3) Underdeveloped nations with iron ore deposits, wishing to embark on iron and steel production and possessing one or more of the several reducing agents. Nations with iron ore and coking coal deposits too small to justify the construction and operation of a blast furnace over a sufficiently long period to recoup the high investment and amortization costs, may also enter upon small-scale iron and steel production with one or more of the alternate processes suitable to local conditions.

Electrical Processes
for Making Iron and Steel

It was inevitable that men would one day think of applying the heat generated by electricity for metallurgical purposes. The first step in that direction was the production of an electric arc between carbon points by Sir Humphry Davy in 1800, using an electric battery. The idea of utilizing the current from a powerful electric battery to heat a small furnace intrigued a number of investigators. Dr. William Siemens, in 1878, with the aid of a dynamo built the first electric arc furnace of any practical importance, and in 1882 melted 20 pounds of steel and 8 pounds of platinum.

A second type of electric furnace was patented in 1883 by Faure, who used the heat generated by the passage of an electric current through solid conducting rods imbedded in the hearth of the furnace, on the same principle as that of a modern electric cooking range. This was called a resistance furnace. It was made a commercial success by the brothers E. H. and A. H. Cowles, who patented it in the United States in 1884. The Cowles furnace was used to reduce a number of metals from their oxides, but iron oxide was not among them.

A third type of electric furnace was invented in Italy by S. Z. Ferranti in 1887. This was an induction furnace. In such a furnace, high-frequency electric current is fed to a primary coil which induces a current to flow through the charge of metal, which acts as a secondary winding of a transformer having a single turn. The electrical resistance of the charge to the passage of the induced current develops heat which melts the charge. Ferranti's furnace was not a commercial success, but later it became very successful in the hands of Kjellin, Colby, and others.

The distinguished French metallurgist, Dr. Paul Héroult, is responsible for the first commercially successful electric arc furnace. In 1886, at the age of twenty-two, he produced metallic aluminum by an electrolytic process in a home-made laboratory. In the same year, an American of identical age, Charles Martin Hall, performed a similar experiment. Neither man knew of the other's existence. By another coincidence, both men died in the same year, 1914. Their electrolytic process laid the foundation for the modern aluminum industry.

Héroult continued his researches with the electric arc principle into other metals, but it was not until 1899 that he produced his first heat of steel.

One of the most important names in the early history of the electric furnace is Henry Moissan of France. In 1892, he discovered that carbon will reduce any metal from its oxides at the temperature attained in an electric arc furnace. Not only would carbon reduce any metal from its oxide but would combine with the metal to form a carbide. Moissan's production of calcium carbide experimentally was followed in the same year by its commercial manufacture in an electric furnace by T. L. Willson. Calcium carbide, in the presence of water, forms acetylene, a valuable illuminating and welding gas. A number of other carbides were also produced in the electric furnace, among them carborundum, but calcium carbide quickly became one of the most important products of the electric furnace and consumed more electrical power in its manufacture than any other.

"It was a financial crisis in the carbide industry," says Stansfield, "that led to the electric smelting of iron, steel, and other iron alloys."[1] Shortly before the turn of the century, according to Stansfield, there was an overproduction of calcium carbide and this led some manufacturers to look for ways to keep their electric furnaces busy. With this object in view, experiments were made "in France and elsewhere about the year 1900" in the production of ferrochrome, ferrosilicon, and other ferroalloys, used in the manufacture of alloy steels. The results were eminently successful, and although Stansfield does not say so directly, he implies that these successes suggested to a number of men the possibility of refining steel in the electric furnace. The carbide furnaces, which were lined with carbon, were not satisfactory for melting steel. Héroult in France, Kjellin in Sweden, and Colby in the United States, successfully adapted the electric furnace to the production of good quality steel. Héroult's was an arc furnace and the other two were induction furnaces.

ELECTRIC IRON SMELTING

In the last decades of the nineteenth century, when men were captivated by the idea of utilizing electrical energy for metallurgical purposes, a number of investigators saw the possibility of circumventing the coke oven-blast furnace cycle and smelting ore and even refining the iron into steel electrically in one operation. Electrical reduction of iron ore was successfully accomplished and has been carried on ever since in Sweden and Norway. It is currently practiced in a number of other nations.

Pioneering in Italy and France

The man who took the first step in the direction of electrical smelting was Captain (also called Major) Ernesto Stassano of Italy. He patented his first furnace in 1898, and when he gave a demonstration of it the following year it created "quite a sensation." The price of electricity was so high, however, that his proposal to use it in competition with coke in the blast furnace appeared "preposterous." Stassano, and others who followed him, simply tried to "electrify" a blast furnace by replacing the tuyeres with carbon electrodes. He intended to work his furnace continuously, like a blast furnace, charging in materials and withdrawing molten metal periodically.

The Captain's exploratory work impressed others with the possibility of electric iron smelting and a "large crop of such processes followed." Foremost among his emulators was the French metallurgist, Charles Keller, who conducted extensive experiments in the years 1901-1905. He had an ambitious plan to reduce iron and refine it into steel in the same operation, but in two stages. His reduction furnace resembled a blast furnace in which there were four vertical electrodes. The steel refining furnace was on a lower level, with its inlet just below the tap hole of the reduction furnace so that the molten iron could flow directly into it. The electrical manufacture of steel by Keller was described as "highly successful" and he was reported to have planned the erection of a battery of reduction furnaces served by one portable electric refining furnace, which was "like a large ladle with electrodes."[2]

Electric Smelting Attempts in Canada

Members of the Canadian government followed with avid interest the progress in electric iron smelting and steel refining in Europe. Canada, with large iron ore and water power resources, saw the possibility of adapting the new process to the development of an iron and steel industry. In 1903, Dr. E. Haanel was appointed head of a commission to investigate electric furnace processes abroad and in the course of its tour the commission consulted Héroult, Kjellin, and Keller. On the commission's return to Canada, both the government and Dr. Haanel were so sanguine over the outlook for electric iron smelting that Dr. Héroult was brought over from France in 1906 to conduct experiments at Sault Ste. Marie. Using a shaft type furnace he demonstrated that his process was "scientifically feasible," but the commercial prospects were not sufficiently promising and the project of establishing electric iron smelting in Canada was abandoned by its supporters.

Electric Iron Smelting in Sweden and Norway

The favorable scientific reports of the electric iron smelting trials in Canada reached the ears of three men in Sweden, Messrs. Grönwall, Lindblad, and Stählhane, and persuaded them to explore the possibilities of electric iron smelting in that country where conditions for its success were held to be more favorable than anywhere else in the world. High-grade iron ore was abundant and electric power from large waterfalls was remarkably cheap. Grönwall, Lindblad, and Stählhane built their first satisfactory furnace in Sweden in 1908 and another in 1910. Both furnaces were the arc type. The 1910 furnace was called an Elektrometall. It was a high shaft type. The upper part resembled a blast furnace and the lower part consisted of a wide melting chamber with six to eight electrodes. Charcoal was used as a reducing agent. In the next ten years, several more Elektrometalls were erected, and by 1918 electrically smelted pig iron in Sweden was estimated to be 100,000 tons annually, or one-eighth of total pig iron production.

A low shaft electric smelting furnace, called the Tysland-Hole, named after the inventors, George Tysland and Ivar Hole, was designed in Norway and went into commercial production in 1928. The furnace uses a mixture of coke and coke breeze as a reducing agent, but anthracite coal, charcoal, or even lignite, may be also used. The largest Tysland-Hole furnaces have a capacity of 225 to 250 tons of iron a day. This type of furnace has almost entirely replaced the Elektrometall because the latter required charcoal as a reducing agent. The Tysland-Hole is the most widely used electric iron smelting furnace in the world, and in 1961 there were thirty-seven such furnaces in fifteen countries and fifteen furnaces were under construction.

ELECTRIC STEELMAKING PROCESSES

Arc Process

Siemens, in designing his electric arc furnace, simply tried to replace coke with electrical power in a crucible furnace. Héroult, on the other hand, adapted the open hearth furnace to his needs. He borrowed from the Wellman tilting open hearth furnace, removed the gas and air ports and put a pair of parallel carbon electrodes through the roof. Although Siemens was the originator of the arc furnace, Héroult's was the prototype of the modern furnace. A powerful current was turned on in both electrodes which were lowered until electric arcs leaped from the ends of the electrodes to the metal in the charge. The intense heat of the arcs melted the steel and kept it liquid so that the refining could be accomplished. His original plan was to produce steel preliminarily in the open hearth furnace and then transfer the molten metal to the electric furnace for further refining and the additions of carbon and alloying elements, as needed. Later, as electric power became cheaper, furnace operators found it feasible to begin with cold scrap, in what became known as the cold melt process, which was adopted in virtually all electric steelmaking furnaces in the United States.

Kjellin patented his induction furnace in Sweden about 1900 and produced good quality steel shortly afterward—perhaps in the same year.

Histories of electric furnace steelmaking in the United States say that it first took place in 1906. Steel was produced at Syracuse in that year by the electric arc process for the first time in this country, but there is good reason to believe that steel was made earlier in the Colby induction furnace. Edward Allen Colby patented his furnace in the United States in 1890 and again in 1900. He undoubtedly made trials with his furnace from 1890 on, but there is no record of them. There are solid grounds to believe that Colby made the first commercial production of electric furnace steel in the United States, possibly as early as 1902, but not later than 1905.[3]

The electric steelmaking furnace was originally looked upon as an improved method for making high-grade tool steel less expensively than by the crucible process. The high cost of crucible steel was due in part to the considerable hand labor involved, but mostly to the excessive amount of coke consumed. The greater portion of the heat from the fuel was carried away in the escaping gases of combustion. In other steelmaking processes, the heat is applied directly to the metal. In the crucible process the heat had to penetrate the crucibles and the slow transmission of the heat to the steel within contributed to the extremely low thermal efficiency of the process. For these reasons, crucible steel was an expensive commodity, selling for 18 to 25 cents a pound in the middle of the last century.

Technical progress in the development of the electric furnace was held up by the limited supply and high cost of electricity and by the inability of manufacturers to make carbon electrodes capable of carrying sufficient current for steel melting. Advance in electric furnace design and practice waited upon expansion of the electric power industry and improvements in electrodes.

ALLOY AND CARBON STEELS

The electric process in its infant years received but passing attention from the American Iron and Steel Institute. In its Annual Statistical Report for 1910, the institute still referred to the electric process as one of the "various minor processes," which also included the cementation and puddling furnaces. In that year, electric furnaces turned out roughly

58,000 tons of a total of 62,000 tons of steel produced by "various minor processes." Of those 62,000 tons of steel, only 680 tons, or 0.011 per cent, were alloy steels. In 1911, due largely to demands from the automotive industry, it may be said that the manufacture of alloy steel in the electric furnaces really began in the United States with an output of 7,500 tons, representing 23 per cent of total electric furnace production.

The electric furnace eventually became identified with the production of the highest grade alloy steels, including stainless steels, and because of this it has been widely assumed—even in steelmaking circles—that the electric process has been devoted almost exclusively to the melting of alloy steels. Such has not been the case, as may be seen in Table 17.

TABLE 17

ELECTRIC FURNACE STEEL PRODUCTION IN THE UNITED STATES,
PERCENTAGES OF ALLOY AND CARBON STEELS:
SELECTED PERIODS, 1911–1961

Year	*(Thousands of Net Tons)* Electric Furnace Steel Production	Per Cent Alloy Steel	Per Cent Carbon Steel
1911	32.6	23	77
1912	20.5	52	48
1914	26.9	39	61
1923	577.8	38	62
1926	730.0	47	53
1929	1,065.6	54	46
1933	471.7	71	29
1939	1,029.1	73	27
1940	1,700.0	76	24
1941	2,869.3	86	14
1943	4,589.1	86	14
1944	4,237.7	86	14
1945	3,456.7	81	19
1946	2,563.0	64	36
1948	5,057.1	41	59
1950	6,039.0	45	55
1952	6,798.0	46	54
1954	5,436.1	47	53
1956	9,147.6	42	58
1957	8,582.1	35	65
1958	7,979.5	33	67
1959	8,532.5	43	57
1960	8,378.7	38	62
1961	8,664.2	43	57

SOURCE: American Iron and Steel Institute.

It will be observed that the proportion of alloy steels produced in the electric furnace reached its maximum of 86 per cent from 1941 through 1944, during World War II. Since alloy steels were so urgently needed in the war, why did their production never exceed 86 per cent of total electric furnace steel output? The explanation is that demand for open hearth steels, both carbon and alloy, was greater than open hearth capacity, with the result that some non-integrated plants installed electric furnaces to provide their own supply of plain carbon steels.

It may also be asked why carbon steels represented such a large part of electric furnace production prior to World War II—going as high as 62 per cent in 1923 and topping 50 per cent in 1926. Some integrated producers possessing both electric and open hearth furnaces found it more economical to fill orders for small tonnages of special carbon steels in the electric furnace than in the open hearth. Electric furnace capacities are generally half or less than half of open hearth furnaces. It was uneconomical to operate an open hearth furnace at considerably less than capacity. Also, companies possessing electric furnaces, but no open hearths, were well suited to produce small tonnages of carbon steels.

It will be noted in Table 17 that since 1948 the proportion of carbon steels produced in the electric furnace has been consistently above 50 per cent, reaching a high of 67 per cent in 1958. The favorable experience gained by non-integrated companies in producing plain carbon steels in the electric furnace during World War II encouraged large integrated steel companies to produce a greater portion of their carbon steel in electric furnaces.

The great advantage of the electric furnace is its source of heat. The temperature and composition of the bath, which are of great importance in steelmaking, can be regulated with a high degree of precision. For that reason, the manufacture of alloy steels to the narrowest chemical specifications is reserved for furnaces heated electrically. This statement applies not only to the arc furnace, but also to the new vacuum melting furnace which utilizes induction heating. When alloy steel producers originally turned from the crucible to the electric arc process for producing steels for tools, dies, cutlery and other special requirements, it was thought that the electric furnace was suitable only for making a limited range of high-cost, high-quality alloy steels for extremely exacting uses. But as furnaces and operating procedure were improved and costs were reduced, the electric furnace became an economical and versatile instrument for making a much wider range of steels. Electric furnace products now include practically all the stainless, tool, and special alloy steels used in the chemical, automotive, aviation, machine-tool, transportation, food processing and many other important industries.

GROWTH OF ELECTRIC ARC FURNACE PRODUCTION

As may be seen in Table 18, the electric furnace industry moved ahead slowly during its first twenty years. Production represented a fraction of 1 per cent of total steel production until 1918, when it first registered more than 1 per cent, and it was not until 1929 that electric furnaces poured more than 1 million tons in a single year. From World War II on, the gains were spectacular, attaining an all-time record of roughly 9 million tons in 1956.

A 1959 report of the United Nations on future trends in the steel industry predicted that in the United States electric furnace steel will constitute 15 per cent of total steel output in 1975. The study said that in Soviet Russia the proportion of electric furnace steel will be doubled in the next seven years, with the same tendency prevailing in the United Kingdom, France, Germany, and other countries.[4]

TABLE 18

GROWTH OF ELECTRIC FURNACE STEEL PRODUCTION
IN THE UNITED STATES: SELECTED PERIODS,
1908–1961

(thousands of net tons)

Year	Total Steel Production	Electric Furnace Production	Electric Furnace Production Per Cent of Total Steel
1908	15,383.1	0.6	1
1909	26,218.0	15.4	1
1910	28,329.7	58.4	1
1914	25,606.1	26.9	1
1918	49,010.1	572.7	1.2
1929	61,742.0	1,065.6	1.7
1933	25,724.6	471.7	1.8
1939	52,798.7	1,029.0	1.9
1940	66,982.7	1,700.0	2.5
1941	82,839.3	2,869.3	3.5
1943	88,836.5	4,589.0	5.2
1944	89,641.6	4,237.7	4.7
1948	88,640.5	5,057.0	5.7
1950	96,836.0	6,039.0	6.2
1952	93,168.0	6,798.0	7.3
1956	115,216.0	9,147.6	7.9
1957	112,715.0	8,582.0	7.6
1958	85,254.9	7,979.5	9.4
1959	93,446.1	8,532.5	9.1
1960	99,281.6	8,378.7	8.4
1961	98,014.5	8,664.2	8.1

SOURCE: American Iron and Steel Institute.
[1] Less than 1 per cent.

In the opinion of one authority, the electric furnace has undergone the "greatest variety and degree of refinement of any steel producing method."[5] Furnace capacities per heat of steel increased from a few tons through successive stages to maximum charges of 50, 75, 90, 100 and 140 tons up to 1954, when two 200-ton furnaces were installed. In the near future, furnaces are expected to have maximum capacities of 250 to 300 tons.

Plans for the construction of the largest electric furnace plant in the world were announced in late 1959 by the United Steel Companies, Ltd., of Sheffield, England. The new shop will replace all of the company's open hearth installations by six electric furnaces with an annual steel-making capacity of 1,485,000 net tons. The largest electric furnace shop in the United States belongs to Republic Steel Corporation and has an annual capacity of 1.1 million net tons.

Electric Induction Process

The two most important induction furnaces patterned after Ferranti's were the Kjellin and the Röchling-Rodenhauser. The Colby furnace which produced the first electric steel in the United States was also the induction type. Shortly after Kjellin installed his first induction furnace at Gysinge, Sweden, in 1900, he was said to be "producing steel of excellent quality, which, when annealed, could readily be cold worked." He attributed the high quality of his steel to the fact that in his furnace the metal did not come in contact with contaminating gases, especially hydrogen, and in this respect he anticipated the modern vacuum melting furnace. Kjellin claimed that where electrical power was cheap he could produce steel as economically as in the open hearth furnace. The Röchling-Rodenhauser furnace was an adaptation of the Kjellin furnace.

A more dependable and efficient method of induction heating was developed by the use of a higher frequency current and is known as the coreless high-frequency induction furnace. The first such furnace for the production of steel was erected at Sheffield, England, and went into operation in 1927. Similar furnaces were producing steel at the Heppenstall Forge and Knife Company plant in Pittsburgh, Pennsylvania, in 1928.

The coreless high-frequency induction furnace is now used chiefly for remelting scrap from fine steels produced in the electric arc furnace and also for melting chrome-nickel alloys and high-manganese scrap. It is not used extensively in steelmaking plants. Such induction furnaces are small and generally range from 200 to 2,000 pounds capacity per heat. The largest in the American steel industry in 1960 was a 7,500-pound unit in a Baltimore plant.

Vacuum Melting Process

The vacuum-melting process is a relatively new method for refining steel and super-alloys for withstanding extremely rigorous stress conditions. Although it was known and practiced on a minor scale early in the century, vacuum melting languished for want of a compelling need for it until World War II and succeeding years when metallurgists suddenly rediscovered it as a means of manufacturing steel and super-alloys with properties unattainable by any other known process. It is the latest answer to needs of the Atomic-Space Age.

Steelmakers have always striven to produce as "clean" a metal as possible. In steel parlance the term means the presence to a minimum degree, or the virtual elimination of unwanted compounds or elements, which may have deleterious effects upon the steel. Each generation thought that it had produced as "clean" a metal as was possible, only to have the succeeding generation come up with one still cleaner. All steelmaking processes considered so far were, or are, conducted in the presence of air. But the interaction of the atmosphere with the molten steel and even with the refractory lining of the furnace, produces compounds or elements which may enter into and contaminate the steel. What may not have been a serious contamination in the past may become so in steels and super-alloys destined for applications of the severest stress and high-temperature service. Metallurgists have become increasingly aware that minute traces of an impurity in a metal may constitute, so as to speak, its Achilles' heel, and may be the cause for the failure of a vital part under great stress—skins of jet passenger planes, turbine parts, valve springs of automobiles, and ball bearings, to cite a few examples. The three offenders which enter steel from the atmosphere are oxygen, nitrogen, and hydrogen. The worst culprit of these three is hydrogen. Hydrogen will dissolve in molten steel, but as the steel cools and solidifies, the hydrogen precipitates. Most of the hydrogen will diffuse out of the steel at room temperature, if sufficient time is allowed, but minute traces of residual hydrogen—from 4 to 8 parts per million, equivalent to 0.0004 to 0.0008 per cent—can cause embrittlement and flaking, the latter manifesting itself in some sheets as internal microcracks which can lead to failure of parts when subjected to great stresses resulting from high speeds at elevated temperatures.

Hydrogen-free steel and alloys therefore become of prime importance as designers importune metallurgists for metals capable of longer service life under ever greater stress and at ever higher temperatures, as the scientific and technological revolution now taking place in the Space Age moves forward at an accelerated pace. "In many fields metals now are being pushed to the extreme limits of their strength," an official of Union Carbide Corporation observed in 1954. "Now, new and stronger alloys must be developed if progress is to be continued."[6] The vacuum melting process offers the brightest hope at present for metallurgy to keep abreast of technology. Vacuum-melted metals can permit advances to go forward not only in jet engines, atomic energy reactors and missiles and vehicles of the Space Age, but also in conventional mundane products such as the automobile. When we begin to drive cars propelled by a gas turbine engine, the metal for critical parts operating at high temperature will probably be vacuum-melted.

Vacuum melting is almost foolproof in eliminating the possibility of elements in the atmosphere from entering into the steel beyond desired limits. Vacuum produced steels are "cleaner" and stronger than those melted in the atmosphere; they have improved mechanical properties at high temperatures, greater ductility and a high degree of uniformity in quality. Some highly reactive metals, notably titanium, cannot be melted successfully except in a vacuum. It has been claimed that vacuum melting promises to more than double and even quadruple the capacities of certain metals to withstand stress.

Steel, super-alloys, and other metals can be vacuum melted. We shall confine our discussion here to the vacuum melting of steel. The steel to be melted is already highly refined and is generally the product of the electric steelmaking furnace, although open hearth steels may also be used. Since the steel to be vacuum-melted is of high purity, the principal function of vacuum melting is to draw off dissolved elements such as oxygen, nitrogen, and hydrogen from the steel in the form of gases. The gases are quite literally sucked out of the steel by powerful pumps which maintain a constant state of vacuum.

The heat for melting the steel in a vacuum furnace is supplied by electrical induction or by an electrical arc.

An induction vacuum furnace consists of a steel shell containing a crucible to hold the charge. The crucible is surrounded by water-cooled copper tubing. A high frequency alternating current is passed through the tubing, and in so doing, induces a high frequency alternating current in the charge, as in induction furnaces previously described. The resistance of the charge to the induced current creates the heat which melts the charge. After the charge is melted, the molten steel is in a state of agitation, rising up along the wall of the crucible and descending at the center. This constant circulation of the molten steel exposes all parts of it to the sucking action of the vacuum and facilitates withdrawal of dissolved gases.

In the arc process, the charge constitutes the electrode which is melted and "consumed" by the heat of the arc. This method is therefore called the consumable-electrode vacuum arc process. The furnace consists of two sections. The upper section, above ground level, is a water-cooled tank which houses the long, round-shaped electrode. The lower section, below ground level, is a water-cooled copper mold in which the metal from the melting electrode accumulates. The electrode is attached to one terminal of the power source and the mold is attached to the opposite terminal.

The furnace is first evacuated of atmosphere by steam-ejector pumps to a condition prevailing at about forty miles above the earth. When the power is turned on, an arc is struck between the end of the electrode and the copper mold. The temperature in the region of the arc is approximately 6,000° F. In this intense heat, the end of the electrode melts, like a melting icicle, and the molten metal drops into the mold. The metal in the mold solidifies almost immediately and builds itself upward in the form of an ingot.

VACUUM CASTING

The advantages of vacuum melting have been extended to the casting of steel in a vacuum. Since the charge of metal to be vacuum-cast is in a molten state, the process does not involve electrical heating, but is included here because it logically follows vacuum melting.

Vacuum casting makes possible the production of large hydrogen-free forgings never before feasible and has been particularly valuable in making giant rotor shafts for turbines and electric generators. Some of these rotors weigh as much as 75 tons and rotate at 3,500 revolutions per minute under heavy loads and at high temperatures. More than minute vestiges of hydrogen in such forgings, made from conventionally produced steel, may in time lead to failure in operation. The electrical industry now specifies vacuum cast steel for all critical applications.

The first vacuum casting unit in the United States was installed by United States Steel Corporation. It casts ingots weighing as much as 480,000 pounds.

In vacuum casting, a ladle of molten steel, produced in an electric or open hearth furnace, is placed over a vacuum tank. In the tank is an ingot mold. A steam-injector system creates a state of vacuum within the tank. The molten steel is allowed to pour slowly from the ladle through the vacuum into the mold below. In its passage, the molten steel separates into many droplets, exposing maximum surface of the steel to the sucking action of the pumps, thus facilitating withdrawal of the gases. As much as 9,600 cubic feet of gases may be drawn off from one ton of steel. Vacuum casting can reduce the dissolved hydrogen in steel to 0.00015 per cent, or to a level below 1.5 parts per million, or lower.

United States Steel has gone a step farther and introduced what is believed to be the first multiple ingot vacuum casting unit. In general construction, it resembles a vacuum casting unit described above. In the vacuum tank is a large turntable resembling a "lazy susan," on which are the ingot molds. The molten steel streams through the vacuum tank, and as one mold is filled, the turntable rotates and positions another empty mold to receive the molten steel. This unit is capable of vacuum casting as many as 7 ingots weighing altogether 45 tons.

Steelmaking Processes—Twentieth Century

Before discussing steelmaking processes now in use and others coming into being, it may be of interest to take a backward glance over the growth and decline of various processes during the past eighty-odd years. The historical review presented in Table 19, is confined to the United States. Comparable statistics for European countries are not available.

Dates shown in the table were selected because of their significance in steel production trends. The year 1906, for example, was chosen because it marked the record production by the Bessemer process. Of historical importance are 1908 and 1909, the years in which electric furnace steel made its first appearance. (The 1908 production of 61 tons of electric furnace steel was included with open hearth steels.) In 1909 electric furnace steel was first reported separately. Production by the new basic oxygen process was included with electric furnace steel in 1957 and 1958 and made its first separate appearance in 1959. The quantity of steel produced in vacuum furnaces was considered too small to be reported.

The table reveals that the positions of the Bessemer converter and open hearth furnace were almost exactly reversed in the period under review. The crucible process died out soon after the electric furnace took a firm hold in 1920 with the production of more than 500,000 tons. The growth of electric furnace steel production, particularly after 1940, has been the most spectacular of all steelmaking processes.

In the "Miscellaneous" column we say farewell to a number of minor processes, chiefly cementation and puddling. The combined miscellaneous processes turned out more steel in 1875 than the fledgling open hearth furnace, and actually reached their peak production as late as 1906 with

16,000 tons. Cementation steel, also called "blister" steel, was the original raw material for the crucible process and may explain why a few cementation "pots" still held doggedly on into the present century. The puddling furnace was of major importance for more than a century for refining pig iron into wrought iron. We finally take official leave of the cementation and puddling furnaces in 1920.

STEELMAKING PROCESSES IN EUROPE

The extent to which various processes are used in European countries varies widely, as may be seen in Table 20. It will be observed that the basic Bessemer process, called in Europe the Thomas process, is still very much in the ascendancy in Luxembourg, Belgium, and the Saar, producing 98, 85, and 75 per cent, respectively of total steel output. The basic Bessemer is favored in those areas because the domestic ores are high in phosphorus, which the process all but eliminates. The basic Bessemer is used least in the United Kingdom and Czechoslovakia where it produced roughly 5 per cent of total steel output. Production by the open hearth process ranges, respectively, from 93, 88, and 83 per cent of total steel output in Poland, the United Kingdom, and Czechoslovakia, down to 2 per cent in Luxembourg. The electric process is utilized to produce a greater proportion of steel in Sweden than in any other important steel center of the world—45 per cent. East Germany and Czechoslovakia rank second as users of the electric process in Europe, relying on it for about 12 per cent of their total steel production. The lowest percentage figure for the electric process—1.2 per cent—is found in the Saar. East Germany, Poland, Sweden, and the United Kingdom were the only countries in 1958 reported as users of one or more of the new steelmaking processes.

HAS THE OPEN HEARTH PASSED ITS ZENITH?

Since the first commercially successful open hearth furnace was operated in Boston in 1871, this type of steelmaking furnace has demonstrated its suitability for large tonnage production of steel in an age of mass production and accounts for nearly nine-tenths of all the steel produced in the United States. From a capacity of 5 tons per heat in 1870, open hearths met the challenge for larger, more economical units, and by 1900 open hearth furnaces of 50 tons capacity were being planned. Furnace capacities continued to grow and now generally range from 150 to 300 tons per heat, with a few as small as 40 tons or as large as 600 tons. The Weirton Steel Company claimed in 1956 to have the world's largest open hearth shop. It consisted of one 600-ton giant and two rated at 550 tons, one at 500 tons and five at 275 tons. A 600-ton furnace was reported to be in China in 1959, and in 1960 several furnaces of the

TABLE 19

PRODUCTION OF STEEL, BY PROCESSES AND PERCENTAGES, OF TOTAL PRODUCTION IN THE UNITED STATES: SELECTED PERIODS, 1875–1961

(thousands of net tons)

Years	Open Hearth (1,000s)		Bessemer (1,000s)		Crucible (1,000s)		Electric (1,000s)		Miscellaneous (1,000s)		Basic Oxygen (1,000s)		Total Steel Production (1,000s)
	Net Tons	% of Total	Net Tons	% of Total	Net Tons	% of Total	Net Tons	% of Total	Net Tons	% of Total	Net Tons	% of Total	Net Tons
1875	9	2.0	375	86.0	39	9.0	—	—	13	3.0	—	—	436
1890	575	11.0	4,130	86.0	80	2.0	—	—	4	1.0	—	—	4,790
1900	3,806	33.0	7,487	66.0	113	a	—	—	5	a	—	—	11,411
1906	12,298	47.0	13,749	53.0	142	a	—	—	16	a	—	—	26,205
1908	8,777b	56.0	6,851	44.0	71	a	—	—	7	a	—	—	15,706
1909	16,233	61.0	10,450	39.0	120	a	16c	a	10	a	—	—	26,830
1916	35,185	73.0	12,386	26.0	145	a	190	a	1	a	—	—	47,907
1920	36,593	77.0	9,949	21.0	81	a	562	1.0	4	a	—	—	47,189
1940	61,573	92.0	3,709	5.5	1	a	1,700	2.5	—	—	—	—	66,983
1950	86,263	89.0	4,535	4.7	—	—	6,038	6.3	—	—	—	—	96,836
1955	105,359	90.0	3,320	3.0	—	—	8,357	7.0	—	i	—	—	117,036
1957	101,658	90.0	2,475	2.0	—	—	8,582d	8.0	—	—	—	—	112,715
1958	75,879	89.0	1,396	2.0	—	—	7,980d	9.0	—	—	—	—	85,255
1959	81,669	87.5	1,380	1.4	—	—	8,532	9.1	—	—	1,864	2	93,446
1960	86,368	87.2	1,189	1.2	—	—	8,379	8.3	—	—	3,346	3.3	99,282
1961	84,502	86.2	881	0.8	—	—	8,664	9.0	—	—	3,967	4.0	98,014

SOURCE: American Iron and Steel Institute.
a Less than 1 per cent.
b Includes 61 tons of electric furnace steel.
c Electric furnace steel first reported separately.
d Includes oxygen converter.

TABLE 20

STEEL PRODUCTION IN SELECTED EUROPEAN COUNTRIES, BY PROCESSES: 1958

(millions of metric tons)

Country	Total Steel Production	Basic Bessemer (Thomas) Production	% of Total	Acid Bessemer Production	% of Total	Open Hearth Production	% of Total	Electric Production	% of Total	Other Production	% of Total
Belgium	6,006	5,135	85.5	27	0.5	571	9.5	273	4.5	—	—
Czechoslovakia*	5,166	242	4.6	—	—	4,273	82.8	651	12.6	—	—
France	14,605	8,684	59.4	114	0.8	4,531	31.0	1,276	8.7	—	—
Germany, East	3,304	340	10.3	63	1.9	2,500	75.7	401	12.1	—	—
Germany, West	22,785	9,180	40.4	85	0.4	11,643	51.2	1,533	6.7	344	1.0
Luxembourg	3,379	3,304	98.0	—	—	75	2.0	—	—	—	—
Poland	5,642	—	—	—	—	5,226	92.6	398	7.0	18	0.3
Saar	3,459	2,643	75.5	—	—	773	22.3	44	1.2	—	—
Sweden	2,400	434	18.0	28	1.1	763	31.3	1,100	45.8	75	3.2
United Kingdom	19,884	964	4.9	233	1.0	17,422	87.9	1,144	5.7	121	0.5

SOURCE: Quarterly Bulletin of Steel Statistics for Europe, United Nations, Geneva, 1958.
* 1957

same size were built in the USSR, where units of 800-900 tons capacity were being designed.[1]

The open hearth furnace, as a mass producer of steel, is facing a challenge similar to that of the blast furnace as the mass producer of pig iron. There are those who say that the open hearth furnace has passed its zenith and will decline in importance, its loss represented by gains of the electric furnace and the new basic oxygen converter. "The trend to oxygen process is clearly established," commented R. N. Merk, Chief Engineer of the Sharon Steel Corporation. "We have probably seen the last large new open hearth shop built in the United States."[2]

Those who hold that the increasing production of carbon steels in electric furnaces constitutes a growing threat to the open hearth furnace point out that electric furnace capacity has been growing more rapidly than that of the open hearth. In the period 1935 to 1960, while open hearth capacity in the United States was less than doubled, electric furnace capacity was increased from 1,053,370 to 14,396,000 tons, or more than thirteen times.

It is noteworthy that Steel, Peech & Tozer of Rotherham, England, announced in 1959 that it was replacing all of its existing open hearth furnaces with the world's largest electric furnace shop, with an annual steelmaking capacity of 1,485,000 net tons.[3]

Meanwhile, some proponents of the open hearth furnace assert that claims that it "has passed its zenith" are "not supported by the facts." They say that the "ability of the open hearth to use as much as 83 per cent hot metal makes it possible to operate independently of fluctuations in the availability and price of purchased scrap. In addition, the versatility of the open hearth in the production of a wide variety of steel grades has not yet been matched by the newer processes." The open hearth of the future, say these authorities, "will be larger, heat times will be shorter, fuel consumption will continue to decline, furnace life will increase—all without sacrificing steel quality."[4]

In support of their claims, defenders of the open hearth furnace cite the impressive gains in production made in recent years through the use of oxygen injection and basic bricks in the roof construction. When trials were first conducted with oxygen injected into the bath by means of a water-cooled lance, open hearth roofs were constructed of conventional silica bricks, but the greater heat created by the oxygen resulted in a shortened roof life. The substitution of basic bricks for silica bricks resulted in a longer roof life, with fewer delays, and was an important factor in greater production through oxygen injection. Using an oxygen lance, U.S. Steel obtained 368 to 498 heats per roof campaign with basic bricks, against 132 to 190 heats with silica bricks. Data collected by U.S. Steel from over 600 heats indicated that with the use of 300 to 600 cubic feet of oxygen per ton of ingots, improvement in heat time was 10 to 25 per cent and saving in fuel was 18 to 35 per cent. Before the use of oxygen in the open hearth furnace, the production of 30 tons of steel an hour was a good performance for the industry as a whole. Shops using oxygen on a regular production basis are making close to 40 tons of steel an hour, an increase of nearly 25 per cent, and production rates of 100 tons per hour have been reported.

OXYGEN STEELMAKING PROCESSES

The idea of using oxygen in iron and steelmaking is not new. Henry Bessemer in 1856 suggested the possibility of using oxygen-enriched air in his converter and actually took out patents (British Pat. 356 and 1292) the same year on the use of oxygen as a refining agent. In 1902, a patent was granted in Austria (Osterr. Pat. 8071, March 1) to an Italian foundry —Fonderia Milanese de Acciaio, Milano—for a procedure whereby oxygen was blown into a metal bath through a nozzle placed in the side wall of the vessel.

The unavailability of pure oxygen in quantity and its very high cost retarded its practical application for many years. In 1923, when oxygen was available only in bottles at $240 a ton, trials in commercial steelmaking furnaces demonstrated the possibility of increasing production through the use of oxygen for both combustion and decarburization purposes. Finally, in the 1920s, Linde and Fraenkl made feasible the volume production of oxygen at moderate cost, clearing the way to freer use of it in experimentation. Around 1936, the price of oxygen dropped to $80 a ton and in 1958 metallurgical oxygen could be manufactured for $12 to $15 a ton and commercial-purity oxygen (95 per cent) produced for about $5 a ton. As a result of these successively lower prices, there was widespread experimentation with oxygen in the United States in both open hearth and electric furnaces and an increasing number of open hearth shops began to use the element in normal operating practices.

But it was in Europe that trials with oxygen as the sole refining agent in steelmaking were brought to fruition. In 1937-1938, Dr. C. V. Schwartz and R. Durrer independently conducted experiments in Germany, using a bottom-blown Thomas converter. They soon learned that blowing high-purity oxygen into the bottom of a vessel created such great heat that the refractory material in the tuyere was rapidly destroyed. The process was reversed and pressurized oxygen was blown from above on the surface of the molten metal bath. The high velocity of the gas enabled it to penetrate the molten metal, converting it into steel. Their work was interrupted by the war. German Patent No. 735,196 directed to this process was issued in 1943. Further experimental work by Durrer and Hellbrügge in Switzerland following the war led to the erection of a pilot plant in Linz, Austria, in 1949. Within a short time, top-blown units produced such favorable results that commercial plants were erected at Linz and Donawitz, Austria. The first commercial heat of 30 tons was poured at Linz in November 1952. Commercial production by the basic oxygen process was begun by Dominion Foundries and Steel, Ltd., of Canada, in October 1954, and two months later by McLouth Steel Corporation in the United States.

The use of oxygen as the principal reagent for steelmaking is not limited to the basic oxygen process. Two other variations have been developed, the Stora Kaldo process, in Sweden, and the Rotor process, in Germany. But the basic oxygen process is enjoying the widest popularity. "In my opinion," said Avery C. Adams, President of Jones & Laughlin Steel Corporation, "the basic oxygen process represents the only major technical breakthrough at the ingot level in the steel industry since before the turn of the century."[5] The immediate threat of this process appears to be to the open hearth furnace. The manager of the Domnarfvet Works in Sweden, said, "We believe that the oxygen steel processes mean the end of open hearth furnace construction."[6] He may have been speaking merely for his own company.

Let us first see how the basic oxygen process works and then examine the advantages claimed for it.

How the Basic Oxygen Process Works

The converter used in the basic oxygen process resembles somewhat a conventional Bessemer converter, but without tuyeres, wind box or blast pipe. The refractory lining is about 20 inches thick and usually consists of magnesite brick. Like the Bessemer converter, the vessel is tilted on its side to receive the charge. Scrap, which constitutes about 25 per cent of the metallics in the charge, is added first, followed by molten pig iron and small quantities of roll scale and lime. The vessel is tilted upright and a water-cooled oxygen lance is lowered to within two to three feet of the charge. The oxygen is turned on, usually under a pressure of 140 to 180 pounds per square inch, and the reaction is instantaneous. Oxygen is dissolved in the metal and results in rapid oxidation of the silicon, manganese, phosphorus, and carbon. The carbon is oxidized to form carbon monoxide gas. The gas causes a vigorous boiling action of the entire charge. In the production of low carbon steel, control of the process can be achieved because the boiling action stops when the carbon content reaches extremely low levels. This point is clearly visible by a drop in the flame at the mouth of the vessel. Then the oxygen lance is withdrawn and the vessel is tilted to a horizontal position to permit skimming off the fluid slag, after which the vessel is tilted about 10 degrees further and the molten metal is poured into a conventional ladle. At one American steel company, the average time per heat, from charge to tap is 38 minutes, from tap to tap 53 minutes.

A commission of the United Nations reported in 1959 that the addition of powdered lime to the jet of oxygen in a basic oxygen converter facilitates de-phosphorization and de-sulfurization of the charge. This modification of the process has been introduced commercially in several steel works in France and Luxembourg, where, it is claimed, the steel was superior in quality to open hearth steel.[7]

Although the basic oxygen process was originally planned for the production of carbon steel, experimentation in several countries has shown that the oxygen converter is capable of producing alloy steels. Chromium, manganese, tool and ball bearing steels have been successfully produced in Austria. A German steelmaker has used the process not only to manufacture low alloy steels, but also steel with 6 to 12 per cent manganese and even stainless steel.[8]

Advantages of Basic Oxygen Process

A major advantage of the process is its remarkable flexibility in handling a wide range of raw materials. The scrap may be either light or heavy and the oxide charge, if used, may be dry iron ore, sinter, pellets, or mill scale. The process can be operated on any kind of hot metal which can be used in the open hearth furnace.

Steel produced by the basic oxygen process has shown itself to be at least equivalent to basic open hearth steel of the same carbon content for a wide variety of products, including welded and seamless tubes, tin plate, hot and- cold-rolled sheets, plates, structural shapes, and bars.

World Trends

Installation of basic oxygen converters is spreading rapidly around the world. In 1960, world annual capacity was 11.5 millon tons. In 1961, there were 120 converters in seventeen nations, with a total annual capacity of 15.5 million tons. In the same year there were nineteen units in seven American steel companies with a total annual capacity of 4.16 million tons, and five units in two Canadian steel companies with 1.4 million tons annual capacity. It has been predicted that world production may reach 120 million tons in 1965, or 35 per cent of the world's steel making capacity.[9]

The Stora Kaldo Process

The Stora Kaldo process was developed by the Stora Kopparbergs Berlags, a 600-year-old Swedish firm. It differs chiefly from the basic oxygen process in that the vessel rotates during operation. Experience at the company's Domnarfvet Works is said to indicate that a Kaldo installation will cost from 50 to 65 per cent less than a new open hearth shop of similar capacity and auxiliaries. The Domnarfvet converter produces 15 to 16 heats in 24 hours, equivalent to 19 tons per heat. Tap to tap time is 90 minutes, of which 40 minutes is actual blowing time.

It is claimed for the Stora Kaldo process that it makes possible the economic production of high quality steels low in sulphur, and the production of medium and high carbon steels without the need of recarburizing. In 1959, there were three Stora Kaldo units in Sweden, three in France, and two units proposed for Sweden. Plans to install the first Stora Kaldo unit in the United States was announced by the Sharon Steel Company in April 1961. It is to contain two furnaces with a total annual steel capacity of 1 million tons.

Rotor Process

The Rotor process was developed at Oberhausen, Germany. Its distinguishing feature is a cylindrical vessel with openings at both ends. The cylinder rotates on its longitudinal axis. Primary oxygen is blown through a water-cooled jet at the entrance end of the vessel below the surface of the hot metal charge. Secondary oxygen is directed across the top of the bath to burn carbon monoxide gas generated by the refining action. Waste gases are drawn off through the opening at the opposite end of the vessel. Blowing time is 50 to 60 minutes and tap to tap time is 2 hours.

In 1959, there were four Rotor units in Germany, four in South Africa, and a license had been issued for one in France.

Local conditions will determine which type of oxygen process is best suitable for a given site.

IRON DIRECTLY INTO STEEL

From the profusion of processes taking shape in ferrous metallurgy have come several which aim at converting iron ore or pig iron directly into steel. Several of them go a step further and roll the steel into strip in one operation.

The Cyclosteel process referred to as "flash reduction" because of the rapidity of the action, is being developed by the British Iron and Steel Research Association. Finely divided iron ore is preheated in a fluidized bed and is then blow into a chamber heated by pulverized fuel partially burnt with oxygen. The object is to reduce the molten ore particles with extreme rapidity at high temperature, and cause them to collect into a bath of steel, or at least to produce molten iron suitable for immediate conversion into steel.

The Cyclosteel process represents a new metallurgical trend: extremely rapid reduction of finely divided iron ore which can be effected at temperatures in excess of 3,000° F. The high temperature presents a problem in refractories, but if these obstacles can be surmounted, it may be possible to obtain large outputs from small units.

A second process of direct steel production from iron ore, has been proposed by Republic Steel Corporation. It aims at nothing less than by-passing the coke oven, blast furnace, open hearth furnace, and the primary rolling mill (blooming mill). The new method consists of three stages. In the first, iron ore is highly purified and reduced to metallic powder. Second, the powder is funneled between four rolls which compress and roll it into a semi-finished strip. Third, the semi-solid strip is fed to a furnace which heats the strip to 2,200° F. in a reducing atmosphere and passes it on through a series of hot strip rolling stands. The rolling stands reduce the strip to the desired gauge and at the end of the line the strip is wound in coils as on a conventional hot strip mill. Republic reported in June 1959 that strip steel made in a laboratory model "offers the same strength, ductility, and ability to be fabricated into finished parts as steel produced by other methods."[10] The next step will be to construct a pilot plant for further experimentation before building a commercial plant. Republic estimates that a commercial plant will cost only 40 to 50 per cent of installations used in conventional melting processes.

Variations of the same process are under investigation in Germany and Sweden. They differ in one important respect from Republic's process in that they begin with pig iron instead of iron ore. In the RZ process (Rodheisen-Zunder), as it is called in Germany, pig iron is granulated into fine particles with high air pressure. During the granulation, the iron droplets are partly oxidized, and the particles have an oxide surface layer surrounding a center with high carbon content. In the reduction of carbon, oxygen at the surface reacts with carbon in the center to form a soft iron with low contents of carbon and oxygen. The mass of powder is slightly sintered together during the decarburization and is made into iron powder by grinding. The iron powder can be rolled into strips in a cold rolling operation, which is followed by heat treatment and further rolling.

In Sweden, Stora Kopparbergs Berlags has developed what it terms the Stora Powder Steel Process. The raw material is ordinary pig iron in which the silicon content has been brought down to the lowest possible level by pre-refining with oxygen. The pig iron is ground into a powder and mixed with a high-grade iron ore concentrate. The mixture is packed in a box of sheet steel containing holes to allow reaction gases to escape. The box is heated to approximately 2,000° F. in a furnace until the reaction between the iron ore and the pig iron is completed. Then the hot box with its contents of sintered iron powder is rolled into steel on a conventional mill. Although Stora has rolled the steel into round and square sections, metal produced by the Powder Steel Process is considered to be best suited for rolling into flat products. The company reports that the steel has good deep-drawing properties, welds easily, and is comparable in quality to electric furnace steel.

It is claimed that the Stora Powder Steel process requires lower capital cost and fewer man-hours per ton than conventional steelmaking methods. Furthermore, the iron yield is said to be higher.

VACUUM MELTING

The refining of steel in a vacuum was described in the previous chapter. It will be recalled that vacuum melting is the latest answer of engineers and metallurgists to the need for steel of greater purity in the atomic-space age. This end is accomplished by the vacuum elimination from steel of contaminating elements, principally hydrogen.

THE FUTURE

There can be no doubt that a revolution is brewing in methods used for the production of steel. The controversy over the relative positions of the conventional electric and open hearth furnaces and the oxygen processes will resolve itself in the near future. Certainly the open hearth furnace will be with us for some time to come, if only because of the heavy investment in existing facilities. Whether the last "large new open hearth shop" has been built in the United States remains to be seen. It appears to be the consensus that oxygen and electricity will be used increasingly as agents for the refinement of iron into steel. Durrer believes that the "main part of steelmaking will involve the utilization of oxygen. The electric furnaces will play an important role as a producer of high-grade products and may also become a mass production tool involving the blowing of pig iron with an oxygen-enriched blast, and the refining of the resulting steel through utilization of electric energy."[11]

The several processes for the direct manufacture of iron ore into steel are still in early stages of development. Their significance lies in the trend which they indicate: the simplification of processes in ferrous metallurgy. Direct methods for ore reduction, some of which employ fuels other than coke, hold promise for small-scale, inexpensive production of iron in underdeveloped countries. The Cyclosteel process aims to convert iron ore into steel in a matter of seconds. Republic Steel Corporation's proposal is aimed at eliminating a number of intermediary steps in the conversion of iron ore into strip steel. The RZ process in Germany and the Stora Powder Steel Process in Sweden begin with pig iron and end with rolled steel products.

Steel in the Atomic-Space Age

When looms weave by themselves man's slavery will end.
                                              —*Aristotle*

Man's long quest to conquer his environment and improve his living conditions has been determined in each age by the toolmaking materials at his command. Stone was replaced by bronze and bronze by iron. Iron served man well until the steam engine gave impetus to the Industrial Revolution in the latter part of the eighteenth century. In the opening phase of the Industrial Revolution, iron performed satisfactorily, but as machines grew heavier and wheels turned faster, and as new industries came into being with more severe requirements, iron could no longer answer all the demands made upon it. A stronger, more durable metal was needed in mass quantities. It was steel, then being made in limited quantities and at high cost. Invention of the Bessemer and open-hearth processes in the second half of the nineteenth century met the need for inexpensive steel in volume production and the Industrial Revolution moved into its second phase.

It became evident by degrees that plain carbon steel had more than met its match in requirements that arose in this second phase of the Machine Age. The steel industry was importuned for stronger and tougher steels with greater resistance to high temperatures and corrosive conditions, for application in high-speed tools, automobiles, aircraft, petroleum refining, and chemical manufacturing. Metallurgists gave the world a virtually new metal in the form of alloy steels with properties of strength, toughness, and resistance to heat and corrosion undreamed of in the opening years of the present century.

Alloy steels met virtually all requirements until the era following World War II, when steam and gas turbines, atomic reactors, jet engines, and rockets overtaxed known alloy steels in some critical applications. The next step in man's search for materials to do service in the Atomic-Space Age was the development of super-alloys, composed of such elements as nickel, cobalt, chromium, columbium, titanium, and others, in varying proportions, with less than half iron. Super-alloys can hold their strength at higher temperatures than steel. Concurrently with the development of super-alloys has been the exploration of cermets, so-called because they are a combination of ceramics and metals containing compounds such as nitrides, borides, carbides, sulfides, and hydrides. Cermets have different properties than their constituents. Metallurgists question the ability of metals to perform at temperatures higher than 1,800° F., while engineers dream of engines able to operate at 2,600° F., or higher. Cermets offer some hope because they can withstand temperatures from 1,700° to 2,500° F.

This, then, has been man's development of industrial materials from the Stone Age to the Atomic-Space Age. Beginning with the generation of steam for propulsive purposes, one of the most persistent problems of the metallurgist has been to find metals capable of performing at ever higher temperatures in order to realize greater thermal efficiency. It continues to be one of his most formidable problems. The designers of steam and gas turbines have probably been the metallurgist's severest taskmasters, continually raising the service requirements of steel. The history of high temperature alloy steels parallels the development of steam and gas turbines. The blades of a turbine are subjected not only to high temperatures, but also to tremendous stresses, and are also exposed to severe corrosive conditions. As far back as 1914, one of the first applications of stainless steel was to answer the needs for stronger turbine blades. Stainless steel since then has been greatly improved and can now operate at 1,200° F. But engineers say that they could double the efficiency of gas turbines if a metal could be found to hold its strength above 1,800° F.

The turbine is the first mechanism for which technological advance has been held up for want of a suitable material. When we turn to nuclear reactors, supersonic aircraft, rockets, and missiles, we find technology far in advance of metallurgy in many respects. Supersonic aircraft are being throttled back to conform to the limitation of metal in the airframes. Although more efficient atomic reactor systems have been designed and some are in the pilot plant stage, materials for their construction are proving to be inadequate. At the present time, steel in the form of plates 9 inches thick is being used. The steel must withstand intense bombardment by high energy nuclear particles—neutrons—from a chain reaction. Prolonged exposure of steel to such radiation impairs its ductility and toughness. Loss of toughness is of concern because after several years service, the steel may become susceptible to sudden fracture. Better steels for nuclear power reactors is the most important need for the further peacetime development of atomic energy. When a long-range missile re-enters the atmosphere at an elevation of 85,000 feet, traveling at Mach 18 (18 times the speed of sound) the outer surface of its nose is heated to 12,000° F. The temperature in the combustion chamber of a rocket engine may reach 2,500° to 4,500° F.

These are some of the conditions with which engineers and metallurgists must grapple in their mutual search for better materials in the Atomic-Space Age.

"The sad fact is," commented Dr. Wernher von Braun, in a speech before the American Iron and Steel Institute in 1959, "that designs of advanced missile and supersonic aircraft are already being limited by the non-availability of suitable materials. . . . Obviously this situation can not long continue else the success of our entire advancing space program may be in jeopardy."[1] He went on to say that the search is on for materials that will be resistant to adverse conditions in outer space. These include extremes of temperature, high vacuum, solar and cosmic radiation, residual gases, and meteoric bombardment.

At the threshold of the Atomic-Space Age, technology has outdistanced metallurgy. Man can generate heat beyond the capacity of any known material to contain it. Engineers have designs on their drafting boards that call for a metal stronger than any available. Much progress has been made and more can be expected in the technological and scientific revolution now underway. An important aspect of this revolution is the rapidity of its progress. Former revolutions went forward at a relatively slow pace. This one is moving at a dizzy rate. The startling innovation of today is soon accepted as commonplace or becomes outdated. At the end of World War II aircraft builders were concerned with breaking the sound barrier. Fifteen years later, man-made satellites were tearing around the earth at 18,000 miles an hour, and in 1961 man himself orbited the earth in a space vehicle. Programs are being pursued for manned space flights to the moon and perhaps other planets, even to other solar systems.

What do these wonders and marvels portend for the metal industries and for the steel industry in particular? Metallurgy is at the center of the technological and scientific revolution now taking place. The metallurgy of steel has entered a new era. Two others preceded it. The first was that of chemical control when man began to understand the chemistry of steel and to develop steels according to chemical composition. In the second, metallurgists with the aid of the microscope, began to see and understand the changes in the properties of steel which had formerly been achieved empirically. This was called "visible microstructure." Now we are in the era of atomic structure.

STEELS OF GREATER STRENGTH

While man is lifting his eyes to the heavens in contemplation of space travel, he is finding a new universe within the atom. Physicists say that the theoretical strength of metals is 1,000 to 10,000 times greater than their actual measured strength.[2] It has been possible in the laboratory to produce pure crystals of molecular iron in the form of a filament with the tensile strength of 2 million pounds per square inch. The strongest steels today have a tensile strength of 280,000 to 300,000 pounds per square inch, and new steels of 350,000 to 600,000 pounds per square inch tensile strength are beginning to appear. From a laboratory experiment to practical application is often a long and tortuous procedure, but the direction has been pointed out. The problem appears to be to get rid of the defects ordinarily existing in iron crystals, and, by rendering them more nearly perfect, to produce steels of much greater strength. Studies are being pursued with the object of producing steels twice as strong as any now known.

Numerous metals are used in supersonic planes and space vehicles. Each metal is chosen for the application to which it is best suited. Steel, and alloys of titanium, aluminum, and magnesium are the most widely used. If there is one all-round metal it is probably steel, which, according to one report, constitutes more than half the metallic weight of the average missile.[3] The important place of steel in space technology accounts for the interest in the possibility of producing steels of much greater strength. Emphasis has been placed so far in this chapter on steel capable of holding its strength at elevated temperatures. Such steel is still very important. It may be pointed out in this connection that metal on the outer surface of a supersonic plane or missile is generally subjected to great heat for a relatively short time. A steel which could not withstand exposure to high temperature for a prolonged period may be able to operate satisfactorily for a short period. The X-15 rocket plane, designed to explore problems of space flight, has ascended to more than fifty-eight miles above the earth. On its return through the atmosphere, its skin surfaces glow red with heat. The skin of the craft is made of a nickel alloy over a structural frame of stainless steel and titanium. Exposure to high temperature in reentering the atmosphere is so brief that any metal softening is not damaging.

With the advent of intercontinental ballistic missiles, the emphasis has shifted from heat-resistant steels to steels with greater strength at room temperature. Beyond the stratosphere, where there is no air friction, the problem of space vehicles traveling at 24,000 miles an hour is not so much one of heat as of strength. A missile, moving at greater speed than a supersonic plane, is exposed to frictional heating for a shorter period. Consequently, designers of space vehicles want steel with vastly greater strength at relatively low temperatures and with greater resistance to corrosion, especially corrosion under stress.

Steel could be fabricated strong enough for any purpose if enough of it were used. The stronger the steel, the less of it is needed for a given application, thereby cutting down on weight. The relationship of strength to weight is spoken of as the strength-weight ratio. A missile may be looked upon as a flying fuel tank. The fuel load diminishes in flight as the fuel is consumed. It is therefore in the launching equipment that engineers look for a higher strength-weight ratio in steel. If steel could be made twice as strong as at present, the weight of steel in the launching equipment could be cut in half. The fuel load could be correspondingly increased, extending the range of the missile.

The need for resistance to corrosion under stress has been accentuated by the use of "exotic fuels" to power vehicles for space travel. Some of these fuels are extremely corrosive and all the more so under conditions of stress. If steel can be developed that can cut the weight of a space vehicle in half, it would avail nothing if it cannot at the same time resist corrosion of fuels within the container.

STEEL IN SPACE VEHICLES

As already mentioned, a number of metals are being used in high-speed aircraft and space vehicles. Each has its special properties which recommend it for a given application. The technology of the Atomic-Space Age is still in its early stages and trials are being conducted with various materials for the same application. The suitability of metals and non-metals now under investigation is far from being evaluated. Certain applications are not made public for security reasons.

Steel predominates as a metal for space vehicles for a variety of reasons. Iron and steel are the oldest structural metals and their technology and metallurgy have been more thoroughly explored than any competitive metal. Titanium has been in commercial use for only a few years. Steel is available in a greater range of properties and forms than any other metal. Most grades are easily formable and lend themselves well to fabrication, a matter of prime importance to design engineers. Steel combines ductility, strength, toughness, and resistance to corrosion and heat to a degree unmatched by any other metal. Few materials can equal steel for sub-zero service, another property which must be given serious consideration by the designers of supersonic planes and space vehicles. The technology and metallurgy of steel is being relentlessly pursued and new areas of service are being developed, with the promise of new achievements yet to come. Mention was made that steels with tensile strengths of 350,000 to 600,000 pounds per square inch are beginning to appear. Steel, with double its present strength, is in the laboratory stage.

Steel finds numerous applications in supersonic aircraft and space vehicles. In a jet plane there may be as many as one hundred different types of stainless and alloy steels. Steel serves as an important structural material in launching towers and auxiliary equipment at missile bases. One of these complicated towers may stand 135 feet high and weigh 360 tons, so constructed that technicians may have access to every part of the missile. At some bases, liquid oxygen is stored in stainless steel tanks because of the metal's cleanliness and toughness at low temperature.

STEEL AND ATOMIC ENERGY

On the mundane level, steel will continue to be man's chief industrial metal, in spite of growing competition from other materials, as far as we can see into the future. It will continue in this role because of its great versatility, which permits it to be manufactured in a greater number of grades for a greater variety of purposes than any other metal, and also because there are abundant iron ore deposits in many parts of the world.

In 1961, the world produced 392,647,000 tons of steel. It has been estimated that in the fourth quarter of this century the quantity may be raised to well over one-half billion tons annually.[4] Whether this tonnage will be realized or even exceeded will depend on a number of factors. In major industrial nations, population growth and general economic expansion can be counted on to raise steel consumption materially. Progress toward industrialization in underdeveloped countries will have an important bearing on the rate of growth in the steel industry of the world. Third, man's success in producing cheap atomic energy and in making it available throughout the world will profoundly affect the future of the steel industry.

It is generally acknowledged that a machine civilization will eventually spread over the earth. What will this mean to the steel industry?

One of the most important problems to be faced by the steel industry will be its future source of energy. As mineral fuels become exhausted, the generation of atomic energy will increase. After about 1980, say the authors of *The Next Hundred Years*, nuclear energy should constitute a significant part of total world power production. By the turn of the century, they foresee nuclear energy accounting for about one-third of total energy consumption. "By the middle of the next century," they write, "it seems likely that most of our energy will be satisfied by nuclear energy, with coal reserved almost entirely for the production of liquid fuels and chemicals."[5]

Nuclear energy will be available at any place on the globe at a fairly uniform cost. While it will be important in the further industrialization of Western and Eastern Europe and Japan, it will be of transcendent importance to underdeveloped regions, poor in energy resources. In such areas, it will make possible and accelerate the growth of a machine economy and in so doing, greatly increase the production and consumption of steel.

The harnessing of nuclear energy to machines will not only bring about an increased production of steel for the myriad wants of an industrialized economy, but will also directly create its own needs for the metal. More steel will be required for the mining of uranium and thorium ores. There will be greater need for steels used in the construction of fissionable fuel processing plants, where the mined ores are prepared for subsequent use as fuel in atomic reactors. An increased demand will develop for steels used in the recovery and safe disposal of radioactive waste materials.

Nuclear energy, as a source of power, will affect the steel industry internally. By the time atomic energy replaces mineral fuels in the steel industry, manufacture of the metal from mines to finished products will be a continuous process. A picture of the steel industry in the year 2056 has been given us by Benjamin F. Fairless, former board chairman of United States Steel and President of the American Iron and Steel Institute. Speaking in 1956 at the dedication of the Socony Mobil Building in New York, he said that in another century the steel industry "will have moved all the way to a continuous operation instead of a batch-type process," using atomic energy. "Iron ore," he said, "will move in at one end of the plant and finished steel products will emerge at the other, without intermediate processes such as soaking, conditioning, hot rolling, annealing, pickling and shearing. Extruding will largely have replaced rolling to produce finished products. Order entry, production planning, mill scheduling, cost control and shipment records all will be handled by an interlocking computer system."

AUTOMATION

Those days are in the future. Meanwhile, we are in the early stages of automation, which, as defined by the dictionary is "automatically controlled operation of an apparatus, process, or system, especially by electronic devices."[6] One of its distinguishing features is the presence of what are termed "feedback" control devices. Installed in a system of continuous or semi-continuous operations, the feedback observes and appraises specific variations in the performance of the machines or the quality or dimension of the product and feeds back this information to a computer control system which initiates corrective action. This is something new under the sun.

A second distinguishing feature of automation is the electronic computer. This instrument is capable of storing and interpreting a vast body of information and of performing both simple and complex mathematical calculations with lightning-like rapidity.

Computers are used both in the business office and in manufacturing processes. The latter application will be discussed first. A structural mill, designed for electronic program control, was put into operation by United States Steel at its South Chicago Works in 1960. Forty-three operations in the rolling of a steel beam from start to finish are performed in sequence with precision. As a result of the new installation, together with rescheduling of product in all structural units of the plant, its wide beam capacity was increased by 40 per cent. The most advanced rolling mill in the

United States is the 80-inch hot-strip mill of the Great Lakes Steel Corporation in Detroit. The instructions supplied to the electronic controls include the number of slabs called for in the production schedule and the width and thickness of the strip to be rolled. These controls make the necessary calculations and adjust the mill settings accordingly. They control the temperature of the slab heating furnace by regulating the gas flame and release a slab from the furnace for rolling only after the slab has met the prescribed temperature. They also control the coiling temperature of the finished strip.

In addition to these two mills, electronic control systems are operating in a number of primary rolling mills and roughing mills in the United States, with many more scheduled to be installed. Electronic controls operate an annealing line and one is due for a sintering plant. Studies are under way to apply computer control to the basic oxygen converter. In other industries, computers control an entire oil plant and a steam-powered generating plant.

Computers in the Business Office

Computers are making more rapid progress in the business office than in manufacturing processes because electronic devices developed so far are more adaptable to office procedures than to industrial machines. In England, Guest Keen & Nettlefolds, Ltd., manufacturers of screws, bolts, nuts, and rivets, adopted a computer for payroll purposes in 1957. Previously, the payroll for 4,000 employees was made up manually by twenty-five clerks and their supervisors. The computer system has reduced the clerical staff by twelve and produces the payroll more accurately, smoothly, and quickly than formerly. The company reported that the danger of errors caused by the manual transcription of information from one document to another is eliminated.[7]

When Dorman Long (Steel), Ltd., of England several years ago started to build new beam mills at its Cleveland and Lackenby plants, it was estimated that the enlarged mill office staff would require eighty additional clerks. Studies on the feasibility of utilizing computers indicated that it would be possible to carry out the majority of the mill office work with computers and ancillary equipment with an over-all reduction of 140 in the clerical staff at a payroll saving of £90,000 and a total saving of between £30,000 and £40,000 a year.[8]

In the United States, virtually all steel companies have instituted electronic data processing for accounting and certain other clerical functions and are pursuing research and development programs to improve and extend the uses of computers. Some companies have made more progress than others, but United States Steel has taken a commanding lead in the practice and theory of computer use. Some of U.S. Steel's principal accomplishments will be described here.

The corporation's objective in its Integrated Data Processing Program was defined as follows:

The effective production, through systematic organization of all related clerical routines, of a coordinated flow of data essential to management in its control, planning, and decision-making function at the lowest possible cost.

In U.S. Steel divisions and subsidiaries, it has been the practice to decentralize accounting and other clerical functions and carry them on at each plant. With the establishment of data processing, the field offices are reduced in number and much of their work is transferred to a central location, resulting in increased efficiency. An advanced data processing project is under way in one of the corporation's divisions. When the project is completed, total centralized control of accounting will be achieved for this division at its headquarters. The system will include all plants of the division, located in several widely scattered states.

Data Processing in a Steel Plant

U.S. Steel confined its initial work with computers to accounting procedures, such as payroll, inventory, and cost records, and statistics. The next step was to utilize computers in purchasing, production planning, customer billing, statistical analysis, forecasting, operations research, and other business functions. As applied at one of its large works, this extension of computer service now makes it possible to process at one site all the data necessary to accept, schedule, produce, ship, and invoice an order and produce the necessary cost, profit, and statistical statements. Faster deliveries can be promised and more dependable production schedules maintained, to the mutual benefit of the plant and the customer. There is better control of product quality and more accurate and timely cost analysis. Comparable systems are being installed or developed for installation in other plants throughout the corporation.

The Near Future

The instructions fed to a computer are of a highly technical nature. Their preparation and entry into a computer require technical training of a high order on the part of the operators. All the more so, since the computer of each manufacturer must be instructed differently. The preparation of directions is time-consuming and costly. U.S. Steel participates in the development of techniques, elaborated in cooperation with manufacturers of computers, whereby instructions will be prepared automatically for any type of computer from directions written in English. This innovation will make it possible to instruct a computer by using certain English words that will be common to all machines, which will automatically translate the English words into technical instructions required to run themselves. The faster preparation of instructions will represent still another way to facilitate the use of computers. Furthermore, the instructions written at one location will be used at all other locations without duplication of effort and additional cost.

Computers are being improved so rapidly that almost as soon as one is installed it is made obsolete by a faster, more efficient model. The United States Navy has recently declassified a computer which goes beyond anything previously available to private business. Its vast data storage capacity enables it to centralize information on a massive basis. It will simultaneously accept data from many locations directly from cards, punched tapes, magnetic tapes, radio or telephone and transmit required information to many locations. A question asked of the machine will be answered in eleven-thousands of a second. The instrument's ability to receive from and transmit to many locations simultaneously can be expanded almost without limit by adding additional units. While answering questions from many locations all at once, the system can at the same time receive and transmit data or make calculations. The machine would give the user access to information on what is transpiring, rather than on what has happened.

Another important advance in electronic technology is "optical scanning." This is performed by a machine that "reads" a typewritten document at the rate of three lines per second and automatically transcribes the text to a punched card or tape for direct entry into a computer. The manual performance of this work consumes a great deal of clerical time. Optical scanning combined with a computer avoids human error and reduces clerical costs.

These advanced electronic devices, in addition to rendering their various services with greater speed, efficiency, accuracy, and monetary savings, will have another over-all advantage. By shortening the time required to accept, acknowledge, schedule, produce, ship, and invoice a customer's order, they will strengthen a company's competitive position.

The Long-range Future

The use of computers in the business office and manufacturing operations has so far followed separate lines. Among the long-range possibilities is the joining of the two systems. If and when that union takes place, the production line will feed information on what it has done into a data processing system.

The known advantages of automation are great. The potential advantages are staggering. Advantages of both kinds account for the vigorous pursuit of automation in major industrial nations. As automation moves ahead within an industry, no member of it will be able to afford to lag behind, any more than a manufacturer could afford to rely on water power after invention of the steam engine. The same may be said of industrial nations engaged in international trade. Domestic rivalries within industries and between industries and competition between nations can be expected to intensify interest in automation and accelerate its progress. The Soviet Union was the first nation to set up an institute to study the industrial applications of automation.[9] The Russians are making a major scientific effort toward automating their industrial production and are ready to move faster than the United States in applying mathematical theories to automation, according to a report prepared in 1961 by a group of mathematicians for the Research Institute for Advanced Studies of the Martin Company in Baltimore. "There is reason to believe," the report concluded, "that the U.S.S.R. can achieve a rapid acceleration in its rate of technological progress by an all-out scientific program in the field of automatic control."[10] France is well-advanced in the development of automation techniques in many fields, while Germany, Japan, and Sweden are rapidly developing automation components and processes for industrial application.

The future pattern of automation in the steel industry is beginning to emerge. Each stage of operation will be separately automated in "islands of automation." Associated islands of automation will next be linked together in an automated process by new area computer systems and these, in turn, will be linked with even newer master computer systems for the entire plant, as foreseen by Mr. Fairless. Administration of the business, with subsidiary functions—sales, accounting, production planning, research, etc.—will be tied in with the plants in an integrated over-all system. Orders and information will pulsate back and forth continuously between administrative nerve centers, sales offices, mines, and plants. The customer will enjoy a speed of service and quality of product never before experienced. Management, in addition to the many other advantages of automation, will have at its command a sensitivity to market trends and conditions never before attainable. Operators in the mills will serve as monitors whose function will be to observe any abnormalities in the flow of operations. Assisting them will be maintenance crews trained to keep the system performing smoothly. Both groups will have to be of a high order of intelligence and technical training.

How far along automation in the steel industry will have advanced by the time nuclear energy becomes an important source of power, only the years ahead will reveal. At the rate automation is proceeding, it may outpace the utilization of atomic energy. But the day will eventually come when automation and nuclear power will constitute the foundation on which a new industrial civilization will rest, with profound repercussions on the industrial, economic, social—and perhaps political—structure of the world.

Automation should not be thought of solely as a great technological revolution, which it actually is, but also as a manifestation of an intellectual revolution in man's concept of supplying his physical and intellectual needs and of his relationship to the processes by which he accomplishes these ends.

Notes

CHAPTER 1/BEFORE MAN KNEW IRON

1. R. J. Forbes, *Metallurgy in Antiquity*, Leyden, Netherlands, 1950, pp. 26f.
2. T. A. Rickard, *Man and Metals: A History of Mining in Relation to the Development of Civilization*, New York, 1932, I, 109.
3. J. Newton Friend, *Iron in Antiquity*, London, 1926, p. 30.
4. Forbes, *op. cit.*, p. 23.
5. *Ibid.*, p. 133.
6. *Ibid.*, pp. 18, 325.
7. Thomas T. Read, "Chinese Iron—A Puzzle," *Harvard Journal of Asiatic Studies*, (Dec. 1937), p. 400.

CHAPTER 2/IRON, EARTHLY AND CELESTIAL

1. T. A. Rickard, "Drift Iron," *The Geographical Review* (Oct. 1934), pp. 525ff.
2. *Ibid*, p. 533.
3. *Ibid.*, pp. 535, 542.
4. George Frederic Zimmer, "The Use of Meteoric Iron by Primitive Man." *Journal of British Iron and Steel Institute*, XCIV (1916), p. 343.
5. Deut. 27:5.
6. 1 Kings 6:7.
7. 1 Chron. 22:3.
8. *Ibid.*, 29:7.
9. T. A. Rickard, *Man and Metals*, New York, 1932, II, 832.
10. *Ibid.*, pp. 832f.
11. *Ibid.*, pp. 835, 851.
12. R. J. Forbes, *Metallurgy in Antiquity*, Leyden, Netherlands, 1950, p. 418.
13. James M. Swank, *History of the Manufacture of Iron in All Ages*, 2d ed., Philadelphia, 1892, p. 7.
14. Forbes, *op. cit.*, pp. 400ff.
15. C. W. Ceram, *The Secret of the Hittites*, New York, 1956, pp. 211f.
16. Judg., 1:19.
17. *Ibid.*, 4:3.
18. I Sam. 13:19.
19. Gen. 4:22.
20. Deut. 4:20.
21. *Ibid.*, 8:9.
22. Job 28:2.
23. *Ibid.*, 20:24.

24. 2 Sam. 12:31.
25. William H. Schoff, "Eastern Iron Trade of the Roman Empire," *Journal of American Oriental Society*, 35 (1915), 224-39.
26. Swank, *op. cit.*, pp. 8f.
27. H. R. Schubert, *History of the British Iron and Steel Industry from C. 450 B.C. to A.D. 1775*, London, 1957, pp. 3f.
28. Sir Cyril Fox, *A Find of the Early Iron Age from Llyn Cerrig Bach, Anglesey*, National Museum of Wales, Cardiff, 1946, p. 1.
29. Schubert, *op. cit.*, pp. 60f.
30. Letters to the author from Fuji Iron and Steel Company, Ltd., Tokyo, Sept. 10 and Nov. 13, 1958.
31. *Steelways*, American Iron and Steel Institute, New York (Nov. 1946).
32. M. H. C. Landrin, Jr., *A Treatise on Steel*, Philadelphia, 1868.
33. Thomas T. Read, "The Early Casting of Iron," *Geographical Review* (Oct. 1934), pp. 545ff.
34. Carleton S. Coon, *The Story of Man*, New York, 1954, p. 264.

CHAPTER 3/STEEL IN ANTIQUITY

1. James M. Swank, *History of the Manufacture of Iron in All Ages*, 2d ed., Philadelphia, 1892, pp. 2, 8.
2. J. S. Jeans, *Steel: Its History, Manufacture, Properties and Uses*, London, 1880, p. 7.
3. Jer. 15:12.
4. Job 20:24.
5. John W. W. Sullivan, *The Story of Metals*, Ames, Iowa, 1951, p. 153.
6. Jeans, *op. cit.*, p. 8.
7. H. R. Schubert, *History of the British Iron and Steel Industry from c. 450 B.C. to A.D. 1775*, London, 1957, p. 29.
8. *New York Times*, Jan. 30, 1961. Letter to author, Feb. 24, 1961.
9. Swank, *op. cit.*, p. 20.
10. Sir Cyril Fox, *A Find of the Early Iron Age From Llyn Cerrig Bach, Anglesey*, National Museum of Wales, Cardiff, 1946, *passim*.

CHAPTER 4/FROM THE CATALAN FORGE TO THE BLAST FURNACE

1. *The Cambridge Economic History of Europe*, Cambridge, 1952, II, 261.
2. *Ibid.*, p. 289.
3. *Ibid.*, pp. 430ff., 470.
4. James M. Swank, *History of the Manufacture of Iron In All Ages*, Philadelphia, 2d ed., 1892, pp. 81, 84.
5. H. R. Schubert, *History of the British Iron and Steel Industry from c. 450 B.C. to A.D. 1775*, London, 1957, p. 129.
6. Swank, *op. cit.*, p. 81.
7. Schubert, *op. cit.*, pp. 133f.
8. Swank, *op. cit.*, p. 46; Ernest Straker, *Wealdon Iron*, London, 1931, p. 82.
9. Swank, *op. cit.*, pp. 25, 82ff.; T. A. Rickard, *Man and Metals*, New York, 1932, II, 885.
10. Swank, *op. cit.*, pp. 24f.
11. Schubert, *op cit.*, pp. 137, 147f.
12. Straker, *op. cit.*, p. 82.
13. Thomas Southcliffe Ashton, *Iron and Steel in the Industrial Revolution*, Manchester, 1924, pp. 7f.
14. R. R. Palmer, *A History of the Modern World*, New York, 1955, p. 113.
15. Bruce L. Simpson, *Development of the Metal Castings Industry*, American Foundrymen's Association, Chicago, 1948, p. 156.

16. *The Making, Shaping and Treating of Steel*, United States Steel Corporation, Pittsburgh, 7th ed., 1957, p. 209.
17. Swank, *op. cit.*, p. 42.
18. Schubert, *op. cit.*, pp. 119f.
19. Swank, *op. cit.*, p. 42.
20. Schubert, *op. cit.*, pp. 119f.
21. Swank, *op. cit.*, p. 42.
22. Schubert, *op. cit.*, pp. 54, 120, 316ff.

CHAPTER 5/ENGLAND LEADS THE WAY

1. H. R. Schubert, *History of the British Iron and Steel Industry: From c. 450 B.C. to 1775 A.D.*, London, 1957, p. 62.
2. Material on the early history of wire was obtained from publications and manuscripts formerly belonging to the Industrial Museum of the American Steel and Wire Division of United States Steel Corporation, in Worcester, Mass. The Museum was closed in 1941 and in 1944 most of the manuscripts and printed matter were donated to the Library of the Harvard School of Business Administration in Cambridge, Massachusetts, where they were consulted by the author.
3. Exod. 39:3.
4. Chronicles 22:3.
5. Schubert, *op. cit.*, pp. 304ff.
6. James M. Swank, *History of the Manufacture of Iron in All Ages*, Philadelphia, 1892, 2nd ed., p. 49.
7. Roy Rutherford, *Romancing in Tin Plate*, Wean Engineering Company, Warren, Ohio, 1951, pp. 43, 123.
8. T. A. Rickard, *Man and Metals*, New York, 1932, II, 890.
9. Swank, *op. cit.*, p. 46.
10. Ernest Straker, *Wealdon Iron*, London, 1931, p. 63.
11. *History of Iron and Steelmaking in the United States*, American Institute of Mining, Metallurgical, and Petroleum Engineers, Inc., New York, 1961, p. 29.
12. Dud Dudley, *Metallum Mortis (Iron Made with Pit-Coale)*, London, 1665.
13. H. R. Schubert, "The Truth About Dud Dudley," *Journal of the Iron and Steel Institute*, London (Nov. 1950).
14. *Ibid.*
15. *Ibid.*
16. *Ibid.*
17. R. A. Mott, "Dud Dudley and the Early Coal-Iron Industry," *transactions of the Newcomen Society*, XV (1933-1935).
18. Arthur Raistrick, *Dynasty of Iron Founders: The Darbys of Coalbrookdale*, London, 1953, pp. 68f.

CHAPTER 6/PRELUDE TO THE INDUSTRIAL REVOLUTION

1. *Rolling Mills, Rolls, and Roll Making*, Mackintosh-Hemphill, Pittsburgh, Pa., 1953, p. 17.
2. A. D. Eppelsheimer, "The Development of the Continuous Strip Mill," *Journal of the Iron and Steel Institute*, London (1938).
3. H. R. Schubert, *History of the British Iron and Steel Industry from c. 450 B.C. to A.D. 1775*, London, 1957, pp. 304ff.
4. *Rolling Mills, Rolls, and Roll Making*, *op. cit.*, p. 22.
5. *Ibid.*, p. 22.
6. Ross E. Beynon, *Roll Design and Mill Layout*, Association of Iron and Steel Engineers, Pittsburgh, Pa., 1956, p. 5.
7. Thomas Sutcliffe Ashton, *Iron and Steel in the Industrial Revolution*, Manchester, 1924, p. 90.
8. Beynon, *op. cit.*, pp. 8f.

9. Ashton, *op. cit.*, pp. 92f.
10. Beynon, *op. cit.*, p. 9.
11. Ashton, *op. cit.*, p. 97.
12. *Ibid.*, pp. 70ff.
13. Thomas Hibben, *Sons of Vulcan*, Philadelphia, 1940, p. 179.
14. J. S. Jeans, *Steel: Its History, Manufacture and Uses*, London, 1880, p. 17.
15. *Ibid.*, pp. 16f.
16. Ashton, *op. cit.*, p. 57.
17. James M. Swank, *History of the Manufacture of Iron in All Ages*, Philadelphia, 2d ed., 1892, p. 43.
18. David Carnegie, *Liquid Steel*, London, 1913, pp. 74.
19. *Ibid.*, pp. 75f.
20. *Ibid.*, p. 77.

CHAPTER 7/MINERS, SMITHS, AND METALLURGY

1. I Sam. 13:19.
2. T. A. Rickard, *Man and Metals*, New York, 1932, I, 208f.
3. Vanoccio Biringuccio, *Pirotechnia*, American Institute of Mining and Metallurgical Engineers, New York, 1932, p. 370.
4. Georgius Agricola, *De Re Metallica*, Tr. Herbert and Lou Henry Hoover, Dover Publications, New York, 1950, pp. 99f.
5. *Ibid.*, p. 217.
6. Gunnar Lowegren, *Swedish Iron and Steel*, English version by Nils. S. Sahlin, Stockholm, 1948, pp. 45f.
7. *Ibid.*, p. 47.
8. Thomas Sutcliffe Ashton, *Iron and Steel In The Industrial Revolution*, Manchester, 2d ed., 1951, p. 189.
9. Agricola, *op. cit.*, pp. 127f.
10. *Ibid.*, pp. 168f.
11. *Ibid.*, pp. 192ff.
12. *Ibid.*, pp. 10f.
13. *Ibid.*, footnote, 44f.
14. *Ibid.*, Preface, p. XXVIII.
15. *Ibid.*, footnote, pp. 44f.
16. Biringuccio, *op. cit.*, p. 13.
17. *Ibid.*, p. 371.
18. Sydney W. Smith, *Roberts-Austen: A Record of His Work*, London, 1941, p. 157.
19. René Antoine de Réamur, *Memoirs on Steel and Iron* (1722), University of Chicago Press, Chicago, 1956, p. XXVL.
20. *Encyclopedia Americana*, 1947 ed., vol. XXI, 784; *Encyclopaedia Britannica*, 1941 ed., vol. VI, p. 98.
21. R. F. Mehl, *A Brief History of the Science of Metals*, American Institute of Mining and Metallurgical Engineers, New York, 1948, pp. 5f.
22. Mehl, *op. cit.*, p. 6.

CHAPTER 8/IRON AND STEEL IN COLONIAL AMERICA

1. C. T. Currelly, "Viking Weapons Found Near Beardmore, Ontario," *The Canadian Historical Review*, XX, 1 (March 1939), pp. 4ff.
2. John B. Pearse, *A Concise History of the Iron Manufacture of the American Colonies Up to the Revolution and of Pennsylvania*, Philadelphia, 1876, p. 89.
3. J. Paul Hudson, "The Story of Iron at Jamestown, Virginia," *The Iron Worker*, Lynchburg, Va. (Summer 1956), pp. 3, 5.
4. E. N. Hartley, *Ironworks on the Saugus*, Norman, Okla., 1957, pp. 32f.

5. *Ibid.*, p. 33.
6. *Ibid.*, pp. 33f.
7. *Ibid.*, p. 34.
8. Charles E. Hatch, Jr. and Thurlow Gates Gregory, "The First American Blast Furnace, 1619–1622," *The Virginia Magazine of History and Biography*, LXX, No. 3 (July 1962), pp. 271f.
9. Hartley, *op. cit.*, p. 35.
10. *Ibid.*, pp. 36f.
11. *Steel Facts*, American Iron and Steel Institute, New York, 39 (March 1940).
12. Hatch and Gregory, *op. cit.*, pp. 273f.
13. Robert Beverly, *The History and Present State of Virginia*, Louis B. Wright (ed.) (Chapel Hill, N. C., 1947), p. 49.
14. Hartley, *op. cit.*, p. 37; *Steel Facts, op. cit.*
15. *Steel Facts, op. cit.*
16. Hartley, *op. cit.*, p. 39.
17. *Ibid.*, pp. 40f.
18. *Ibid.*, p. 39.
19. Hatch and Gregory, *op. cit.*
20. Thurlow Gates Gregory, "Iron of America Was Made First in Virginia," manuscript, 1947.
21. Hatch and Gregory, *op. cit.*, p. 277.
22. *Ibid.*, p. 290.
23. *Ibid., loc. cit.*
24. *Ibid.*, p. 291.
25. *Ibid.*, p. 294.
26. Hartley, *op. cit.*, p. 128.
27. *Ibid.*, pp. 134, 139, 144, 163f., 219.
28. *Ibid.*, pp. 222, 237, 243, 251, 262.
29. James M. Swank, *History of the Manufacture of Iron in All Ages*, Philadelphia, 2d ed., 1892, pp. 113ff.
30. Pearse, *op. cit.*, pp. 104f.
31. Charles S. Boyer, *Early Furnaces and Forges in New Jersey*, Philadelphia, 1931, p. 151.
32. Swank, *op. cit.*, p. 136.
33. *Ibid.*, p. 434.
34. Earl Chapin May, *Principio to Wheeling, 1715–1945*, New York, 1945, pp. 150f.
35. H. G. Warren, "History of the Wire Industry," *Various Phases of the Wire Industry: By Men Prominent in the Industry*, Union Wire Corporation, June 1, 1931.
36. *Furnaces and Forges in the Province of Pennsylvania*, Pennsylvania Society of the Colonial Dames of America, Philadelphia, 1914, pp. 6f.
37. Arthur C. Bining, *Pennsylvania Iron Manufacture in the Eighteenth Century*, Harrisburg, Pa., 1938 (Pennsylvania Historical Commission), p. 75.
38. *Steel Facts, op. cit.*, 49 (Sept. 1941).
39. *Ibid.*, 48 (June 1941).
40. Pearse, *op. cit.*, pp. 104f.
41. Swank, *op. cit.*, pp. 479ff.
42. *Ibid.*, p. 482.
43. Bining, *The Rise of American Economic Life*, 3d ed., New York, 1955, p. 93.

CHAPTER 9/RISE OF THE YOUNG REPUBLIC

1. B. F. French, *History of the Rise and Progress of the Iron Trade of the United States from 1620 to 1857*, New York, 1858, pp. 16ff.
2. James M. Swank, *History of the Manufacture of Iron in All Ages*, 2d ed., Philadelphia, 1892, pp. 509f.
3. Harold Underwood Faulkner, *American Economic History*, 7th ed., New York, 1954, p. 265.

4. *Farmers in a Changing World*, U.S. Department of Agriculture, Washington, D.C., 1940, p. 228.
5. Charles A. Beard and Mary R. Beard, *The Rise of American Civilization*, 3rd ed., New York, 1933, II, 144f.
6. Ernest Staples Osgood, *The Day of the Cattleman*, 2d ed., Minneapolis, Minn., 1954, pp. 182, 192; Edward Everett Dale, *The Range Cattle Industry*, Norman, Okla., 2d ed., 1960, p. 111.
7. Lloyd Wendt and Herman Kogan, *Bet A Million: The Story of John W. Gates*, New York, 1948, pp. 30ff.
8. Walter Prescott Webb, *The Great Plains*, Boston, 1931, pp. 316f.
9. Swank, *op. cit.*, pp. 134, 144, 448.
10. *Ibid.*, p. 450.

CHAPTER 10/THE INDUSTRIAL REVOLUTION COMES TO AMERICA

1. *Rolling Mills, Rolls, and Roll Making*, Mackintosh-Hemphill Company, Pittsburgh, 1953, p. 32.
2. James M. Swank, *The Manufacture of Iron in All Ages*, 2d. ed., Philadelphia, 1892, pp. 440, 512.
3. Arthur C. Bining, *Pennsylvania's Iron and Steel Industry*, Gettysburg, Pa., 1954, p. 10.
4. Ross E. Beynon, *Roll Design and Mill Layout*, Association of Iron and Steel Engineers, Pittsburgh, 1956, p. 9.
5. *Rolling Mills, op. cit.*, pp. 29f.
6. Beynon, *op. cit.*, p. 79.
7. Charles Singer, *et al.* (eds.) (J. C. 405), *A History of Technology*, Oxford, 1954–1958, IV, 474f.
8. Carl A. Zapffe, *A Brief History of Alloy Steel*, American Society of Metals, 1948, p. 10.
9. Stephen L. Goodale, Chronology of Iron and Steel, Cleveland, 1931, p. 131; *Encyclopaedia Britannica*, XXI, 478, under "Structural Engineering."
10. *History of Technology, op. cit.*, pp. 472f.
11. *Rolling Mills, op. cit.*, p. 40.
12. Col. W. A. Starrett, *Skyscrapers and the Men Who Build Them*, New York, 1928, p. 27.
13. *Rolling Mills, op. cit.*, p. 30.
14. D. L. Burn, *The Economic History of Steelmaking: 1867–1939*, Cambridge, 1940, p. 56.
15. Bruce L. Simpson, *Development of the Metal Castings Industry*, Chicago, 1948, pp. 191f.
16. C. D. King, *Seventy-Five Years of Progress in Iron and Steel*, New York, 1948, p. 13.
17. Swank, *op. cit.*, p. 370; Bining, *op. cit.*, p. 12.
18. King, *op. cit.*, p. 15.
19. Swank, *op. cit.*, pp. 383f.
20. *Ibid.*, p. 385.
21. *Ibid.*, p. 393.

CHAPTER 11/INVENTION OF THE BESSEMER PROCESS

1. *Sir Henry Bessemer: An Autobiography*, London, 1905, p. 130f.
2. *Ibid.*, pp. 130ff.
3. *Ibid.*, p. 136.
4. *Ibid.*, pp. 146ff.
5. *Ibid.*, pp. 164.
6. *Ibid.*, p. 168.
7. *Ibid.*, p. 170.

8. *Ibid.*, pp. 170ff.
9. Charles Singer, *et al.* (eds.), *A History of Technology,* Oxford, 1954–1958, V, p. 55; *American Metal Market,* New York, July 25, 1959.
10. *Sir Henry Bessemer, op. cit.,* pp. 174ff.
11. *The Bulletin,* American Iron and Steel Association, Philadelphia, April 1, 1898.
12. Fred M. Osborn, *The Story of the Mushets,* London, 1952, p. 40.
13. *Ibid.,* p. 41f.
14. *Ibid.,* p. 43.
15. *Ibid.,* pp. 44ff.
16. *Ibid.,* p. 47f.
17. *Sir Henry Bessemer, op. cit.,* p. 341f.
18. Osborn, *op. cit.,* p. 49f.; Herbert N. Casson, *The Romance of Steel: The Story of a Thousand Millionaires,* New York, 1907, p. 6.
19. John W. Boucher, *William Kelly: A True History of the So-Called Bessemer Process,* Greensburg, Pa., 1924, p. 17.
20. Photostat of Commissioner Shugert's order.

CHAPTER 12/THE STEEL AGE BEGINS

1. Fred M. Osborn, *The Story of the Mushets,* London, 1952, p. 42.
2. *Sir Henry Bessemer; An Autobiography,* London, 1905, p. 335.
3. James M. Swank, *History of the Manufacture of Iron in All Ages,* Philadelphia, 2d ed., 1892, pp. 415, 440.
4. Swank, *op. cit.,* p. 421.
5. Stephen L. Goodale, *Chronology of Iron and Steel,* Cleveland, 1931, p. 175.
6. Charles Singer, *et al.* (eds.), *A History of Technology,* Oxford, 1954–1958, V, 61.
7. D. L. Burn, *The Economic History of Steelmaking: 1867–1939,* Cambridge, 1940, pp. 21, 28.
8. *History of Technology, loc. cit.*
9. Burn, *op. cit.,* p. 65f.
10. *Ibid.,* p. 74.
11. *Ibid., passim.*
12. Burton J. Hendrick, *Life of Andrew Carnegie,* New York, 1932, I, 171f.
13. *Ibid.*
14. Hal Bridges, *Iron Millionaire: Life of Charlemagne Tower,* Philadelphia, 1952, pp. 135ff.
15. Bridges, *op. cit.,* p. 245.
16. Henry Oliver Evans, *Iron Pioneer: Henry W. Oliver, 1840–1904,* New York, 1942, pp. 191f.
17. Hendrick, *op. cit.,* II, 11.
18. Herbert N. Casson, *The Romance of Steel: The Story of a Thousand Millionaires,* New York, 1907, pp. 118f.
19. Evans, *op. cit.,* pp. 192, 202f.
20. Hendrick, *op. cit.,* pp. 11, 18ff.

CHAPTER 13/ENTER AUTOMOBILES, EXIT HORSES

1. Edward G. Budd, Jr., *Edward G. Budd (1870–1946): Father of the Streamliners and The Budd Company,* Address before the Newcomen Society, New York, Jan. 26, 1950, p. 9f.
2. George L. Kelley, *Life and Work of Edward G. Budd,* Address at the Franklin Institute, Philadelphia, Feb. 16, 1949, p. 17.
3. *A Chronicle of the Automotive Industry in America, 1893–1952,* Automobile Manufacturers Association, Detroit; Budd, *op. cit.,* p. 17.
4. Budd, *op. cit.,* p. 20.
5. Christy Borth, *True Steel: The Story of George Matthew Verity and His Associates,* Indianapolis, 1941, p. 150.

6. Stephen Badlam, "The Evolution of the Wide Strip Mill," *Yearbook of the American Iron and Steel Institute, 1927,* Philadelphia, 1928, p. 385.
7. Frank H. Fanning, *Wide Strip Mills: Evolution or Revolution,* Paper read before the General Meeting of the American Iron and Steel Institute, New York, May 21-22, 1952.
8. Borth, *op. cit.,* pp. 146f.
9. Verbatim Record of the Proceedings of the Temporary National Economic Committee, XIII, No. 4, 1940, Bureau of National Affairs, Inc., Washington, D. C., pp. 122, 129.
10. Max Lerner, *America As A Civilization,* New York, 1957, p. 96.
11. *Electrical Merchandising Week,* Annual Statistical and Marketing Issue, Jan. 23, 1961.

CHAPTER 14/ALLOY STEELS—I

1. Sir Robert A. Hadfield, *Faraday and His Metallurgical Researches with Special Reference to Their Bearing on the Development of Alloy Steels,* London, 1931, pp. 35-39.
2. *Ibid.,* p. 2.
3. *Ibid.,* p. 262.
4. Mitchell Wilson, *American Science and Invention,* New York, 1954, p. 246.
5. Charles Singer, *et al.* (eds.), *A History of Technology,* Oxford, 1954–1958, V, 65.
6. Christy Borth, *True Steel,* Indianapolis, 1941, pp. 140f.
7. Carl A. Zapffe, *A Brief History of Alloy Steel,* The American Society for Metals, 1948, p. 11.
8. Carl A. Zapffe, "Who Discovered Stainless Steel?" *Iron Age,* CLXII (Oct. 14, 1948).
9. Hadfield, *op. cit.,* p. 285.
10. Zapffe, *Iron Age, op. cit.,* p. 120.
11. Douglas A. Fisher, *Steel in the War,* United States Steel Corporation, New York, 1946, pp. 25f.

CHAPTER 15/ALLOY STEELS—II

1. Most of the information from this point on in the chapter was obtained from the following sources: *Resources for Freedom,* A Report to the President's Materials Policy Commission (Paley Report), Washington, D.C., 1952, Vol. I; *Minerals Yearbook,* U. S. Department of the Interior, Washington, D.C., Vol. I, 1956, 1960; *Mineral Facts and Problems,* U. S. Bureau of Mines, Washington, D.C., 1956.

CHAPTER 16/THE FABULOUS COAL CHEMICALS

1. *Coke and Coal Chemicals in 1960,* U.S. Bureau of Mines, Washington, D.C.
2. *The Age of Coal Chemicals,* United States Steel Corporation, Pittsburgh, 1958, p. 8; *History of Iron and Steelmaking in the United States,* American Institute of Mining, Metallurgical, and Petroleum Engineers, Inc., New York, 1961, p. 44.
3. *Ibid.*
4. *Ibid.,* pp. 44f.
5. Carl A. Meissmer, "Modern By-Product Coke Ovens," 1913 *Yearbook,* American Iron and Steel Institute, New York.
6. *History of Iron and Steelmaking, op. cit.,* pp. 46f.
7. *Ibid.,* pp. 47f.
8. *Ibid.,* p. 48.
9. *Age of Coal Chemicals, op. cit.,* p. 13.
10. *History of Iron and Steelmaking, op. cit.,* p. 49.

11. *Coke and Coal Chemicals, op. cit.*
12. *Coal Chemical Materials Produced at Coke Plants in The United States,* 1948–1957, U.S. Bureau of Mines, Washington, D.C., 1959, p. 1; *Minerals Yearbook,* 1959, U.S. Department of the Interior, Washington, D.C., Vol. I (Fuels), 230.
13. *Coke and Coal Chemicals, op. cit.*
14. William Haynes, *This Chemical Age,* New York, 1942, pp. 42ff. The remainder of this section, Discovery and Applications of Coal Chemicals, up to the work of Dr. Baekeland, is based on *This Chemical Age.*

CHAPTER 17/WIRE AND WIRE PRODUCTS

1. *Mighty Mac,* Wayne University Press, Detroit, 1958, p. 18f.

CHAPTER 18/PLATES, PIPES AND TUBES, RAILS AND BARS

1. Charles Singer, *et al.,* (eds.), *A History of Technology,* Oxford, 1954–1958, II, 62.
2. Thomas Sutcliffe Ashton, *Iron and Steel in the Industrial Revolution,* Manchester, 1924, p. 70ff.
3. *Rolling Mills, Rolls and Roll Making,* Mackintosh-Hemphill Company, Pittsburgh, 1953, p. 29.
4. Stephen Badlam, *Evolution of the Hot Strip Mill,* American Iron and Steel Institute Yearbook 1927, New York, p. 407.
5. Robert Daley, *The World Beneath the City,* Philadelphia, 1959, p. 11.
6. Bruce L. Simpson, *Development of the Metal Castings Industry,* Chicago, 1948, p. 150.
7. *Ibid., loc. cit.*
8. *History of Technology, op. cit.,* pp. 259ff.
9. *Ibid.,* pp. 262ff.
10. *Ibid.,* p. 629.
11. *New York Times,* March 17, 1958.

CHAPTER 19/COATINGS FOR STEEL

1. *Minerals Yearbook 1960,* U.S. Department of the Interior, Washington, D.C., I, Metals and Minerals (except Fuels), pp. 1, 111.
2. *Ibid.,* pp. 1, 103.
3. "Vinyl-Metal Laminates—up 1800% in Two Years," *Modern Plastics,* New York (April 1958).
4. The Society of the Plastics Industry, Inc., New York.
5. *Encyclopaedia Britannica,* Chicago, 1959 ed., XVIII, 241f; *Porcelain Enamel—From Egyptians to Jets,* Porcelain Enamel Institute, Washington, D.C., 1959.
6. *Porcelain Enamel—From Egyptians to Jets, op. cit.*
7. Paul M. Corbett, "Steel Porcelain Enameling—Past, Present and Future," *Journal of the Canadian Ceramic Society,* Toronto (vol. 27, 1958); H. N. Davis, "Porcelain Enamels on Steel," *Mineral Industries School of Mineral Studies,* Pennsylvania State College, State College, Pa. (Jan. 1951).

CHAPTER 20/WORLD IRON AND STEELMAKING RESOURCES

1. *Economic Bulletin of Asia and the Far East,* United Nations, New York, X, No. 1, 2f.
2. *Economic Commission for Asia and the Far East,* Annual Report, March 16, 1958–March 19, 1959, Supplement No. 2, United Nations, Bangkok, 1959, p. 27.
3. Address at Conference on The World Population Crisis, New York, May 12, 1961.

CHAPTER 21/THE BLAST FURNACE, 1881-1960

1. "Progress in Steel," *Barron's* (March 30, 1959).
2. "Iron Ore Reduction and the Arc-Furnace," *Carbon and Carbide News*, National Carbon Company, (Dec. 1957), IV, No. 4, 1f.
3. "Iron Making—Past Achievements, Present Recommendations, and Future Prospects," *Blast Furnace, Coke Oven and Raw Materials Committee Proceedings*, American Institute of Mining, Metallurgical and Petroleum Engineers, 1958, 17, 304.
4. C. D. King, *Seventy-Five Years of Progress in Iron and Steel*, New York, 1948, pp. 88f.
5. *Long-term Trends and Problems of the European Steel Industry*, Economic Commission for Europe, United States, Geneva, 1959, p. 93.
6. *Advances in Steel Technology in 1956*, United Nations, Geneva, 1958, p. 5f.
7. R. Durrer, "Considerations on the Development of the Production of Iron," *A Study of the Iron and Steel Industry in Latin America*, United Nations, Department of Economic Affairs, New York, 1954, pp. 184ff.
8. *Advances in Steel Technology, op. cit.*, p. 6.
9. *Ibid.*, p. 7.
10. "Static Control Provides Blast Furnace Automation," *Iron and Steel Engineer*, (Feb., 1959).
11. William C. Bell, "Review of European Operating and Technology Practices," paper presented before general meeting of American Iron and Steel Institute, May 27–28, 1953.

CHAPTER 22/GOLIATH IS CHALLENGED

1. "Alternative Processes for Making Iron and Steel," *Iron and Coal Trade Review* (July 25, 1958), p. 211.
2. "Progress in Steel," *Barron's* (March 30, 1959).
3. *A Study of the Iron and Steel Industry in Latin America*, United Nations, New York, 1954, II, 192f.
4. "Krupp-Renn Expansion," *Journal of Metals* (Dec. 1959).
5. *Survey of World Iron Ore Resources*, United Nations, New York, 1955, p. 136.
6. *Study of Iron and Steel In Latin America, op. cit.*, pp. 204ff.
7. *Processes of Iron Manufacture Without Coking Coal and Their Applicability in ECAFE Countries*, Economic Commission for Asia and the Far East, United Nations, Bangkok, Thailand, 1955, p. 65.
8. "Sponge Iron by the HyL Process, *Journal of Metals* (May 1959).
9. *Study of Iron and Steel in Latin America, op. cit.*, Introduction.
10. F. Weston Starratt, "Low-Shaft Blast Furnace Holds New Promise," *Journal of Metals* (Nov. 1957).
11. "Progress in Steel," *op. cit.*
12. "Alternative Processes," *op. cit.*, p. 214.
13. *Survey of World Iron Ore Resources, op. cit.*, p. 135.

CHAPTER 23/ELECTRICAL PROCESSES FOR MAKING IRON AND STEEL

1. Alfred Stansfield, *The Electric Furnace*, New York, 1914, p. 13.
2. J. Wright, *Electric Furnaces and Their Industrial Applications*, New York, 1907, pp. 114f.
3. Stansfield, *op. cit.*, p. 237.
4. *Long-term Trends and Problems of the European Steel Industry*, United Nations, Economic Commission of Europe, 1959, p. 105.

5. "Production of Quality Steels in the Electric Furnace," *Carbon and Graphite News*, National Carbon Company, New York, 2 (Dec. 1955).
6. "Muscular Metals," *Wall Street Journal* (Dec. 15, 1954).

CHAPTER 24/STEELMAKING PROCESSES—TWENTIETH CENTURY

1. *Long-term Trends and Problems of the European Steel Industry*, United Nations, Economic Commission for Europe, Geneva, 1959, pp. 102, 105.
2. *American Metal Market* (March 11, 1959).
3. *Ibid.* (Dec. 7, 1959).
4. "Basic Open-Hearth Steelmaking in the U.S.A.," *Journal of the Iron and Steel Institute* (July 1958).
5. *American Metal Market* (Sept. 23, 1959).
6. *Business Week* (May 1959).
7. *Long-term Trends and Problems, op. cit.*, p. 97.
8. *Ibid.*, p. 98.
9. *Steel* (Feb. 9, 1959).
10. *American Metal Market* (June 19, 1959).
11. R. Durer, "Considerations on the Development of the Production of Iron." *A Study of the Iron and Steel Industry in Latin America*, United Nations, New York, 1954, II, p. 187.

CHAPTER 25/STEEL IN THE ATOMIC-SPACE AGE

1. *American Metal Market*, May 28, 1959.
2. Carl A. Zappfe, *A Brief History of Alloy Steels*, American Society for Metals, New York, 1948.
3. *Steel Facts*, American Iron and Steel Institute, Feb. 1959.
4. C. R. Wheeler, "Raw Material Supplies and the Future Development of the Iron and Steel Industry," *Journal of the* (British) *Iron and Steel Industry* (June 1958).
5. Harrison Brown, James Bonner, and John Weir, *The Next Hundred Years*, New York, 1957, p. 109f.
6. Webster's New Collegiate Dictionary, Springfield, Mass., 1956.
7. *Conference on Computers in the Iron and Steel Industry*, The British Iron and Steel Research Association, April 15, 1958, pp. 32ff.
8. *Ibid.*, pp. 32ff.
9. *Electronics and Automation*, A Financial Times Survey, Financial Times, London, Dec. 1, 1958.
10. *New York Times*, Jan. 8, 1961.

Index

Adams, Avery C., 308
Africa, west, iron ores, 266
Agricola, Georgius, 57-61
Agriculture:
  first large American iron market, 92-93, 97
  steel products used in, 151, 224-225, 227, 238
A. I. S. I. steels, 158
Alan Wood Steel Company, 287
Alchemy, 62-64
Alloy steels:
  antiquity in, 24
  future demands anticipated, 166-167, 169
  high-strength low-alloy steels. *See* High-strength steels
  post-World War II period, 166
  research and development, early, 153-160
  service limits of, 313-314
  World Wars I and II and, 164-165
Alloying elements:
  characteristics, deposits, production, consumption, 168-196
  chief uses in steel, 169
Aluminum:
  coating for steel, 170, 219-220
  steelmaking, uses in, 170
American colonies:
  Falling Creek (Virginia) ironworks, 67-70
  iron industry, characteristics of, 81-83
  iron plantations, 78, 84-85
  ironworkers, 73, 83, 87
  Revolutionary War period, 85-87
  Saugus River (Hammersmith, Mass.) ironworks, 70-72
  steelmaking in, 75, 77
American iron ores:
  Eastern seaboard, South, and West, 262
  Lake Superior. *See* Lake Superior iron ores

American iron ores—*Continued*
  reserves, 259
  reversal in exports and imports, 259-260
American Rolling Mill Company (Armco), 140, 144-146
American steel industry:
  reversal in exports and imports, 251
Ammonia:
  anhydrous, 203-204, 206, 216
  coke-oven gas constituent, 198, 203
Ancony, semi-finished wrought iron, 33
Aristotle, 10, 21-22, 62
Arthur D. Little, Inc., 288
Atomic-Space Age. *See* Nuclear energy and *see also* Automation
  greater strength steels needed in, 315-317
  problems of heat resistance, 314-316
  steel applications for, 317-318
  technology ahead of metallurgy, 314-315
Automation (automatic controls):
  blast furnace in, 269, 277-278
  combined in mills and offices, 323
  combined with nuclear energy, 319, 323
  electronic computers in business functions, 320-322
  in mills, 319-320
Automobile:
  all-steel, development of, 138-139
  "horseless carriages," 137-138

Barbed wire:
  invention of, 93
  in opening American West, 93-94
Bars:
  shapes and sizes of, 240
  reinforced concrete in, 227
  standard wrought iron product, 33, 82
Bar mills:
  established in United States, 98-99
  origin and development of, 49, 240

Basic oxygen process:
  advantages of, 309
  invention and development of, 307-308
  number and total capacity of convert-
    ers, 309
  operation of, 308-309
Basic process (Thomas-Gilchrist):
  Bessemer process in, 128
  Britain and Europe in, 130
  open hearth process in. *See* Open
    hearth process
  revolutionary effects in America, 129
Beehive coke ovens, development and
  operation of, 110
B. F. Goodrich Company, 246
Bellows, 17, 27, 83
Beneficiation:
  coal, 274-275
  iron ores, 253, 260-261, 275-277
Bessemer, Sir Henry, 114-123
Bessemer process:
  acid, 128
  America, established in, 121-122
  basic, 128
  England and Europe, established in,
    119
  invention and development of, 114-122
  vs. open hearth process, 126-127
Bessemer steel:
  initial production of, 118-122
  production related to Bessemer rails
    (table), 125
  rails, replace wrought iron in, 123-124
Bethlehem Steel Company (Bethlehem
  Iron Company), 79, 155, 222, 287
Biringuccio, Vanoccio, 57, 63
Bituminous coal:
  blast furnaces, as fuel in, 109
  distillation of, 198
  yield per ton in coking, 203
Blast furnace:
  air consumed in, 270
  automatic controls in, 269, 277-278
  blowing devices, 17, 27, 51, 83, 270
  challenged by new processes, 267
  charging methods, 83, 111, 268
  coke consumption rate, 275
  in Colonial America, 71, 83
  cost of, 274
  efficiency of, 271
  future furnaces, 277-278
  gas, volume produced, 270
  hot blast in, 51-52, 110-111
  iron disposal, 31, 269
  new fuels for, 273
  nitrogen behavior in, 272
  origin of, 27-29
  oxygen-enriched blast, 272-273
  pressure blowing, 271-272

Blast furnace—*Continued*
  raw materials
    handling, 268-269
    per ton of pig iron, 269-270
  sizes, growth of, 271, 277
  slag disposal, 269
  water consumed by, 270
Blister steel. *See* Cementation process
Bloom:
  iron product of early furnaces, 27
  steel bloom, origin of, 105
Blooming mill, evolution of, 105-106
Boiler plate, 99, 230-232
Boron, addition to steel, 166
Brazil, iron ores, 265
Brearley, Harry, 159-160
Bridges:
  iron in, 103
  steel in, 103, 163
  suspension, 220-222
Bronze, 3-4
Budd, Edward G., 138-139, 161
Buildings:
  cast iron, 102, 104
  forerunners of skyscrapers, 104-105
  wrought iron beams in, 104-105

Canada, iron ores, 262
Carbide, chemical formula of, 65
Carbon:
  cast iron, content of, 17
  effects in steel, 168
  identified as causing differences in
    wrought iron, cast iron, and steel,
    64-65
  steel, content of, 168
  wrought iron, content of, 17
Carbon steels:
  carbon content in, 168
  electric furnace production of, 295-296;
    see also table, 295
  future demand compared to alloy steels,
    166-167, 169
  properties of, 168-169
Carburizing, 18-19
Carnegie, Andrew (Carnegie Steel Company, 105, 111, 122, 132-134, 232,
  269
Case-hardening, 18-19
Cast iron. *See* Iron castings
Casting:
  metals cast in antiquity, 3-4
  where and when begun, 3
Cementation process (steel), 23, 34, 53,
  75, 111-112, 302-303
Chafery forge, 33, 71
Chalybia (chalybes), 10; *see also* Iron
  Age

Charcoal:
  blast furnace, consumption in, 84
  charcoal to coke in blast furnace. *See*
    Coke
  depletion in Britain, 41-43, 85
  how made, 41
  iron refining in, 33, 41
  iron smelting in, 16-19, 26, 41, 108
  steelmaking in, 22-23, 54
Chariot, iron war chariot, 10, 14, 24
China, Communist:
  iron ore reserves, 264
  steel industry, character of, 264
Chromite:
  consumption and sources of, United
    States, 171
  production of, 171, 173
  reserves, 172
Chromium:
  content reduction in steel, 163
  ferrochromium, 153
  future demands for, 169
  multiple alloys in, 157, 159, 164
  properties imparted to steel, 153, 159,
    170-171
  properties and uses of, 153, 155, 157,
    163
Coal:
  anthracite, in blast furnaces, 108-110
  beneficiation of, 274-275
  bituminous. *See* Bituminous coal
  iron smelting in, 43-45
Coal chemicals:
  American industry, 208-209
  discovery and applications of, 206-217
  principal products recovered, 198
  production of, 202; *see also* table, 204-
    205
  products derived from, 197, 216
  value of, 198; *see also* table, 204-205
Coal chemical recovery, origin and de-
    velopment of, 198-203
Coatings for steel:
  aluminum, 170, 219
  porcelain enamel, 246-247
  tin for tin plate. *See* Tin plate
  tin for wire, 219
  vinyl, 245-246
  zinc. *See* Galvanizing
Cobalt:
  consumption, production, sources of,
    United States, 174-175
  future demands for, 169
  mineral sources of, 172
  reserves, world, 175
  steel, uses in, 174
Coke:
  blast furnace consumption rate, 275
    established in America, 108-110
    replaces charcoal in, 41-47

Coke—*Continued*
  beehive ovens. *See* Beehive ovens
  high-grade, vanishing supply of, 275
  ovens for producing. *See* Coke ovens;
    Beehive ovens
  yield per ton of coal, 203
Coke ovens:
  description and operation of, 202-203
  development of, 199-202
  see also Beehive ovens; Coal chemical
    recovery; Coke
Coke-oven gas:
  constituents of, 198, 203
  yield per ton of coal, 203
  see also Coal chemical recovery; Coke
Cold reduction mill, development and
    importance of, 146, 148
Cold rolling, development of, 147
Columbia Steel Company, 145
Columbium-tantalum:
  columbium, uses in steel, 176-177
  consumption, production, sources of,
    United States, 177-179
  mineral sources of, 175, 177
  production, reserves, Free World, 177-
    178
Connecticut, colonial iron and steelmak-
    ing, 74-75
Constructional alloy steels, 158
Continuous mills:
  continuous hot strip mill, 143-146
    invention and development of, 143-
    146
  development of, 100-102
Cooper, Peter, 104
Copper:
  coating for steel, 179
  first metal smelted and cast, 2-3
  properties imparted to steel, 179
Cermets, 314
Corrosion resistance:
  chromium, imparted by, 158-159
  copper, imparted by, 179
  nickel, imparted by, 186
  stainless steel of, 160-162
  under stress, for Atomic-Space Age, 316
Cort, Henry, 49-51, 240
Crucible process (steel):
  description of, 54
  established in United States, 111-112
  origin of, 22-23
  revival in England, 52-54
Cupola, 31-32, 51, 106
Cyclosteel process, 310, 312

Damascus, swords of, 21-22
Darby, Abraham, 43, 45-47
Delaware, colonial iron industry, 79
Direct reduction:
  advantages of, 279, 289

Direct reduction—*Continued*
  H-Iron process, 287
  hydrogen as reducing agent, 283, 287-288
  Krupp-Renn process, 281-282
  low shaft furnaces in, 285-286
  Nu-Iron process, 287-288
  production, per cent of iron and steel, 279
  products of, 279
  R-N process, 288
  sponge iron processes, 282-284
Dominion Foundries and Steel, Ltd. (Canada), 308
Dorman Long (Steel) Ltd. (England), 320
Du Pont de Nemours, E. I. & Company, 211
Durham boats, 78
Durrer, R., 272, 285-286, 307, 312

Electric arc furnaces:
  carbon and alloy steels, relative production, 294-296; *see also* table, 295
  invention and development of, 291-294
  iron smelting in. *See* Electric smelting
  production growth, American, 296-297; *see also* table, 297
  production trends, 297
  steel products of, 295-296
  vs. open hearth furnaces, 296, 303, 306, 312
Electric smelting:
  advantages of, 280-281
  development of, 291-293
  number and location of furnaces, 281
  types of processes (furnaces), 288-289, 293
Electrical power, replaces steam, 129
Electrolytic tin-plating, development and operation of, 243-245
Employment, steel, costs per hour, United States and eight other nations (table), 252; *see also* Smiths
European Coal and Steel Community (E.C.S.C.), iron ores, 262
Extrusion, 240-241

Fairless, Benjamin F., 319, 323
Faraday, Michael, 153
Fence:
  barbed wire. *See* Barbed wire
  varieties of, 225
Ferroalloys, 119, 153, 171, 176, 180, 185, 188-190, 193
Finery forge, 33, 71
Fluxes, 19, 75, 83
Ford, Henry, 137
Ford Motor Company, 164

Forging:
  crucible steel ingots, 105
  hydraulic press, 107-108
  steam hammer, 107
  tilt hammer, 29, 71
Fox, Sir Cyril, 15
Furnaces:
  Bessemer converters. *See* Bessemer process
  blast furnace. *See* Blast furnace
  bloomery. *See* Iron smelting
  crucible. *See* Crucible process
  cupola, 31-32, 51, 106
  open hearth. *See* Open hearth furnaces
  puddling, development of, 50-51
  reverberatory, 50, 116
  stückofen. See Smelting furnaces

Galvanizing:
  sheets of, 151, 245
  wire of, 219
Galvanized steel, applications of, 151, 245
Gas:
  blast furnace. *See* Blast furnace
  coke-oven. *See* Coke-oven gas
Göransson, Göran Frederik, 118
Great Lakes Steel Corporation, 320
Guest Keen & Nettlefolds, Ltd. (England), 320
Guillet, Leon, 157, 159

Hadfield, Robert A., 155-156
Hammer. *See* Forging
Hand hot mills:
  operation of, 99, 140-142
  origin of, 49
  see also Hand-rolled sheets
Hand-rolled sheets:
  applications of, 40, 82, 113, 138-139
  deficiences of, 140, 142, 146
Heat resistance:
  Atomic-Space Age, problems in, 314-316
  chromium, imparted by, 158-159, 170-171
  cobalt, imparted by, 174
  molybdenum, imparted by, 184
  nickel, imparted by, 186
  stainless steel of, 160-162, 317
Héroult, Paul, 291-293
High-strength steels (low-alloy steels), development and uses of, 163-164
Hittites, early monopoly of iron, 10
Hojalatay y Lamina (Mexico), 284
Holley, Alexander L., 121-122
Homer, mention of iron, 12-13
Hook, Charles R., 144, 146
Hoover, Herbert and Lou Henry, 57

Hot-dip tin-plating, 113, 243-244
Huntsman, Benjamin, 52-54, 105
Hydrogen:
  coke-oven gas constituent, 198, 203
  elimination of in vacuum melting proc-
    ess, 299-301
  reducing agent as, 283, 287-288

India, iron ore, 265
Induction furnaces:
  invention and development of, 290, 298
  vacuum steel melting for. *See* Vacuum
    melting process
Ingot:
  origin of term, 105
  steel, 105-106
Iron:
  biblical mention of, 7, 10-11
  cast. *See* Iron castings
  meteoric. *See* Meteoric iron
  pig, origin of term, 31-32
  wrought. *See* Wrought iron
Iron Age:
  dispersion of, 11-16
  Halstatt period, 13-14, 19
  La Tène period, 13-14
  Llyn Cerrig Bach relics, Wales, 14-15,
    24
  when and where established, 7-11
Iron castings (cast iron):
  American colonies in, 69-70, 82, 87
  antiquity, production in, 19-20, 29-31
  bells and cannon, first products, 29-31
  buildings and bridges in, 102-104
  carbon content of, 17
  displace wrought iron, 47
  malleable, 32, 106-107
  pipes in water lines, 234
Iron consumption, per capita, United
  States, 89
Iron industry:
  in American colonies, 66-87
  Middle Ages to Industrial Revolution,
    25-52
  primitive, 6-20
  in United States, after Revolutionary
    War, 88-91, 97-98
Iron ore:
  in American colonies, 67, 70-71, 73,
    75-76, 79, 80, 83-84
  beneficiation of. *See* Beneficiation
  bog ore, 70-71, 73, 75, 83
  briquettes (briquetting), 276
  Lake Superior. *See* Lake Superior iron
    ores
  nodules (nodulizing), 276
  pellets (pelletizing), 276
  price, freight costs in, 257-259, 262-263
  price-quality ratio, 256, 258
  reserves, world, 253

Iron ore—*Continued*
  sinter (sintering), 276-277
  trade:
    in Africa, Asia, Europe, North and
      South America, 259-266
    effects on new metallurgical proc-
      esses, 253-254
    future of international, 258-259
    international trends, 257-258, 266
    price-quality ratio, market determi-
      nant, 256
  United States. *See* American iron ores
Iron smelting:
  description of, 16-17
  early shortcomings and remedies of,
    9-10, 18-19
  see also Smelting furnaces

Japan:
  iron ore trade, import sources, 264
  steel industry, resurgence of, 264
Jones, Captain Bill, 129, 269
Jones & Laughlin Steel Corporation, 269,
  273
Jones mixer. *See* Ladles

Kelly, William, 114, 120-122
Kentucky:
  colonial ironmaking, 81
  Hanging Rock district, 90
Ketona Chemical Company, 203
Koppers Company, 201

Ladles:
  closed, torpedo-shaped, 269
  Jones mixer, 129, 269
Lake Superior iron ores:
  beneficiation of, 260-261
  characteristics of, 260-261
  discovery and development of, 131-136
  mining of, 134-135
  ranges, historical development, 131-
    136
  shipments of, 131, 133, 135-136
  source of, primary, 260-261
  taconite, 261
Landore Siemens Steel Company (England), 235
Lukens Steel Company, 232

Machine tools, innovation of, 154
Manganese:
  production, world (table), 182-183
  properties imparted to steel, 155, 180
  reserves, foreign suppliers in U. S.,
    180-181, 183
  reserves, world, 180-181; *see also* table,
    181
  slag, recovery from, 181, 183

Manganese—*Continued*
   steel. *See* Manganese steel
   steelmaking, purpose in, 179
Manganese steel:
   applications of, 155, 158
   development of, 155
   properties of, 155, 180
Martin, Emile and Pierre, 125-126
Maryland, colonial iron industry, 79-80
Massachusetts:
   colonial iron industry, 73
   Saugus River (Hammersmith) iron-
     works, 70-73
McLouth Steel Corporation, 308
Merchant mill, 143, 240
Merk, R. N., 306
Merritt brothers, 133-134
Mesabi iron ore range, discovery and
   development of, 133-135
Metallurgy:
   behind technology, 314-315
   three eras of, 315
   see also Atomic-Space Age
Metals:
   ancient attitude toward, 61-63
   ancient beliefs on origin of, 62-63
   first discovery of, 2
   theoretical strength of, 316
Meteoric iron (meteors):
   American Indians, use by, 66
   earliest source of iron, 6-7
   nickel content of, 8
   mystical properties, 7
   reproduction of, 153
Mining:
   American colonies in, 83
   antiquity and Middle Ages, 56-61
   Lake Superior iron ores, 133-135
Molybdenum:
   content reduction in steel, 163
   future demands for, 169
   production and consumption in U.S.,
     185
   production, world, 185
   properties, imparted to steel, 184
   steel. *See* Molybdenum steels
Molybdenum steels, history and uses, 164,
   184
Mushet, Robert F., 114, 123, 154, 157

Nails:
   cut, 95
   nailmaking machines, 95-96
   wire, 95-96
   wrought iron, hand-made, 38-39, 72,
     82, 94-95
National Lead Company, 288
Neilsen, James Beaumont, 51-52
New Jersey, colonial iron and steelmaking, 75-77

New York, colonial iron industry, 77
Nickel:
   consumption, imports, production in
     U.S., 186
   content in meteoric iron, 8
   content reduction in steel, 166, 186
   multiple alloys in, 157, 185
   production, world, 186-187; *see also*
     table, 187
   properties imparted to steel, 185-186
Nickel steel:
   applications of, 157, 163, 185-186
   properties of, 185-186
Nitrogen, blast furnace behavior in, 272,
   285
North American Cyanamid Company
   (Canada), 206
North Carolina, colonial ironmaking, 81
Nuclear (atomic) energy:
   combined with automation, 319, 323
   future impact on steel industry, 318-
     319
   steel in reactors, 162, 314

Ohio, Hanging Rock district, 90
Oliver, Henry W., 133-134
Open hearth process (furnace):
   basic, development of, 129
   invention and development of, 125-126
   oxygen injection in, 306
   position challenged, 306-307
   vs. Bessemer process, 126-128
   vs. electric arc process, 296, 303, 306,
     312
Oxygen:
   enrichment in blast furnace, 272-273
   injection in open hearth furnace, 306
   steelmaking processes, 307-310
   trend toward in ferrous metallurgy, 286,
     306, 308, 312
Ore boats (vessels):
   ocean-going, 258-259
   on Great Lakes, 135

Pack rolling, 140-142
Page Woven Wire Fence Company, 225
Pennsylvania, colonial iron and steelmaking, 77-79
Perkin, William Henry, 206-207
Phlogiston theory, 64-65
Phosphorus:
   deleterious effect in steel, 117
   control by basic process, 128-130
Pig iron. *See* Iron
Pipe:
   butt-weld process, 235
   cast iron, 234-235
   early history of, 233-235
   electric-welded, 237

Pipe—*Continued*
  wooden, 60
  see also Pipes and tubes
Pipes and tubes:
  ancient and modern civilization in, 233
  see also Pipe; Tubes
Plastics, 212-214
Plate:
  applications of, 231, 237, 314
  boiler. *See* Boiler plate
  change from iron to steel, 230-231
  definition of, 231
  plate mills. *See* Plate mills
Plate mills, development of, 232-233
Plow, 16, 92-93
Pneumatic process, 120
Porcelain enamel, 246-247
Pressed steel. *See* Stamping
Puddling furnace:
  development of, 50-51
  United States, establishment in, 98

Quenching, 18-19, 63

Rail mill, 239
Rails:
  Bessemer rails related to Bessemer steel
    production (table), 125
  iron
    evolution of, 91-92
    production of, 99, 124
  open hearth replaces Bessemer steel in,
    127
  production, rise and decline of, 238-239
  steel *vs.* wrought iron, 123-124, 129-130
  to guide a vehicle, 59
Railroads:
  early American, 91
  growth of, related to Bessemer steel
    and rail production (table), 125
  streamlined trains, 161, 163
  see also Rails; Bessemer Steel
Raw (natural) steel, 23, 34
Réamur, René Antoine de, 32, 64
Reinforced concrete, 227
Republic Steel Corporation, 272, 288, 311
Rhode Island, colonial iron industry, 73-74
Rockefeller, John D., 132, 134
Rod mills, continuous mills, 100-102, 218-219
Rods, steel replaces iron in, 102
Rolling mills:
  blooming mill. *See* Blooming mill
  continuous. *See* Continuous mills
  grooved rolls, 49-51, 98-99, 240
  hand mills. *See* Hand hot mills
  hot, origin of, 39, 48-49
  origin of, 48
  plate mills. *See* Plate mills

Rolling mills—*Continued*
  reversing, 100, 232
  rod mills. *See* Rod mills
  sheet mills. *See* Sheet mills
  strip mills. *See* Continuous hot strip
    mill
  structural mills. *See* Structural mills
  three-high, 99-100, 232
  water-driven, 49
Rotor (oxygen) process, 278, 310
RZ (Rodheisen-Zunder) process, 311

Scrap, 128, 279-281, 306
Seamless tubes:
  applications of, 236-238
  cold-drawn, 236
  development of process, 235-236
  growth of industry, 236
  pressure cylinders for, 238
Selenium, 188
Sharon Steel Corporation, 306
Sheets:
  applications of, 40, 82, 113, 138-139,
    148-149, 151, 156, 242-247
  cold-reduced, 146, 148, 151
  distinction from strip, 140
  electrical, 156-157, 188
  hand-rolled. *See* Hand-rolled sheets;
    Hand hot mills
  production of, 1925-1955 period, 149
  shift from heavy to light steel products
    in United States, 149, 151; *see also*
    table, 150
  tin plate for, 40, 82, 113, 148, 151,
    242-245
Sheet mills:
  early, 49, 99, 140-142
  modern, development of, 143-145
  see also Hand hot mills; Hand-rolled
    sheets; Continuous hot strip mill
Siemens-Martin furnace. *See* Open hearth
  furnace
Silicon:
  electrical sheets in. *See* Sheets, elec-
    trical
  properties, imparted to steel, 188
Silicon steel, electrical sheets, 156
Sinter (sintering), 276-277
Slag:
  blast furnace, disposal of, 269
  manganese. *See* Manganese
Slitting mill, 38-39, 49, 71-72, 79, 82
Smelting:
  direct reduction. *See* Direct reduction
  where and when begun, 3-4
Smelting furnaces:
  blast furnace. *See* Blast furnace
  bloomery, 27, 36, 77
  Catalan forge, 26-27
  direct reduction. *See* Direct reduction

Smelting furnaces—*Continued*
  primitive, 17
  stückofen, 27-29
Smiths (ironworkers, miners):
  American colonies in, 73, 83, 87
  early Britain in, 35, 56
  status in primitive society, 55-56
  working conditions, early, 56-59
Soviet bloc:
  iron ore, trade and trends in, 263-264
  see also Soviet Union
Soviet Union:
  automation, advances in, 323
  blast furnaces, 271, 273, 277
  electric steel production, future, 297
  iron ore beneficiation, 275
  iron ore trade in. *See* Soviet bloc
Spain, iron ore, 263
Spiegeleisen, in Bessemer process, 119
Springs:
  applications of, 218, 227
  machine manufacture begun, 226-227
  principal types of, 226
  sizes of, 226
Stainless steels:
  development and applications of, 160-162, 318
  discovery of, 159-160
  properties of, 158, **160-163**
Stamping, 138, 143, 147
Standard Oil Company, 288
Steam power,
  introduced in iron industry, 51-52
Steel:
  alloy. *See* Alloy steels; Alloying elements
  Atomic-Space Age requirements, 315-317
  Biblical mention of, 11, 21
  carbon. *See* Carbon steels
  cementation (blister). *See* Cementation process
  crucible. *See* Crucible steel
  earliest find in Britain, 24
  first American-made, 75
  raw (natural) steel, 23, 34
  space vehicles in, 317-318
  stainless. *See* Stainless steels
  tensile strength of, 316
  versatility of, 318
  wootz. *See* Wootz steel
Steel Age:
  Germany wrests lead from Britain, 129-130
  launched by Bessemer process, 123
  slow growth of, 127-128
Steel capacity:
  world planned capacity and production, 252; *See also* table, 254-255

Steel industry:
  American. *See* American steel industry
  Atomic-Space Age in, 315, 318-319, 323
  future growth, factors in, 248-250
  primitive, 21-24
  underdeveloped nations in. *See* Underdeveloped nations
Steelmaking:
  antiquity, three processes in, 21-23
  Bessemer process. *See* Bessemer process
  cementation process. *See* Cementation process
  crucible process. *See* Crucible process
  direct processes, 310-312
  open hearth process. *See* Open hearth process
  oxygen processes, 307-310
  processes and production, American 303; *see also* table, 304
  processes and production, Europe, 303; *see also* table, 305
  revolution in, 310-312
Steel, Peach & Tozer (England), 306
Steel production:
  explosion in, 250-251
  world
    future prediction of, 318
    in 1961, 318
    production and planned capacity, 252; *see also* table, 254-255
Stora Kaldo (oxygen) process, 309-310
Stora Kopparbergs Berlags (Sweden), 283, 309, 311
Stora Powder Steel Process, 311-312
Strategic alloying elements:
  exploration and production of, 170-171, 174, 177, 186, 191-192
  stockpiling of, 166, 193
Strip, distinction from sheets, 140
Strip mills. *See* Continuous hot strip mill
Structural iron, innovation of, 102-104
Structural iron and steel:
  bridges. *See* Bridges
  buildings. *See* Buildings
Structural mills:
  steel, development of mills for, 104
  wrought iron, first rolling of, 103-104
Super-alloys, 171, 176, 184, 186, 189, 299-301, 314
Sweden, iron ore, 263

Technology. *See* Atomic-Space Age
Taconite, 261
Tantalum. *See* Columbium-tantalum
Tennessee, colonial ironmaking, 81
Thomas-Gilchrist process. *See* Basic process
Tilt hammer. *See* Forging

Tin:
  consumption for tin-plating, 242-243
  wire coating, 219
  See also Tin plate
Tin plate:
  American industry established, 112-113
  applications of, 82, 151, 243
  electrolytic. *See* Electrolytic tinning
  food preservation for, 40-41, 242
  hot-dipped. *See* Hot-dip tinning
  origin of industry, 39-41
Titanium:
  occurrences, 189-190
  properties of, 189
  steelmaking, uses in, 189
Tool steel:
  early development of, 154-155
  high-speed, 155, 171, 174, 190, 193
Tubes. *See* Pipes and tubes; Seamless
    tubes
Tubs, for air blast, 83
Turbines, 161, 270, 313-314
Tungsten:
  consumption, production, imports in
    United States, 190-191
  future demands for, 169, 191-192
  production, world, (table), 194-195
  properties imparted to steel, 190
  reserves, world, 191-192; *see also*
    table, 192
Tungsten steel:
  invention of, 154
  properties of, 154-155, 190
Tytus, John Butler, 140

Underdeveloped nations:
  direct reduction, advantages for, 279-
    280
  steel producers, 250
  steelmaking aspirations, 250
  steelmaking, obstacles to, 249-250
Union Carbide Corporation, 299
United Kingdom, iron ores, 263
United States Rubber Company, 246
United States Steel Corporation, 197,
  200, 201, 206, 222, 228, 232, 244, 246,
  268, 270-271, 277, 287, 301, 306, 319-
  321
Unloaders, iron ore, 135

Vacuum melting process:
  for Atomic-Space Age steels and super-
    alloys, 299-300
  consumable-electrode process, 300
  hydrogen elimination in, 299-301
  induction process, 300

Vanadium:
  production, American, 193-194
  production, world, 195; *see also* table,
    196
  properties imparted to steel, 193
  reserves, 193-195
Venezuela, iron ores, 265-266
Vinyl-coated steel, 246-247
Virginia:
  colonial iron industry, 67-70, 81
  Falling Creek ironworks, 67-70

Wanamaker, John, 104
Washburn, Ichabod, 102, 147
Washington, George, 78, 80, 87
Von Braun, Wernher, 315
Wheeling Steel Corporation, 80
Wilkinson, John, 32, 51, 106
Wire:
  barbed. *See* Barbed wire
  drawing, description of, 219
  early history of, 36-37
  first drawn in America, 82
  grades, shapes, and sizes, 220
  metallic coatings on, 219-220
  miscellaneous products (bolts, screws,
    rivets, bale ties, stitching wire,
    strapping wire), 228
  nails. *See* Nails
  poultry netting, 225
  reinforcing fabric, 227
  springs. *See* Springs
  stainless steel, uses of, 229
  tensile strength of, 220
  woven, origin and development of, 225
Wire rope:
  antiquity in, 37
  applications of, 220-225
  origin and development of, 220
Wootz steel:
  Britain, use of, 52-53, 152-153
  origin and manufacture of, 21-23
Wrought iron:
  bar, standard product, 33
  carbon content of, 17
  colonial America, production in, 69-70
  conversion from pig iron, 33
  early deficiencies of, 18-19
  manufacturing techniques acquired, 19
  rails *vs.* steel rails, 123-124, 129-130
  smelting of. *See* Iron smelting

Zapffe, Carl A., 159-160
Zirconium:
  nuclear reactors in. *See* Nuclear energy
  reserves, world, 196
  steelmaking, uses in, 196